Catalogue of
EUROPEAN
PAPER MONEY
since 1900

By ALBERT PICK

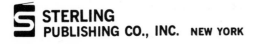
STERLING
PUBLISHING CO., INC. NEW YORK

Oak Tree Press Co., Ltd.
London & Sydney

COIN AND STAMP BOOKS

Second Printing, 1972
Copyright © 1971
by PRESIDENT COIN CORP.
4 Warwick Place, Port Washington, N.Y. 11050
Translated from "Papiergeld Katalog Europa seit 1900"
© 1970 by Ernst Battenberg Verlag, Munich, Germany
British edition published by Oak Tree Press Co., Ltd., Nassau, Bahamas
Distributed in Australia by Oak Tree Press Co., Ltd.,
P.O. Box 34, Brickfield Hill, Sydney 2000, N.S.W.
Distributed in the United Kingdom and elsewhere in the British Commonwealth
by Ward Lock Ltd., 116 Baker Street, London W 1

Manufactured in the United States of America
All rights reserved
Library of Congress Catalog Card No.: 76–151707
ISBN 0–8069–6030 2   UK 7061 2295 X
6031 0

CONTENTS

INTRODUCTION

During the past few years, interest in collecting paper money has greatly increased. The number of collectors specializing in paper currency is still small compared to those whose main interest is stamps or coins but more and more numismatists and philatelists are bringing printed notes into their field of interest.

North American and European notes of the 20th century have been the most popular among collectors. Aside from a few plentiful issues such as the French assignats, notes issued before 1900 are seldom seen and those that do still exist are treasured by their owners and seldom offered for sale. A complete collection of just the 20th century notes would be nearly impossible to put together. Completeness alone should not, therefore, be a collector's goal.

The literature previously available has consisted mainly of mimeographed catalogues and price lists, mostly full of errors, which unfortunately have not always guided the collector properly. This is not surprising, of course, in a hobby so relatively new and with so few serious studies available. The following books, however, are excellent sources of information and are highly recommended: Dr. Arnold Keller "Das Papiergeld des ersten Weltkrieges" and "Das Papiergeld des zweiten Weltkrieges"; A. Platbarzdis "Coins and Notes of Estonia, Latvia and Lithuania" and "Sveriges Sedlar 1661–1961"; Maurice Muszynski "Catalogue des Billets de la Banque de France."

This catalogue deals only with paper money issued by governments and banks plus those regional and military notes that were widely circulated. Germany has contributed perhaps the greatest number of local notes, so of the bank issues only those after 1900 are taken up and the local and private issues of Notgeld (emergency money) have been excluded altogether. The catalogue numbers of regional notes are preceded by an R, the military notes by an M.

Arranging the notes of all the countries according to a uniform scheme was not practical but, so far as possible, the listings are in order by date of issue. The dates are given in the European manner as they appear on the notes with the first numeral indicating the day, the second numeral the month, and the third numeral the year of issue. Dates of issue which do not actually appear on the notes are given within parentheses. The dates following the listings are examples taken from notes actually observed. The listings further indicate the principal devices and vignettes that appear on the obverses of the notes and the main colors of each. Further description is given only where it was necessary to distinguish a note from other issues. Signature and serial variety numbers are noted and watermarked paper is pointed out.

Catalogue evaluations have previously, for the most part, been geared to types only with all notes of the same design shown at one price rather than with a separate value for each of the various issues which can be differentiated by date, series, etc. Consequently, it has been very difficult for a collector to determine the right price at which to buy, sell or trade. In this catalogue, only one price is given for each note, this for notes in average used condition as they are generally available. Very fine condition or uncirculated notes are naturally higher priced, poorly preserved notes are worth less.

A base price of 15¢ was established for the commonest notes and actual dollar prices were quoted only up to $50. An R signifies a price range of $50 to $100, RR indicates a price upwards from $100, and RRR denotes an issue that would realize well in excess of $100. Current notes are not given any valuation at all since they are usually available from foreign exchange dealers for their face value plus perhaps a small service charge. Some notes that now seem to be scarce may be lying unknown and unappreciated in some dealer's stock or in someone's bureau drawer. Government emission offices may sell off retired or cancelled notes or whole issues that were never officially released. Searching through archives and printers' records may turn up some previously unreported issues. Any of these factors can make further price adjustments necessary.

In general, specimen notes are rarer than regular issues. Collectors nevertheless usually favor the actual notes. For certain issues with high face value such as the German 500 and 1,000 rentenmark notes of 1923, it has been practical to quote a value only for specimens. The price given in such a case is understandably for these specimen notes. Only under Czechoslovakia were separate values given for specimen notes, since most of the issues up to 1953 were given out in large quantity to collectors and dealers.

The notes illustrated are through the courtesy of the Bayerischen Hypotheken und Wechsel Bank of Munich and Coin & Currency Institute, Inc. of New York.

Albert Pick

FOREWORD

The values in this catalogue are quoted in U.S. dollars, a unit familiar in all parts of the world and one which readers everywhere can readily convert into their own currencies.

At the rate of U.S. $2.40 to the British pound, the common valuations of $ .50 = £ .21, $1.00 = £ .42, $2.50 = £1.04, $5.00 = £2.08, $10.00 = £4.17. At the rate of U.S. $1.12 to the Australian (or New Zealand) dollar, $ .50 = A$ .45, $1.00 = A$ .90, $2.50 = A$2.23, $5.00 = A$4.47, $10.00 = A$8.94. At the rate of U.S. $1.40 to the South African rand, $ .50 = R .36, $1.00 = R .72, $2.50 = R1.79, $5.00 = R3.57, $10.00 = R7.14.

ALBANIA (Shqipni)

From the Middle Ages until 1912 when it became a principality, Albania was a province of Turkey. During World War I, both Italy and Austria occupied the country. A republic was proclaimed in 1925 under President Achmed Zogu who assumed the title of king in 1928. Albania was occupied by Italy from 1939 to 1943 and thereafter by Germany until the end of World War II. The country was declared a communist People's Republic on January 12, 1946.

1 Frank Ar (gold franc) = *5 Lek* = *100 Quindtar Ar* (gold cent)

Banka Kombetare e Shqipnis, Banca Nazionale d'Albania (National Bank of Albania)

1.	(1925)	5 Lek — 1 Frank Ar, brown with green, grey and rose background. Printed by Richter & Co., Naples	$15.00
2.	(1926)	5 Franka Ari, green. Boy's head at right (two signature varieties)	4.00
3.	(1926)	20 Franka Ari, blue. Youth's head at left	5.00

190 × 104

4.	(1926)	100 Franka Ari, lilac. President Achmed Zogu at right	30.00
5.	(1939)	100 Franka Ari. Same as #4 but head of Zogu overprinted with black double-headed eagle	R
6.	(1939)	5 Franga, green and blue. Watermarked with head of King Victor Emmanuel III	2.50
7.	(1939)	20 Franga, green. Seated figure of Roma with she-wolf at right	4.00
8.	(1944)	100 Franga, lilac brown. Peasant woman with sickle and sheaves at right	7.50
9.	(1944)	2 Lek, violet on brown. Man's head at right	1.00
10.	(1944)	5 Lek, blue on yellow. Female profile on reverse	1.25
11.	(1944)	10 Lek, red on brown. Female profile on reverse	1.50

#7
185 × 105

Banka e Shtetit Shqiptar

12.	(1945)	20 Franka Ari. Same as #3 but with impressed double-headed eagle and new bank name	R
13.	(1945)	20 Franga. Same as #7 but impression as #12	50.00
14.	(1945)	100 Franga. Same as #8 but impression as #12	R
15.	1.5.1945	1 Franga	15.00
16.		5 Franga, green, blue and brown. Helmeted man's head at left	20.00
17.		20 Franga	25.00
18.		100 Franga	30.00
19.	1947	10 Leke, green on brown. Soldier with weapon at right	7.50
20.		50 Leke, brown on green. Type of #19	10.00
21.		100 Leke, violet. Type of #19	15.00
22.		500 Leke, brown on violet. Type of #19	25.00

178 × 90

23.		1,000 Leke, brown, blue and yellow. Type of #19	R
24.	1949	10 Leke, red, blue and green. Double-headed eagle	4.00
25.		50 Leke, violet on green. Bearded man's head at right	5.00
26.		100 Leke, green. Soldier at left	7.50
27.		500 Leke, brown violet. Peasant woman with sheaf at left	15.00
28.	1957	10 Leke. Type of #24	1.50
29.		50 Leke. Type of #25	2.50

30.		100 Leke. Type of #26	4.00
31.		500 Leke. Type of #27	6.00
32.		1,000 Leke, brown, lilac and green. Bearded man's head at left	15.00
33.	1964	1 Lek, green and blue. Peasant man and woman	—
34.		3 Leke, brown and lilac. Woman with basket of grapes	—

125 × 65

35.	5 Leke, lilac and blue. Truck and train	—
36.	10 Leke, dark green. Woman at loom	—
37.	25 Leke, dark blue. Peasant woman with sheaf	—
38.	50 Leke, red brown. Marching soldiers	—
39.	100 Leke, brown lilac. Worker and youth on dike	—

Berat, Bashkia e Beratit

R1.	19. Dhetuer (Dec) 1925 50 Quindtar	25.00

Koritza (Korce), a republic founded by the French in 1917

R2.	1. 3.1917	½ Franc. Double-headed eagle with inscription "Shqiperie Vetqeveritare, Korce." Serial letter "A"	25.00
R3.		1 Franc. Type of #R2	25.00
R4.	25. 3.1917	½ Franc. Type of #R2 but serial letter "B"	12.50
R5.		1 Franc. Type of #R4	12.50
R6.	10.10.1917	½ Franc. Type of #R2 but inscription "Republika Shqipetare, Korce." Serial letter "C"	12.50

108 × 71

R7.		1 Franc. Type of #R6	12.50
R8.	Feb. 1918	½ Franc	25.00
R9.		1 Franc	25.00
R10.	1.11.1918	50 Centimes. Serial letter "A." City view on reverse	12.50
R11.		1 Franc. Type of #R10	12.50

R12.	1.12.1918	50 Centimes. Type of #R10 but serial letter "B"	12.50
R13.		1 Franc. Type of #R12	12.50
R14.	10.12.1918	50 Centimes. Type of #R10 but serial letter "C"	12.50
R15.		1 Franc. Type of #R14	12.50
R16.	March 1920	50 Centimes. Type of #R2 with "Territoire de Koritza"	12.50
R17.		1 Franc. Type of #R16	12.50
R18.	1. 4.1920	1 Franc, multicolored	25.00
R19.		2 Franc, multicolored	25.00
R20.	1. 8.1920	1 Franc	12.50

Skutari (Shkodre)

R21.	30. 1.1920	5 Qindtar. Text reads "Sigurim arke i perlimt ares se Shkodres permbi"	7.50
R22.		10 Qindtar. Type of #R21	7.50
R23.		20 Qindtar. Type of #R21	7.50
R24.		50 Qindtar. Type of #R21	7.50

Vlora, Bashkia e Vlores

R25.	1. 5.1924	10 Qindtar	10.00
R26.		25 Qindtar	10.00
R27.		1 Frank	10.00
R28.		2 Frank	10.00

ANDORRA

Tracing its history back for more than 1,000 years, Andorra is an independent free state on the Franco-Spanish border high in the Pyrenees mountains. The republic is under the joint protection of the President of France and the Spanish Bishop of Urgel. During the Spanish civil war of 1936–39, necessity money was issued with text printed in the Catalonian dialect.

1 Peseta = 100 Centimes

1.	19.12.1936	1 Peseta, blue with colored stamp	$10.00
2.		2 Pesetas. Type of #1	10.00
3.		5 Pesetas. Type of #1	12.50
4.		10 Pesetas. Type of #1	15.00
5.		50 Centimes, brown with impressed stamp	7.50
6.		1 Peseta. Type of #5	6.00

100 × 75

7.	2 Pesetas. Type of #5	6.00
8.	5 Pesetas. Type of #5	6.00
9.	10 Pesetas. Type of #5	10.00

AUSTRIA (Osterreich)

In 1869, Austria was linked with Hungary in a dual monarchy under Emperor Francis Joseph (1848–1916). The old monarchy was broken up after World War I with parts going to make up the present-day republics of Austria, Hungary, Czechoslovakia and Yugoslavia. Other pieces went to Italy and to Rumania. The Austrian Republic was called "Ostmark" while under German control from 1938 until 1945. Occupied by Allied troops after World War II, Austria was restored to independence and guaranteed neutrality under a 1955 treaty.

1 Gulden = 100 Kreuzer (until 1892)
1 Krone = 100 Heller (until 1924)
1 Schilling = 100 Groschen (1924–38 and 1945-   )

Osterreichisch-Ungarische Bank, Osztrak-Magyar Bank (Austro-Hungarian Bank)

1.	1. 5.1880	10 Gulden, blue. Woman's head at left and right	$10.00

154 × 108

2.		100 Gulden, blue. Boy with sickle and sheaf at left, boy with book at right	25.00
3.		1,000 Gulden, blue. Child's head at left and right	RR
4.	31. 3.1900	10 Kronen, lilac. Putti (cupids) at left and right	7.50
5.		20 Kronen, red and green. Woman's head with putti	12.50
6.	2. 1.1902	50 Kronen, blue. Seated woman at left and right	5.00
7.		100 Kronen, green. Seated woman and child at left, blacksmith at right	50.00
8.		1,000 Kronen, blue. Woman's head at right	1.50
9.	2. 1.1904	10 Kronen, blue violet on red and green. Girl's head (Princess Rohan) at right	2.50
10.	2. 1.1907	20 Kronen, blue on red brown and green. Woman's head at right	4.00
11.	2. 1.1910	100 Kronen, blue. Woman with flowers at right	30.00

12.	2. 1.1912	100 Kronen, green on red and blue. Woman's head at right	.75
13.	2. 1.1913	20 Kronen, blue on green and red. Woman's head at left	.50
14.		20 Kronen. Type of #13 but with "*II Auflage* (2nd issue)"	·50
15.	2. 1.1914	50 Kronen, blue and green. Woman's head	.75
16.	5. 8.1914	1 Krone. Woman's head. Trial printing	RR
17.		2 Kronen, blue. Girl's head	
		a. Thin paper with serial letter "A" or "B" (two control number varieties)	3.00
		b. Hard paper with serial letter "C"	.75
18.		5 Kronen. Woman's head. Trial printing	RR
19.	2. 1.1915	10 Kronen, blue and green. Boy's head at right	.50
20.	1.12.1916	1 Krone, red. Woman's head at left and right. Serial numbers 1,000–1,700	.25
		For serial numbers over 7,000 see Hungary # 10.	
21.	1. 3.1917	2 Kronen, red. Woman's head at left and right. Serial numbers 1,000–1,600 and A1,000–1,100 (two control number varieties)	
		For serial numbers over 7,000 see Hungary # 11.	
22.	1.10.1918	5 Kronen. Woman's head at left and right. Trial printing	RR
23.	27.10.1918	25 Kronen, blue on grey brown. Girl's head at left. Serial numbers to 2,000	4.00
		For serial numbers over 3,000 see Hungary #12 and #13.	
24.		200 Kronen, green on rose. Girl's head at left. Serial letter "B"	6.00
		For serial letter "A," see Hungary #14 and #16.	
25.	2.11.1918	10,000 Kronen, violet. Woman's head at right	2.00

Kriegsdarlehenskasse (War Loan Office Notes)

26.	26. 9.1919	250 Kronen, red and green. Three allegorical figures at right	10.00
27.		2,000 Kronen, green and brown. Type of #26	10.00
28.		10,000 Kronen, Lilac and blue. Type of #26	10.00
		Also see Hungary #1–3.	

Osterreichisch-Ungarische Bank (Austro-Hungarian Bank, Treasury Notes)

29.	3.10.1918	100,000 Kronen, violet and brown. Printed reverse	RR
30.	25.10.1918	5,000 Kronen	RRR
31.	26.10.1918	1,000 Kronen. Printed reverse	RR
32.	28.10.1918	1,000 Kronen, green. Blank reverse	RR
33.	30.10.1918	1,000 Kronen, green. Type of #32 except date	RR
34.	4.11.1918	10,000 Kronen. Printed reverse	RR
35.	18.11.1918	1 Million Kronen, red brown. Blank reverse	RR
36.	5. 2.1919	5,000 Kronen. Printed reverse	RR
37.	23.12.1921	1,000 Kronen, green	R
38.		5,000 Kronen, olive	RR
39.	23.12.1921	10,000 Kronen, blue	RR

217 × 128

40.		100,000 Kronen, violet	RRR

For Treasury Notes of the Hungarian branches of the Bank, see Hungary #4–9.

Osterreichisch-Ungarische Bank (Austro-Hungarian Bank), overprinted *"Ausgegeben nach dem 4. Okt. 1920"*

41.	1.12.1916	1 Krone. Same as #20 but overprinted in green	2.50
42.	1. 3.1917	2 Kronen. Same as #21 but overprinted in green	3.00
43.	2. 1.1915	10 Kronen. Same as #19 but overprinted in red	4.00
44.	2. 1.1913	20 Kronen. Same as #13 but overprinted in red	7.50
45.		20 Kronen. Same as #14 but overprinted in red	4.00
46.	2. 1.1914	50 Kronen. Same as #15 but overprinted in red	4.00
47.	2. 1.1912	100 Kronen. Same as #12 but overprinted in red	4.00
48.	2. 1.1902	1,000 Kronen. Same as #8 but overprinted in red	5.00

Osterreichisch-Ungarische Bank (Austro-Hungarian Bank), overprinted *"Deutschoster-reich 1919"* or *"1920"*

49.	1.12.1916	1 Krone. Same as #20 but overprinted in green	.25
50.	1. 3.1917	2 Kronen. Same as #21 but overprinted in green	.25
51.	2. 1.1915	10 Kronen. Same as #19 but overprinted in red	.25
52.	2. 1.1913	20 Kronen. Same as #13 but overprinted in red	.25
53.		20 Kronen. Same as #14 but overprinted in red	.25
		a. With additional stamp *"Note echt, Stempel falsch* (note genuine, stamp false)"	7.50
54.	2. 1.1914	50 Kronen. Same as #15 but overprinted in red	.25
		a. With additional stamp as #53a	7.50
55.	2. 1.1912	100 Kronen. Same as #12 but overprinted in red. Hungarian reverse	.25
		a. With additional stamp as #53a	7.50
		b. With additional stamp *"Note echt, Stempel nicht konstantierbar* (note genuine, stamp not verified)"	12.50
56.		100 Kronen. Same as #55 but German reverse	.25
57.	2. 1.1902	1,000 Kronen. Same as #8 but overprinted in red. Hungarian reverse	1.00
		a. With additional stamp as #53a	7.50

128 × 192

58.	1,000 Kronen. Same as #57 with additional black overprint *"Echt, Osterr.-ungar. Bank, Hauptanstalt Wien* (Genuine, Austro-Hungarian Bank, Head Office, Vienna)"*	10.00
59.	1,000 Kronen. Same as #57 but German reverse	.25
60.	1,000 Kronen. Obverse same as #57 but reverse has ornaments and woman's head at left and right	.25
61.	1,000 Kronen. Same as #60 but additional red overprint *"II Auflage (2nd issue)"*	·25
62.	2.11.1918 10,000 Kronen. Same as #25 but overprinted in red. Hungarian reverse	30.00
	a. With additional stamp as #53a	12.50
63.	10,000 Kronen. Same as #62 with additional overprint as #58	25.00
64.	10,000 Kronen. Obverse same as #62 but German reverse	2.00
65.	10,000 Kronen. Obverse same as #64 but reverse has ornaments and woman's head at left and right	1.00
66.	10,000 Kronen. Same as #65 but additional overprint *"II Auflage"*	1.50

Donaustaadt Noten (Danube Area Notes)

Only half printed, these unissued notes were used as lottery tickets. All have numerals but no indication of denomination. The first column is the value for the note only while the second column is the price for a specimen with the lottery overprint.

67.	No date	10 Green and red brown. Girl's head at right	7.50	1.00
68.		20 Green and violet. Girl's head at right	7.50	.75
69.		50 Blue and lilac. Woman's head at right	7.50	1.25
70.		100 Blue and brown. Woman's head at right	7.50	.75

| 71. | | 1,000 | Green and blue. Girl's head at right | 10.00 | 1.25 |
| 72. | | 10,000 | Red brown and olive. Rev. Heads of 11 children | 12.50 | 1.50 |

Osterreichisch-Ungarische Bank, Osterreichische Geschaftsfuhrung (Austro-Hungarian Bank, Austrian Management)

73.	2. 1.1922	1	Krone, red		.25
74.		2	Kronen, red. Woman's head at right		.25
75.		10	Kronen, blue violet. Child's head at right		.25
76.		20	Kronen, lilac. Bearded man's head at right		.25
			a. Error: Without colored background		R
77.		100	Kronen, green. Girl's head (Princess Rohan) at right		.25
78.		1,000	Kronen, blue. Woman's head at right		.25
79.		5,000	Kronen, green and red brown. Woman's head in picture frame at right		1.75
80.		50,000	Kronen, red brown and green. Woman's head in picture frame at right		6.50

195 × 131

81.		100,000	Kronen, blue and green. Woman's head in picture frame at right	7.50
82.	11. 9.1922	1,000,000	Kronen, blue green	RR
83.		5,000,000	Kronen, blue green	RR
84.	20. 9.1922	500,000	Kronen, brown lilac. Woman and three children at right	22.50

Osterreichische Nationalbank (Austrian National Bank)

Currency Reform, 1924: *10,000 Kronen = 1 Schilling*

85.	2. 1.1924	10,000	Kronen, violet and green. Girls head at right	1.50
86.		1	Schilling. Same as #85 but overprinted with new denomination	1.75
87.	1. 7.1924	1,000,000	Kronen	RR

88.	2. 1.1925	5 Schilling, green. Youth's head (E. Zwiauer, painter) at right	7.50
89.		10 Schilling, brown violet. Man's head at right	10.00
90.		20 Schilling, green. Woman's head at right	15.00
91.		100 Schilling, blue on multicolored. Woman's head at right	30.00

204 × 97

92.		1,000 Schilling, blue on green and red brown. Woman's head at right	R
93.	3. 1.1927	10 Schilling, blue on green and red. Mercury	10.00
94.		100 Schilling, violet on green. Woman's head (personification of Knowledge) at right	15.00
95.	1. 7.1927	5 Schilling, blue on green. Young man with pair of dividers at left	5.00
96.	2. 1.1928	20 Schilling, green. Girl's head at left, peasant at right	10.00
97.	2. 1.1929	50 Schilling, blue on brown olive. Woman's head at left, man's head at right	20.00
98.	2. 1.1930	1,000 Schilling, blue violet on green. Woman with a statuette of Athena	50.000
99.	2. 1.1933	10 Schilling, blue. Young woman in native costume	
		a. Corner numerals on diagonal lines	5.00
		b. Numerals on crosshatched lines	5.00
100.	2. 1.1935	50 Schilling, blue violet on green. Boy's head at right (Hubert Sterrer)	15.00
101.	2. 1.1936	100 Schilling, dark green on multicolored. Young woman with edelweiss (not officially issued)	25.00

From 1938 through 1945, the following German bank notes were in circulation: #171, #173, #174, #179–190.

Alliierte Militarbehorde (Allied Military Authority)

102.	1944	50 Groschen, red brown	
		a. Watermarked with "Military Authority" (not visible on most notes, occasionally part of a word shows)	2.00
		b. Watermarked with wavy lines	.75

103.	1 Schilling, blue on green	
	a. Watermarked as #102a	2.00
	b. Watermarked as #102b	.50
104.	2 Schilling, blue	
	a. Watermarked as #102a	2.00
	b. Watermarked as #102b	.75
105.	5 Schilling, lilac	.75
106.	10 Schilling, green	1.00
107.	20 Schilling, blue on blue violet	1.25

138 × 78

108.	25 Schilling, brown on lilac	10.00
109.	50 Schilling, brown on yellow brown	1.75
110.	100 Schilling, green	2.50
111.	1,000 Schilling, blue on green and multicolored	15.00

Republik Osterreich (Austrian Republic), issues of the Russian border garrison

112.	(20.12.1945)	50 Reichspfennig, brown on orange (not issued, pattern notes only)	R
113.		1 Reichsmark, green	5.00

Osterreichische Nationalbank (Austrian National Bank)

114.	29. 5.1945	10 Schilling, blue. Type of #99 — color varies from blue to violet (two control number varieties)	1.00
115.		10 Schilling, blue. Type of #114 but "Zweite Ausgabe" below design (two control number varieties)	6.00
116.		20 Schilling, blue green. Type of #96 but many color shades (two control number varieties)	1.00
117.		50 Schilling, dark green. Type of #100 but many color shades	4.00
118.		100 Schilling, blue violet to violet. Type of #94 but many color shades	1.00
119.		100 Schilling, blue violet. Type of #118 but design and "Zweite Ausgabe" at right	15.00
120.		1,000 Schilling, green. Type of #98	37.50
121.	4. 9.1945	5 Schilling, blue or violet on grey green. Type of #95 but many color shades (Also see #131)	2.00

122.	2. 2.1946	10	Schilling, multicolored. Woman's head at right	2.50
123.		20	Schilling, multicolored. Woman's head in middle	3.00
124.	2. 1.1947	100	Schilling, dark green. Young woman in native costume at right	6.25

184 × 92

125.	1. 9.1947	1,000	Schilling, dark brown on grey green. Type of #120 but design and "Zweite Ausgabe" at left	50.00
126.	3. 1.1949	100	Schilling, dark green. Cupids at left, woman's head at right	5.00
127.		100	Schilling, dark green. Same as #126 but overprinted "2 Auflage" at bottom left	4.00
128.	2. 1.1950	10	Schilling, violet. Prince Eugen on horseback	2.00
129.		10	Schilling, violet. Same as #128 but overprinted "2 Auflage" on upper reverse	2.00
130.		20	Schilling, brown on multicolored. Joseph Haydn at right	2.50
			Error: "OESTERREICHISC*E*E" in background printing on obverse	25.00
131.	1951	5	Schilling, violet on grey green. Same as #121 but overprinted "Ausgabe 1951" at left	2.00
132.	2. 1.1951	50	Schilling, lilac and violet. Jakob Prandtauer at right	4.00
133.	2. 1.1953	500	Schilling, dark brown on blue and red. Wagner v. Jauregg at right	25.00
134.	2. 1.1954	100	Schilling, green. Franz Grillparzer at right	4.50
135.		1,000	Schilling, blue. Anton Bruckner at right	45.00
136.	2. 7.1956	20	Schilling, brown on red brown and olive. Auer von Welsbach at right	1.50
137.	1. 7.1960	100	Schilling, green, violet and multicolored. Johann Strauss at right	—
138.	2. 1.1961	1,000	Schilling, dark blue and multicolored. Viktor Kaplan at right (size 148 × 75 mm)	R
139.		1,000	Schilling, dark blue and multicolored. Type of #138 but blue lined background to edge (size 158 × 85 mm)	—

140.	2. 7.1962	50 Schilling, violet. Richard Wettstein at right	—
141.	1. 7.1965	500 Schilling, red brown. Josef Ressel at right	—
142.	1. 7.1966	1,000 Schilling, dark blue and violet. Bertha von Suttner at right	—
143.	2. 7.1967	20 Schilling, brown. Carl Ritter von Ghega at right	—
144.	2. 1.1969	100 Schilling, dark green. Angelika Kauffmann at right	—

AUSTRIA (continued)

Notes of the Austrian Provinces 1918-1921

Karnten (Carinthia)

R1.	11.11.1918	10 Kronen, black. One-sided trial printing (not issued)	2.00
R2.		10 Kronen, orange. Type of R1	2.00

124 × 72

R3.		20 Kronen, blue. Both sides printed with control numbers (not issued)	7.50
R4.		100 Kronen, black. One-sided trial printing (not issued)	2.50
R5.		100 Kronen, orange. Type of R4	2.50
R6.	1. 3.1920	10 Heller, black and lilac on light brown	.25
R7.		20 Heller, black and blue on light brown	.25
R8.		50 Heller, black and green on light brown	.25

Niederosterreich (Lower Austria)

R9.	May 1920	10 Heller, dark green. Mountains with railroad bridge	.25
R10.		20 Heller, blue grey. Steamboat on the Danube	.25
R11.		50 Heller, brown. Peasant plowing with horses	.25
R12.	July 1920	10 Heller, green to dark green. Peasant woman with cows, "II Auflage"	.25
		Error: Picture on both sides	5.00
		Trial printing: One-sided on orange or lilac colored paper	7.50
R13.		20 Heller, blue to dark blue. Landscapes with horse and wagon, "II Auflage"	.25
		Trial printing: One-sided on white or lilac colored paper	7.50
R14.		50 Heller, brown. Castle, "II Auflage"	.25
		Error: Picture on both sides	5.00
		Trial printing: Light blue ink	12.50
		Trial printing: One-sided on lilac colored paper	7.50

Oberosterreich (Upper Austria)

R15.	1. 3.1920	20 Heller	
		a. Green blue, white paper	.25
		b. Green blue, bluish paper	.25
		c. Blue, grey paper	1.00
		d. Violet	1.00
		e. Green	6.00
		f. Brown	7.50
R16.		50 Heller	
		a. Dark brown	.25
		b. Red	.35
R17.	1. 6.1920	10 Heller	
		a. Rose paper	.25
		b. Grey violet paper	.25

78 × 53

R18.	21. 6.1920	80 Heller, red and grey	·40
R19.	1921	10 Heller	
		a. Red	.25
		b. Green	.25
		c. Orange	.35
		d. Brown	.25
		e. Blue	.25
R20.		20 Heller	
		a. Brown	.25
		b. Violet	.25
		c. Black	.25
		d. Green	.25
		Error: Wrong reverse picture (Steyr with fountains) in nine different colors, each	7.50
R21.	1. 2.1921	50 Heller, orange	.35

Osterreich ob der Enns (Austria on the Enns)

R22.	30.11.1918	5 Kronen, brown on green	1.50
R23.		10 Kronen, green on blue grey	2.00
R24.		20 Kronen, blue on grey brown	4.00
R25.		50 Kronen, brown on light brown	7.50

Salzburg

R26.	1.10.1919	10 Heller, blue on green	.25
		Error: No background color	2.50
R27.		20 Heller, black on yellow	.25
R28.		50 Heller, blue on rose	.25
		Error: No background color	2.50

R29.	May 1920	10 Heller, black and red. View of Salzburg about 1500	.35
		Error: Obverse or reverse without red plate	2.50
R30.		20 Heller, black and red. View of Salzburg about 1600	.35

78 × 61

R31.		50 Heller, black and red. View of Salzburg about 1700	.25
		Error: Obverse or reverse without red plate	2.50
R32.	1921	5 Kronen. Mirabelle Castle on reverse (not issued)	
		a. Obverse brown on red-brown background, reverse brown. Name of printing firm in middle (with and without control numbers)	2.50
		b. Type of R32a but name of printing firm at right, design at left	2.50
		c. Type of R32a but reverse lilac. Without name of printing firm	7.50
		d. Type of R32a but obverse brown on green	12.50
R33.		10 Kronen. Summer riding school in Salzburg on reverse (not issued)	
		a. Type of R32a	2.50
		b. Type of R32b	2.50
		c. Type of R32c	7.50
		d. Type of R32d	7.50
R34.		20 Kronen. Residenz Castle in Salzburg on reverse (not issued)	
		a. Type of R32a	2.50
		b. Type of R32b	2.50
		c. Type of R32c	7.50
		d. Type of R32d	12.50

Steiermark (Styria)

R35.	17.10.1919	10 Heller, blue	.25
R36.		20 Heller, green	.25
R37.		50 Heller, red brown on grey green	.25
R38.		50 Heller, red brown, "II Auflage"	
		a. Blue background	.35
		b. Green background	.35
		c. Yellow-brown background	.35
		d. Rose background	.35

Tirol (Tyrol)

R39.	1. 9.1919	10 Heller, orange	.35
R40.		20 Heller, grey	.35
R41.		50 Heller, green	.35
R42.	1.10.1920	10 Heller, green	.35
R43.		20 Heller, brown	.35
R44.		50 Heller, blue	.35

Vorarlberg

R45.	1.10.1919	10 Heller, green	.35
R46.		20 Heller, light brown	.35
R47.		50 Heller, blue	.35
R48.	1. 5.1921	50 Heller	
		a. Brown	.50
		b. Violet	.50
		Error: Reverse inverted	2.50

AZORES (Acores)

A group of islands in the Atlantic Ocean, the Azores is now a self-supporting province of Portugal.

1 Milreis = 1,000 Reis (Insulanos)
1 Escudo = 100 Centavos

Various notes of the Bank of Portugal are known with black imprints "Moeda Insulana" and "Acores" or a red imprint "Acores." Each new type of note has a different plate number ("Ch" for chapa = plate).

 124 × 82

1.	2,500 Reis. Alf. de Albuquerque, "Ch.1"	$15.00
2.	5,000 Reis. Tejo u. Douro, "Ch.3"	20.00
3.	10,000 Reis. Don Henrique, "Ch.3"	25.00
4.	10,000 Reis. Symbolic figures, "Ch.4"	25.00
5.	20,000 Reis. Symbolic figures of Mechanics and History, "Ch.3"	35.00
6.	50,000 Reis. Pero de Alenquer and Diogo Cao, "Ch.2"	45.00
7.	20 Escudos. Marques de Pombal, "Ch.4"	RR
8.	50 Escudos. Christovao da Gama, "Ch.3"	RR
9.	100 Escudos	RRR
10.	500 Escudos	RRR
11.	1,000 Escudos	RRR

Since 1931, regular Portuguese notes without imprints have circulated.

BELGIUM (Belgique - Belgie)

After Napoleon's defeat in 1815, Belgium became a part of the Netherlands but in 1830 it proclaimed its independence and chose Prince Leopold of Saxe-Coburg as King. The same ruling family has continued ever since. The country was occupied by Germany during both World Wars. King Leopold III (1937–51) was held a prisoner by the Germans during World War II and, in 1945, a regency was set up under Prince Charles (brother of Leopold III) until Prince Baudouin came of age in 1951.

1 Franc (Frank) = 100 Centimes (Centiemen)
1 Belga = 5 Francs

Most of the Belgian notes carry the date of printing, so many types exist with several different date varieties. The official designations of the note types are thus usually the name of the designer or engraver. Because of the two official languages, French and Flemish, Belgian notes carry inscriptions in both languages.

Banque Nationale de Belgique—Nationale Bank van Belgie (National Bank of Belgium)

Notes issued before World War I with printings continuing to 1922

1.	1.7.1914	5 Francs, brown and orange. (Hendrickx-Doms type) Allegorical figures	$10.00
		a. 25.1.1919 date (two signature varieties)	12.50
2.	1.7.1914	5 Francs, green and brown. Similar to #1 (Hendrickx-Doms type)	4.00
		a. 29.12.1918 date	2.50
		b. 30.12.1919 date	2.50
		c. 3.1.1921 date (two signature varieties)	2.50
3.	Various dates	20 Francs, wine red and green. Minerva with lion at left (Titz-Biet type, four signature varieties)	5.00
4.		50 Francs, blue and black. Woman's head in medallion and children (1887 type, three signature varieties)	37.50

#5

159 × 97

5.	50	Francs, green. Man with scythe at left, two women with book at right (Montald type, four signature varieties)	20.00
6.	100	Francs, blue and black. Man seated at left, woman with scepter at right (Hendrickx-Doms-Ligny type)	50.00
7.	100	Francs, blue, red and black. Type of #6 but denomination in red	50.00
8.	100	Francs, green. Quadriga with lions at left and right, lion in middle (Montald type)	37.50
9.	100	Francs, brown and black. Type of #8 but watermarked with medallion, white border below and arabesque imprinted at right (dated to 1914, two signature varieties)	7.50
10.	100	Francs, brown and black. Type of #9 but no arabesque (dated after 1914, two signature varieties)	5.00
11.	500	Francs, blue, red and black. Women and cupids (Hendrickx-Doms type). Bank name and value in red (three signature varieties)	R
12.	500	Francs, blue and green. Type of #11 but bank name and denomination (Francs only) in green (three signature varieties)	37.50
13.	1,000	Francs, black and blue. Neptune with trident at left, woman with scepter at right (Hendrickx-Pannemaker-Doms type)	R

220 × 134

14.	1,000	Francs, green and brown. Type of #13 (three signature varieties)	50.00
15.	1,000	Francs, green and brown. Type of #14 but no edge printing (provisional)	R

Banque Nationale de Belgique—Nationale Bank van Belgie (National Bank of Belgium)

Comptes Courants (War Issues)

16.	27.8.1914	1 Franc, blue on grey	.75

17.	2 Francs, brown on grey	1.50
18.	20 Francs, grey and brown. Leopold I	10.00
19.	100 Francs, grey, blue and red. Leopold I	30.00
20.	1,000 Francs, brown and red. Leopold I	RR

Societe Generale de Belgique

The notes issued by this bank during the German occupation and after the war show various printing dates between 1915 and 1920.

21.	1 Franc, violet. Queen Louise-Marie	.75
22.	2 Francs, brown. Queen Louise-Marie	1.00
23.	5 Francs, green. Queen Louise-Marie	5.00

137 × 88

24.	20 Francs, blue. Peter Paul Rubens	12.50
25.	100 Francs, brown. Queen Louise-Marie	37.50
26.	1,000 Francs, green. Peter Paul Rubens	RR

Bank Nationale de Belgique—Nationale Bank van Belgie (National Bank of Belgium)

Post war types, denominations in francs only, various dates from 1920

27.	1 Franc, blue. King Albert and Queen Elizabeth (Nationale type)	.50
28.	5 Francs, blue. Type of #27 (two signature varieties)	1.25
	See #46 and 47 for notes overprinted "Tresorerie."	
29.	20 Francs, brown. Type of #27 (two signature varieties)	5.00
	See #48 and 49 for notes overprinted "Tresorerie."	

182 × 105

30.	100 Francs, lilac brown. Type of #27 (three signature varieties)	4.00
31.	1,000 Francs, blue. Type of #27 (three signature varieties)	10.00

Denominations in both francs and belgas, various dates from 1927

32.	50 Francs = 10 Belgas, green. Type of #5 (Montald)	30.00
33.	50 Francs = 10 Belgas, blue. Peasant woman with sheaves and two horses (Anto-Carte type)	15.00
34.	50 Francs = 10 Belgas, green. Type of #33 but dated after 1928 See #50 for notes overprinted "Tresorerie."	5.00
35.	100 Francs = 20 Belgas, blue. King Albert and Queen Elizabeth (Nationale type)	2.50
36.	100 Francs = 20 Belgas, grey and light brown. Woman with crown and fruit in middle, Queen Elizabeth at left, King Albert at right. Serial number side in French (Vloors type, four signature varieties)	1.00

177 × 108

37.	100 Francs = 20 Belgas, grey and light brown. Type of #36 but serial number side in Flemish	2.50
38.	100 Francs = 20 Belgas, orange. Type of #36	20.00
39.	100 Francs = 20 Belgas, orange. Type of #37	20.00
40.	500 Francs = 100 Belgas, blue and green. Frame with women and cupids (Hendrickx-Doms type). Signatures on obverse only	4.50
41.	500 Francs = 100 Belgas, blue and green. Type of #40 but signatures on both sides (dated from 1938, two signature varieties)	4.00
42.	1,000 Francs = 200 Belgas, green. Type of #31 (Nationale). Signature on obverse only (three signature varieties)	2.50
43.	1,000 Francs = 200 Belgas, green. Type of #42 but signatures on both sides (two signature varieties)	2.50
44.	1,000 Francs = 200 Belgas, red. Type of #42 (issued 1944)	RRR
45.	10,000 Francs = 2,000 Belgas, blue and red. Quadrigas at left and right, lion in middle (three signature varieties)	45.00

Tresorerie-Thesaurie (State Treasury Notes)

Issues from 1926

46.	5 Francs, blue. Same as #28 (Nationale) but overprinted "Tresorerie—Thesaurie" on obverse	.75

125 × 75

| 47. | 5 Francs, blue. Same as #28 but overprinted "Tresorerie" on obverse, "Thesaurie" on reverse | 1.00 |

47.   5 Francs, blue. Same as #28 but overprinted "Tresorerie" on obverse, "Thesaurie" on reverse — 1.00

48.   20 Francs, brown. Same as #29 but overprinted "Tresorerie—Thesaurie" on obverse (two signature varieties) — 3.00

49.   20 Francs, brown. Same as #29 but overprinted "Tresorerie" on obverse, "Thesaurie" on reverse (four signature varieties) — 1.25

50.   50 Francs = 10 Belgas, green. Same as #34 but overprinted "Tresorerie—Thesaurie" on obverse (six signature varieties) — .75

Bank Nationale de Belgique—Nationale Bank van Belgie (National Bank of Belgium)

Printed in England, dated 1.2.1943 but issued in 1944

51.   1.2.1943   5 Francs = 1 Belga, red — .50
52.   10 Francs = 2 Belgas, green — .75
53.   100 Francs = 20 Belgas, red and green — 2.50
54.   500 Francs = 100 Belgas, violet, lilac and green — 12.50
55.   1,000 Francs = 200 Belgas, brown and violet — 35.00

Issues after 1944

56.   100 Francs, brown, rose and yellow. Leopold I at left, Grand Place, Brussels in middle (Dynastie type, two signature varieties) — 15.00

57.   100 Francs, brown and multicolored. Leopold I at left, Frere Orban on reverse (Centenaire type, three signature varieties) — —

58.   100 Francs, lilac brown. Lambert Lombard at left (Lombard type) — —

59.   500 Francs, brown and yellow. Leopold II in military cap at left, view of Antwerp in middle (Dynastie type, two signature varieties) — 20.00

60.   500 Francs, lilac and brown. Leopold II without cap (Centenaire type, three signature varieties) — —

61.   500 Francs, blue and brown. Bernard Van Orley (Van Orley Type) — —

180 × 94

62.	1,000 Francs, blue. King Albert I in steel helmet at left (Dynastie type, three signature varieties)	35.00
63.	1,000 Francs, blue and multicolored. King Albert I in civilian dress (Centenaire type, three signature varieties)	—
64.	1,000 Francs, brown. Gerard Kremer, known as Mercator, at left (Mercator type)	—

Tresorerie—Thesaurie (State Treasury Notes)

Issues after 1945

65.	20 Francs, lilac and violet. Roland de Lassus. Dated 1.7.1950 or 3.4.1956 (two signature varieties)	1.25
66.	20 Francs, blue, green and multicolored. King Baudouin. Dated from 1964	—
67.	50 Francs, yellow, green and multicolored. Peasant woman with fruit at left, peasant man at right. Dated 1.6.1948 or 3.4.1956 (two signature varieties)	1.50
68.	50 Francs, brown. King Baudouin and Queen Fabiola. Dated from 1966	—

Armee Belge—Belgisch Leger (Belgian Army)

Notes issued for Belgian troops in Germany after World War II

M1.	1 Franc, green and blue	2.00
M2.	2 Francs, green and violet	2.50
M3.	5 Francs, green and red	2.50
M4.	10 Francs, brown and blue	6.00
M5.	20 Francs, brown and green	10.00
M6.	50 Francs, brown and red	17.50

150 × 75

| M7. | 100 Francs, grey blue and violet | 30.00 |
| M8. | 500 Francs, grey blue and green | 50.00 |

BOHEMIA—MORAVIA (see Czechoslovakia)

BULGARIA

Under Turkish rule from 1396, Bulgaria was declared an independent principality in 1878 under Prince Alexander Joseph. Ferdinand of Saxe-Coburg-Gotha came to the throne in 1887, declaring himself King in 1908. Bulgaria took the German side in both World Wars and was invaded by Russia in 1944. King Simeon III was deposed in 1946, the nation then becoming a communist People's Republic.

1 Lev (ЛЕВ) = *100 Stotinki* (СТОТИНКИ)
БЪЛГАРСКА НАРОДНА БАНКА = *Bulgarskata Narodna Banka* (Bulgarian National Bank)
ЦАРСТВО БЪЛГАРА = *Carstvo Bulgarija* (State Notes)
НАРОДНА РЕПЧБЛИКА БЪЛГАРИЯ = *Narodna Republika Bulgarija* (Bulgarian People's Republic)
ЛЕВ СРЕБРО = *Lev Srebro* (Silver Lev)
ЛЕВ ЗЛАТО = *Lev Zlato* (Gold Lev)

Bulgarskata Narodna Banka (Bulgarian National Bank)

Russian printing (without name of printing firm), values in "Lev Srebro." Issued from 1879 (undated) on unwatermarked paper with some signature varieties.

1.	5 Leva Srebro, blue border and red frame. Arms without script on reverse. Design in vertical format	$20.00
2.	5 Leva Srebro, green border with lilac and violet frame. Arms with "Carstvo Bulgaria" on reverse. Vertical format (issued August 1909)	10.00

91 × 142

3.	10 Leva Srebro, blue border, multicolored frame. Vertical format	7.50

4.	20 Leva Srebro, multicolored. Vertical format	20.00
5.	50 Leva Srebro, multicolored. Vertical format	25.00
6.	100 Leva Srebro, brown, blue and green. Vertical format	37.50
7.	500 Leva Srebro, grey, rose and blue. Vertical format	50.00

Russian printing (without name of printing firm), values in "Lev Zlato." Issues from 1885 (undated), on unwatermarked paper, some signature varieties.

8.	5 Leva Zlato. Same as #1 but "Srebro" crossed out and "Zlato" overprinted at left and right	8.50
9.	10 Leva Zlato. Same as #3 but "Srebro" crossed out and "Zlato" overprinted at left and right	10.00
10.	20 Leva Zlato, rose border, red and blue frame. Design in horizontal format	10.00
11.	50 Leva Zlato, rose border, blue and green frame. Horizontal format	12.50
12.	100 Leva Zlato, rose border, grey frame. Horizontal format	17.50

200 × 127

13.	500 Leva Zlato, rose border, rose and green frame. Horizontal format	20.00

Printed at Reichsdruckerei in Berlin (without name of printing firm). Issued in 1916 but undated. Watermarked with cross and small ring pattern.

14.	1 Lev Srebro, green and blue. Horizontal format	.75
15.	2 Leva Srebro, green and rose. Horizontal format	1.50
16.	5 Leva Srebro, yellow border, blue and grey ornamentation. Vertical format	3.00
17.	10 Leva Srebro, green-blue border, rose and lilac ornamentation. Vertical format	4.00
18.	20 Leva Zlato. Vertical format	5.00
19.	50 Leva Zlato, green-blue border, brown ornamentation. Horizontal format	12.50
20.	100 Leva Zlato, green border, blue, lilac and violet ornamentation. Horizontal format	15.00

Printed by Giesecke & Devrient, Leipzig, (name imprinted on notes). Issued in August 1917 but undated. All notes are watermarked with letters.

| 21. | 5 Leva Srebrni. Horizontal format | 1.50 |
| 22. | 10 Leva Zlatni. Horizontal format | 2.00 |

158 × 100

23.	20 Leva Zlatni. Horizontal format	4.00
24.	50 Leva Zlatni. Horizontal format	17.50
25.	100 Leva Zlatni. Woman with sheaf at left. Horizontal format	10.00

Notes #8 through #25 also exist with a Serbian overprint increasing the value from 50 to 100%.

Various issues until 1928

26.	(1920)	1 Lev Srebro, green. Woman at right, buildings on the reverse. Printed by Waterlow & Sons. Watermarked with zigzag lines	.75
27.	(1920)	2 Leva Srebro, brown. Type of #26	1.25
28.		100 Leva Zlato. Same as #20 with red overprint "БНБ" and "СЕРИЯ А"	RR
29.	(1918)	1,000 Leva Zlatni, blue green and light brown. Printed by Gebr. Parcus, Munich	30.00
30.	5.6.1924	1,000 Leva Zlatni. Same as #29 with overprint meaning "this note is good only within the kingdom"	37.50
31.	Nov. 1925	1,000 Leva Zlatni. Same as #29 with overprint meaning "This certificate has a value in the kingdom of one banknote of 1,000 Leva, Sofia, Nov. 1925"	37.50
32.		1,000 Leva Zlatni. Same as #29 but both overprints as on #30 and #31	37.50
33.	(1920)	1,000 Leva Zlatni. Same as #29 but printed by Bradbury-Wilkinson Company, London	30.00
34.	(1924)	1,000 Leva Zlatni. Same as #33 with overprint as on #30	37.50
35.	1924	5,000 Leva	R

Carstvo Bulgarija (State Note)

36.   10.5.1916   1,000 Leva, grey blue. Printed in Bulgaria. Watermarked with cross and small ring pattern   40.00

Bulgarskata Narodna Banka (Bulgarian National Bank)

Issues after the currency reform of 1928.

37.   1922   5 Leva. Printed by the American Bank Note Company   1.00
38.   10 Leva. Type of #37   1.50
39.   20 Leva. Type of #37   6.00
40.   50 Leva. Type of #37   8.50

152 × 86

41.   100 Leva. Type of #37   12.50
42.   500 Leva. Type of #37   20.00
43.   1,000 Leva. Type of #37   45.00
44.   (1928)   20 Leva, brown. King Boris III facing left   17.50
45.   1925   50 Leva, brown. King Boris III at right. Printed by
                    Bradbury   4.00
46.   100 Leva, blue. Type of #45   6.50
47.   500 Leva, dark green. Type of #45   15.00
48.   1,000 Leva, brown and blue. Type of #45   37.50
49.   5,000 Leva, dark violet. Type of #45   50.00

152 × 84

50.   1929   200 Leva, green. King Boris III at right. Printed by De
                    La Rue & Company   5.00
51.   250 Leva, lilac. Type of #50   12.50
52.   500 Leva, blue. Type of #50   30.00

53.		1,000 Leva, brown. Type of #50	50.00
54.		5,000 Leva, brown. Type of #50	R
55.	1938	500 Leva, lilac, brown and green. King Boris III at left. Printed by Giesecke & Devrient	12.50
56.		1,000 Leva, lilac, brown and green. Type of #55	15.00
57.		5,000 Leva, green. Type of #55	20.00
58.	1940	500 Leva, blue and green. King Boris III at right. Printed by Reichsdruckerei, Berlin	4.00
59.		1,000 Leva, red and brown. Type of #58	5.00
60.	1942	500 Leva, blue, green and brown. King Boris III at left	2.50

182 × 91

61.		1,000 Leva, red and brown. Type of #60	3.00
62.		5,000 Leva, brown. Printed by Giesecke & Devrient	6.50
63.	1943	20 Leva, blue, green and rose (date at lower right of obverse)	1.00
64.		200 Leva, brown. King Simeon III as a child at left. Printed by Reichsdruckerei, Berlin	2.50
65.		250 Leva, green. Type of #64	3.00
66.		500 Leva, blue. Type of #64	2.00
67.		1,000 Leva, dark red. King Simeon III at right. Printed by Reichsdruckerei, Berlin	2.50
68.	1944	20 Leva, brown (date at lower right of obverse)	1.50
69.	1945	200 Leva, green and ochre. Without portrait of the Czar	5.00
70.		250 Leva, green and brown. Type of #69	6.25

155 × 81

71.		500 Leva, blue. Type of #69	8.75
72.		1,000 Leva, brown. Type of #69	12.50
73.		5,000 Leva, multicolored. Type of #69	20.00

Bulgarskata Narodna Banka (People's Republic, Bulgarian National Bank)

74.	1947	20 Leva, dark blue (date below, with name of printing firm)	3.50
75.	1948	200 Leva, brown. Arms with "9.IX.1944" at left (date below, with name of printing firm)	15.00
76.		250 Leva, green. Type of #75	20.00
77.		500 Leva, blue. Type of #75	25.00
78.		1,000 Leva. Type of #75 with soldier at right	37.50
79.	1950	20 Leva, brown	3.00
80.	1951	10 Leva, red brown. Tractor	.25
81.		25 Leva, grey blue. Track layer	.25
82.		50 Leva, brown. Peasant woman with basket and flowers	.40
83.		100 Leva, green and blue. Woman grape picker and grapes	.75

175 × 90

84.		200 Leva, grey blue and multicolored. Tobacco harvest	1.50
85.	1962	1 Lev, brown lilac. Tower	—
86.		2 Leva, green. Woman grape picker and grapes	—
87.		5 Leva, red brown. Seashore scene	—
88.		10 Leva, blue. Factory	—
89.		20 Leva, brown lilac. Factory	—

Narodna Republika Bulgarija (Bulgarian People's Republic, State Notes)

90.	1951	1 Lev, brown	.25
91.		3 Leva, green	.25
92.		5 Leva, blue and green	.25

CROATIA (Hrvatska)

Until 1918, Croatia was part of the Kingdom of Hungary. In that year, along with Serbia and Slavonia, it became part of the Kingdom of Yugoslavia. During the 1941–44 German occupation, Croatia was declared an independent state. In 1945, Croatia was returned to Yugoslavia and is now part of the Federated Peoples Republic.

1 Kuna = 100 Banica (1941–44)

Nezavisna Drzava Hrvatska (Autonomous State of Croatia)

1.	26.5 (Svibnja).1941	50 Kuna, red brown	$1.25
2.		100 Kuna, blue grey	.50
3.		500 Kuna, green. Three sheafs of cereal at right	2.00

4.		1,000 Kuna, brown. Peasant girl at left	1.25
5.	30.8 (Kolovoza).1941	10 Kuna, olive	1.00
6.	25.9 (Rujna).1942	50 Banica, blue on light brown	1.00
7.		1 Kuna, dark blue on brown	.50
8.		2 Kuna, dark brown on red brown	.75
9.	15.1 (Siecnja).1944	20 Kuna, brown (not issued)	5.00
10.		50 Kuna, green (not isssued)	10.00

Hrvatska Drzavna Banka (Croatian State Bank)

11.	1.9 (Rujna).1943	100 Kuna, dark blue and brown	4.00
12.		1,000 Kuna, dark brown on yellow and green	1.50
13.		5,000 Kuna, red brown, blue and brown	1.50
14.	15.8 (Srpnja).1943	5,000 Kuna, brown on lilac and green. Girl in national costume at left	2.00

CZECHOSLOVAKIA (Ceskoslovenska)

When World War I brought about the collapse of the Austro-Hungarian Empire, the ancient territories of Bohemia, Moravia and Slovakia were united to form the new Republic of Czechoslovakia. In 1938, the Treaty of Munich separated the Sudetenland from the Republic and, in 1939, the independent state of Slovakia was formed. German troops occupied the rest of the country, forming the Protectorate of Bohemia-Moravia. After World War II, Czechoslovakia was re-established and, since 1948, it has been a Communist People's Republic.

1 Krone = 100 Heller

Notes of the Austro-Hungarian Bank with counterstamps or overprints added in 1919

1.	2.1.1915	10 Kronen. Austrian note #19 with "heller" overprinted in blue	$2.50
2.	2.1.1913	20 Kronen. Austrian note #13 with "heller" overprinted in red	2.00
3.	2.1.1914	50 Kronen. Austrian note #15 with "heller" overprinted in brown	2.00
4.	2.1.1912	100 Kronen. Austrian note #12 with "heller" overprinted in orange brown	2.00
5.	2.1.1902	1,000 Kronen. Austrian note #8 with "heller" overprinted in black red	5.00

> Numerous marking and overprint falsifications are known. In addition to notes #1–5 above, overprints are known on the 10 Kronen of 2.1.1904, the 20 Kronen of 2.1.1907, the 20 Kronen of 2.1.1913 (II issue) and the 100 Kronen of 2.1.1910. These are not, however, official stamps.

Most of the following notes marked "specimen" were released in large quantities for collectors. Up to 1945 the notes were perforated with holes spelling the words "Specimen" or "Neplatne." Specimen notes issued after 1945 were also perforated but with much smaller holes. The first column of prices is for regularly issued notes, the second column for specimens. The difference in value is often very large.

Bankovni urad Ministertva Financi (Authorized Bank of the Finance Ministry)

6.	15. 4 (Dubna).1919	1 Krone, blue	.75	—
7.		5 Kronen, red. Two girls' heads	1.00	—
8.		10 Kronen, violet and yellow. Two girls' heads	4.50	—

9.		20 Kronen, red. Two men's heads	7.50	—
10.		50 Kronen, olive, green and brown. Two women's heads	17.50	—
11.		100 Kronen, violet. Two women's heads	37.50	—

175 × 119

12.		500 Kronen, red and brown. Woman's head and two eagles	R	—
13.		1,000 Kronen, blue. Allegorical figures with globe	50.00	12.50
14.		5,000 Kronen, red. Woman's head at right (like Austria #8)	RR	R
15.	14. 1 (Ledna).1920	100 Kronen, green. Pagan priestess at right	20.00	10.00
16.	6. 7 (Cervence).1920	5,000 Kronen, brown violet. Elbe river with Rip mountain, girl in costume at right (also see #42)	20.00	2.50
17.	28. 9 (Zari).1921	5 Kronen, blue and brown. J. A. Comenius	1.50	—
18.	12. 7 (Cervence).1922	50 Kronen, blue, brown and red. Peasant with castle in background on the reverse	12.50	—
19.	6.10 (Rijna).1923	500 Kronen, brown. Head of Legionaire at right	R	50.00

Narodna Banka Ceskoslovenska (National Bank of Czechoslovakia)

20.	1.10 (Rijna).1926	20 Kronen, blue, brown and red	1.50	.50
21.	2. 1 (Januara).1927	10 Kronen, lilac and light brown. Type of #8	1.50	.50
22.	2. 5 (Maja).1929	500 Kronen, red. Type of #19	10.00	1.00
23.	1.10 (Oktobra).1929	50 Kronen, red. Girl's head at left	2.50	.75
24.	10. 1 (Ledna).1931	100 Kronen, green. Boy with falcon at left, woman's head at right	2.00	.75
25.	8. 4 (Dubna).1932	1,000 Kronen, blue. Type of #13	12.50	2.00

198 × 105

26. 25. 5 (Kvetna).1934   1,000 Kronen, green and blue.
Woman with book and two
children at left   5.00   1.00

Protectorate of Bohemia-Moravia, 1939–1945 (Issued during German occupation).

27. (1940)   1 Krone, blue. Girl's head at right. Unissued Czechoslovakian note with stamp
"Bohmen und Mahren"
a. Handstamp   2.50   —
b. Machine stamp   5.00   —
c. Without stamp   10.00   —
28.   5 Kronen, lilac and violet. Man's head at
right (J. Jungmann). Unissued Czecho-
slovakian note with stamp "Bohmen und
Mahren"
a. Handstamp   2.50   —
b. Machine stamp   7.50   —
c. Without stamp   15.00   —
29.   1 Krone, brown. Girl's head at right   1.00   .50
30.   5 Kronen, green. Woman's head at right   1.25   .50
31. 28. 8.1940   100 Kronen, blue. View of Prague with Hrad-
schin and Charles Bridges on red reverse   1.50   .50
32.   100 Kronen, blue. Type of #31 but "II
Auflage" on blue reverse   1.00   .50
33. 12. 9.1940   50 Kronen, dark brown and grey. Women's
head at right   2.50   1.00
34.   8. 7.1942   10 Kronen, brown. Girl's head at right (two
control number varieties)   1.00   .50
35. 24. 1.1944   20 Kronen, green. Boy's head at right (two
control number varieties)   1.00   .50
36. 25. 9.1944   50 Kronen, grey. Woman's head at right   2.00   .50

Nationalbank fur Bohmen und Mahren (National Bank for Bohemia-Moravia)

37. 24. 2.1942   500 Kronen, dark brown. P. Brandl, artist, at
right   7.50   1.00

38.		500	Kronen, dark brown. Type of #37 but "II Auflage" on reverse	6.00	1.00
39.	24.10.1942	1,000	Kronen, dark green. P. Parler, sculptor, at right	10.00	2.50
40.		1,000	Kronen, dark green. Type of #39 but "II Auflage" on reverse. Ornament (guilloche) of blue and brown	7.50	1.00
41.		1,000	Kronen, dark green. Type of #39 but multicolored ornament (guilloche)	10.00	1.50
42.	6. 7.1920	5,000	Kronen, brown violet. Same as #16 with red overprint "Nationalbank fur Bohmen und Mahren." Known only as a specimen (issued 25.10.1943)	—	6.00

189 × 90

43.	24. 2.1944	5,000	Kronen, grey. St. Wencelas at right	15.00	1.50

CZECHOSLOVAK SOCIALIST REPUBLIC

State note issued by the Slovakian State Bank

44.	1945	2,000	Kronen, blue and green	R	20.00

State notes, Russian printing

45.	1944	1	Krone, brown	.75	.50
46.		5	Kronen, blue		
			a. Background of horizontal wavy lines	1.00	.50
			b. Background of vertical wavy lines	1.00	.50
47.		20	Kronen, dark blue on brown (two control number varieties)	1.25	.50
48.		100	Kronen, green (two control number varieties)	2.00	.50
49.		500	Kronen, red	5.00	.75
50.		1,000	Kronen, dark blue on green	7.50	1.00

State notes with stamps

51.	7.10.1940	100	Kronen, blue. Slovakian note #9 with yellow stamp (issued in 1945)	4.00	1.00
52.		100	Kronen, blue. Slovakian note #10 with yellow stamp "II Emisia" on reverse	5.00	1.00

53.	12. 7.1941	500 Kronen, green. Slovakian note #13 with orange stamp (issued in 1945)	7.50	1.50
54.	25.11.1940	1,000 Kronen, brown. Slovakian note #12 with red stamp (issued in 1945)	5.00	1.00

168 × 84

55.	1944	100 Kronen, green. Same as #48 with blue stamp (issued in 1945)	2.50	1.00
56.		500 Kronen, red. Same as #49 with blue stamp	6.00	1.00
57.		1,000 Kronen, dark blue on green. Same as #50 with blue stamp	8.50	1.25

States notes issued to 1.6.1953

58.		1 Krone, blue. Type of #27c but no background	2.50	—
59.	(1945)	5 Kronen, red brown	.75	.50
60.		10 Kronen, green	.75	.50
61.		20 Kronen, blue on green. Karel Havlicek at left	1.50	.50
62.		50 Kronen, lilac on green. General Stefanik at left	2.00	.50
63.		100 Kronen, dark green. Tomas Masaryk at left	2.00	.75
64.		500 Kronen, brown. J. Kollar at left	2.00	1.00
65.		1,000 Kronen, grey black. King George von Podiebrad	2.50	1.00
66.	16. 5 (Kvetna).1945	100 Kronen, grey brown. Woman's head at right	1.50	.50
67.	3. 7.1948	50 Kronen, blue green. General Stefanik at right (three control number varieties)	2.50	.50
68.	25. 1 (Ledna).1949	5 Kronen, red brown. Type of #59	1.00	.50
69.	1. 5 (Kvetna).1949	20 Kronen, red brown. Girl with floral wreath at right		
		a. Bluish paper with fibers in left edge	2.00	.50
		b. Yellowish paper without fibers	2.00	.50

70.	4. 4.1950	10 Kronen, green. Type of #60	.75	.50
71.	29. 8.1950	50 Kronen, violet brown. Miner at right		
		a. Bluish paper with fibers in left edge	2.00	.50
		b. Yellowish paper without fibers	2.00	.50
72.	25. 2 (Unora).1953	20 Kronen, blue (not issued)	RRR	—

Narodna Banka Ceskoslovenska (Czechoslovakian National Bank)

Issues to 1.6.1953

73.	16. 5 (Kvetna).1945	1,000 Kronen, grey. Girl's head at right		
		a. Thick, yellowish paper watermarked with a dark cross between light lines	3.00	1.00
		b. Transparent, bluish paper watermarked as #73a	3.00	1.00
		c. Thick, yellowish paper watermarked with a light cross and dark beams	3.00	1.00
		d. Transparent, bluish paper watermarked as #73c	3.00	1.00
74.	1.11 (Listopadu).1945	5,000 Kronen, dark brown. Smetana at right	4.00	1.00
75.	12. 3.1946	500 Kronen, brown. Type of #64	2.50	1.00

Statni Banka Ceskoslovenska (Czechoslovakian State Bank)

76.	9. 5 (Kvetna).1951	1,000 Kronen, brown. Type of #73 (not issued)	RR	—

149 × 70

77.	24.10 (Rijna).1951	100 Kronen, brown. Woman's head at right (not issued)	RR	—

States notes of the CSSR from 1.6.1953

78.	1953	1 Krone, brown	1.00	—
79.		3 Kronen, blue	2.00	—
80.		5 Kronen, green	3.00	—

81.	1961	3 Kronen, blue	—	—
82.		5 Kronen, green	—	—

Statni Banka Ceskoslovenska (Czechoslovakian State Bank)

83.	1953	10 Kronen, brown	4.00	—
84.		25 Kronen, blue. Equestrian statue of J. Ziska (two control number varieties)	6.00	—
85.		50 Kronen, green. Partisan fighter and Russian soldier at left	4.00	—
86.		100 Kronen, brown. Worker and peasant at left (two control number varieties)	3.00	—
87.	1958	25 Kronen, blue. J. Ziska at left	4.50	—
88.	1960	10 Kronen, brown. Two girls with flowers	—	—
89.	1961	25 Kronen, blue. Type of #87	—	—
90.		100 Kronen, green. Worker and peasant girl	—	—
91.	1964	50 Kronen, red brown. Partisan fighter and Russian soldier	—	—

DANZIG (Gdansk)

Danzig was annexed to Prussia in 1793, declared a free city by Napoleon in 1807 and returned to Prussia in 1814. Following World War I, Danzig was made a free state again by the League of Nations. In 1939, the city was again occupied by Germany. Today, it is a part of Poland.

1 Mark = 100 Pfennig
1 Gulden = 100 Pfennig

Magistrat der Stadt (Municipal Council of the City)

Emergency issues prior to 1920

1.	10. 8.1914	50 Pfennig, violet	
		a. Watermarked with flakes	$10.00
		b. Watermarked with wavy lines	7.50
		c. Watermarked with spades	7.50
2.		1 Mark, brown	
		a. Watermarked with wavy lines	10.00
		b. Watermarked with spades	7.50
3.		2 Mark, rose	10.00
4.		3 Mark, green	
		a. Watermarked with spades	10.00
		b. Watermarked with crosses in squares	12.50
5.	9.12.1916	10 Pfennig, blue	1.00
6.		50 Pfennig, light brown	1.00
7.	12.10.1918	5 Mark, black on green	
		a. Watermarked with small drops	7.50
		b. No watermark	4.00
8.		20 Mark, black on brown	
		a. Watermarked with small drops	15.00
		b. Watermarked with spades	12.50
		c. No watermark	7.50
9.	1.11.1918	50 Pfennig, brown. Guild Hall	.75

129 × 79

10.	15.11.1918	20 Mark, black on lilac brown. Sailing ship "Kogge" at left	3.00

11.	15. 4.1919	50 Pfennig, brown and violet. City view on reverse	.50
12.		50 Pfennig, dark green and olive green. Type of #11	.50

Senat der Stadtgemeinde (Senate of the Free City Government)

Emergency money issued after 1920 with denominations in marks

1 Milliarde = 1 Billion (American) = 1,000,000,000

13.	31.10.1922	100 Mark, green on grey. Marian church	1.50
14.		500 Mark, blue. Krantor on the reverse	1.50
15.		1,000 Mark, olive green and dark brown. Sailing ship "Kogge"	1.50
16.	15. 3.1923	1,000 Mark, dark green. Type of #15	2.00
17.	20. 3.1923	10,000 Mark, dark blue on dark brown. City view at left and right	1.00
18.		50,000 Mark, light green on yellow. Marian church	1.25
19.		50,000 Mark, dark brown and brown. Type of #18	1.50

147 × 87

20.	26. 6.1923	10,000 Mark, dark brown and blue. Painting of a Danzig merchant by Hans Holbein the Younger	1.00
21.	8. 8.1923	1,000,000 overprinted on 50,000 Mark. Note #19 with new value in red	1.00
22.		1,000,000 overprinted on 50,000 Mark. Note #19 with new value in dark blue	2.50
23.		1,000,000 Mark, lilac and green. Chodowiecki	.50
24.		5,000,000 overprinted on 50,000 Mark. Note #19 with new value in green	1.00
25.	31. 8.1923	10,000,000 Mark, green. J. Hevelius	.50
26.		10,000,000 Mark. Same as #25 but border imprint inverted	1.50
27.	22. 9.1923	100 Million Mark, black on orange	
		a. Watermarked with triangles	.50
		b. Watermarked with small drops	2.50
28.	26. 9.1923	500 Million Mark, dark brown on violet. Schopenhauer. Border script light blue or light yellow	.50
29.		500 Million Mark. Same as #28 but border script inverted	1.50

30.	11.10.1923	5 Milliarde Mark, black on blue	.75
31.		10 Milliarde Mark, black on brown	
		a. Watermarked with entwined lines	.75
		b. Watermarked with small drops	1.25

Danziger Zentralkasse (Danzig Central Treasury)

32.	22.10.1923	1 Pfennig	2.00
33.		2 Pfennig	2.50
34.		5 Pfennig	
		a. Paper watermarked with entwined lines	3.00
		b. Paper watermarked with octagons	7.50
35.		10 Pfennig	
		a. Paper watermarked with entwined lines	3.00
		b. Paper watermarked with sailing ship "Kogge"	4.00
36.		25 Pfennig	4.00
37.		50 Pfennig	5.00

93 × 64

38.		1 Gulden	
		a. Paper watermarked with entwined lines	7.50
		b. Paper watermarked with sailing ship "Kogge"	12.50
39.		2 Gulden	20.00
40.		5 Gulden	
		a. Paper watermarked with entwined lines	20.00
		b. Paper watermarked with sailing ship "Kogge"	25.00
41.		10 Gulden	20.00
42.		25 Gulden	30.00
43.	1.11.1923	1 Pfennig	10.00
44.		5 Pfennig	12.50
45.		10 Pfennig	17.50
46.		25 Pfennig	20.00
47.		50 Pfennig	20.00
48.		1 Gulden	25.00

Bank von Danzig (Bank of Danzig)

49.		2 Gulden	40.00
50.		5 Gulden	50.00
51.		50 Gulden	R

52.	1.11.1923	100	Gulden		RR
53.	10. 2.1924	10	Gulden		R
54.		25	Gulden		RR
55.		100	Gulden, blue		22.50
56.		500	Gulden, green		10.00

170 × 93

57.		1,000	Gulden, red orange	12.50
58.	1.10.1928	25	Gulden, dark green	22.50
59.	1. 7.1930	10	Gulden, brown	6.00
60.	2. 1.1931	25	Gulden, dark green	7.50
61.	1. 8.1931	100	Gulden, blue	8.50
62.	2. 1.1932	20	Gulden, lilac brown	6.00
63.	5. 2.1937	50	Gulden, brown	7.50
64.	1.11.1937	20	Gulden, dark green	5.00

DENMARK (Danmark)

Denmark became a constitutional monarchy in 1848 under King Frederick VII (1848–63). The present King, Frederick IX, came to the throne in 1947. The country was occupied by Germany during both World Wars.

1 Krone = 100 Ore.

Most Danish banknotes are known with many date and signature varieties

Nationalbanken i Kjobenhavn (National Bank in Copenhagen)

1.	1898–1904	5 Kroner, blue. Ornament made up of the numeral "5" and the words "Fem Kroner"	$15.00
2.	1891–1904	10 Kroner, black on brown. Arms at left. Ten one-krone coins on the reverse	20.00
3.	1883–1904	50 Kroner, brown. Crown above seated woman at left	37.50
4.	1888–1904	100 Kroner, green. Woman with inscribed ribbons	50.00
5.	1875–1910	500 Kroner, grey blue. Head of Hermes at left, head of Neptune at right	R
6.	1904–11	5 Kroner, blue. Type of #1 but watermarked with wavy lines	12.50

142 × 87

7.	1904–12	10 Kroner, black on brown. Type of #2 but watermarked with wavy lines	15.00
8.	1904–10	50 Kroner, brown. Type of #3 but watermarked with wavy lines	32.50
9.	1904–10	100 Kroner, green. Type of #4 but watermarked with wavy lines	45.00

Nationalbanken i Kjobenhavn (National Bank in Copenhagen)

War issue

10.	1914	1 Krone, black on reddish paper. A fish in the arms for Iceland on the reverse	11.00

120 × 76

11.		1 Krone, black on reddish paper. A falcon in the arms for Iceland on the reverse	5.00
12.	1916	1 Krone, blue on blue green	1.50
13.	1918	1 Krone, blue on blue green. Same as #12 except date	1.25
14.	1920	1 Krone, blue on blue green. Same as #12 except date	1.25
15.	1921	1 Krone, blue on blue green. Same as #12 except date	1.00

Statsbevis (State Treasury Notes)

With 5% interest, but passed as legal tender.

169 × 102

16.	1.10.1914	10 Kroner	30.00
17.		50 Kroner	50.00
18.		100 Kroner	R
19.		500 Kroner	R

Nationalbanken i Kjobenhavn (National Bank in Copenhagen)

Inscription begins "Vexles med Guldmont," paper watermarked with dark numerals of the notes' denominations.

20.	1912–31	5 Kroner, blue green. Pre-historic grave	7.50
21.	1913–30	10 Kroner, brown. Head of Mercury on reverse	11.50
22.	1911–30	50 Kroner, blue green. Fisherman with boat and nets	30.00
23.	1910–30	100 Kroner, brown. Sea-god with triton horn at left and right of reverse	37.50
24.	1910–31	500 Kroner, grey blue. Farmer plowing with horse	50.00

Inscription begins "Nationalbankens Sedler," paper watermarked with light numerals of the notes' denominations.

25.	1931–36	5 Kroner, blue green. Type of #20	4.50
26.	1930–36	10 Kroner, brown. Type of #21	6.00
27.		50 Kroner, blue green. Type of #22	20.00

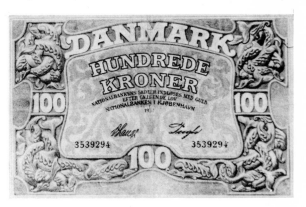

154 × 100

28.	1930–38	100 Kroner, brown. Type of #23	25.00
29.	1931–39	500 Kroner, grey blue. Type of #24	R

Danmarks Nationalbank (National Bank of Denmark)

30.	1937–43	5 Kroner, blue green. Type of #20 but different bank name	.75
31.		10 Kroner, brown. Type of #21	1.00

156 × 100

32.	1937–44	50 Kroner, blue green. Type of #22	5.00
33.	1938–44	100 Kroner, brown. Type of #23	11.50
34.	1939–44	500 Kroner, grey blue. Type of #24	37.50

For overprinted notes of above type, see Faroe Islands #3–12.

Issues after 1944

35.	1944–50	5 Kroner, blue green. New type note without illustration	3.00

131 × 80

36.	1944–45	10 Kroner, brown. Type of #35, arms on the reverse	4.00
37.	1945–50	10 Kroner, dark green. Obverse type of #31, reverse type of #36	
		a. Handmade paper, watermarked with flower design	5.00
		b. Watermarked with wavy lines (later issue)	3.00
38.	1944–55	50 Kroner, violet. Type of #32 but different design on reverse	12.50
39.	1944–45	100 Kroner, dark green. Type of #33, but only arms on reverse	22.50
40.	1946–60	100 Kroner, light green. Type of #39	20.00
41.	1944–63	500 Kroner, orange. Type of #34 but different design on reverse	—

Danmarks Nationalbank (National Bank of Denmark)

The modern type 5 and 10 kroner notes carry only the date of authorization, 7.4.1936. The other denominations have various dates.

42.	1952–61	5 Kroner, blue green. Thorvaldsen at left	1.50
43.	1952–53	10 Kroner, olive brown. Andersen at left, reverse printed in green	4.50
44.	1954–	10 Kroner, brown. Andersen at left, reverse printed in black	—
45.	1956–	50 Kroner, blue green. Ole Romer at left	
		a. Watermarked with crowns	12.50
		b. Watermarked with lines and "50"	—
46.	1961–	100 Kroner, red brown. H. C. Orsted at left	
		a. Watermarked with narrow waves	20.00
		b. Watermarked with "100"	—
47.	1964–	500 Kroner, green. Chr. D. F. Reventlow at left	—

Allierede Overkommando til Brug i Danemark (Issues of the Allied High Command for Denmark)

M1.	(1945)	25 Ore, brown and lilac	1.50
M2.		1 Krone, lilac	2.00
M3.		5 Kroner, green	5.00

138 × 78

M4.	10 Kroner, dark brown	8.75
M5.	50 Kroner, violet	25.00
M6.	100 Kroner, green blue (pattern, not issued)	RR

Danske Krigsministerium, Den Danske Brigade (Danish War Ministry, The Danish Brigade)

Military currency for Danish troops stationed in Germany

M7.	(1945)	5 Ore, blue	1.00
M8.		10 Ore, brown	1.25
M9.		25 Ore, blue	1.00
M10.		1 Krone, brown	2.50
M11.		5 Kroner, blue	5.00

111 × 70

M12.	10 Kroner, brown	10.00

ESTONIA (Eesti)

Estonia was under Danish and then Swedish rule until 1710, when it passed to Russian domination. An independent republic was declared in 1918 which lasted until 1940 when the country was occupied first by the Russians, then by German troops. Estonia was reabsorbed by Russia during World War II.

1 Ruble = 100 Kopecks (1918)
1 Marka = 100 Penni (1919–27)
1 Kroon = 100 Senti (1928)

Eesti Wabariigi 5% Wolakohustus (Obligation notes of the Estonian State bearing 5% interest).

Authorized legal tender

1.	to 1.5.1919, serial letter A	50 Marka, grey	$8.50
2.		100 Marka, grey	10.00
3.		200 Marka, grey	15.00
4.		500 Marka, grey. Both sides printed	17.50
5.		500 Marka, grey. Reverse not printed	20.00
6.		1,000 Marka, grey	37.50
7.	to 1.6.1919, serial letter B	50 Marka, yellow brown. Both sides printed	7.50
8.		50 Marka, yellow brown. Reverse side printed	8.50

208 × 135

9.	100 Marka, yellow brown	7.50

10.		200 Marka, yellow brown. Both sides printed	10.00
11.		200 Marka, yellow. Reverse not printed	12.50
12.		500 Marka, yellow brown	15.00
13.		1,000 Marka, yellow brown	50.00
14.	to 1.7.1919, serial letter D	50 Marka, green	10.00
15.		100 Marka, green	14.00
16.		200 Marka, green. Both sides printed	17.50
17.		200 Marka, green. Reverse not printed	20.00
18.		500 Marka, green. Both sides printed	22.50
19.		500 Marka, green. Reverse not printed	32.50
20.		1,000 Marka, green	R
21.	to 1.11.1919	50 Marka, grey	10.00
22.		100 Marka, yellow brown	12.50
23.		200 Marka, orange	17.50
24.		500 Marka, green	20.00
25.	to 1.12.1919	50 Marka, grey	10.00
26.		100 Marka, yellow brown	12.50
27.		200 Marka, orange	17.50
28.		500 Marka, green	20.00
29.	to 1. 1.1920	50 Marka, grey	7.50
30.		50 Marka, green	9.00
31.		100 Marka, grey	7.50
32.		100 Marka, yellow brown	9.00
33.		200 Marka, orange	17.50
34.		500 Marka, grey	15.00
35.		500 Marka, green	32.50
36.		1,000 Marka, green	R
37.	to 1. 5.1920	100 Marka, grey	7.50
38.		200 Marka, grey	10.00

Eesti Vabariigi Kassataht (State Loan Office Notes)

39.	(1919)	5 Penni, green	.50
40.		10 Penni, brown	.75
41.		20 Penni, yellow. Windmill	.75
42.	1919	50 Penni, blue	1.00
43.		1 Marka, brown	1.25
		For notes #42 and 43 stamped "Pohjan Pojat Rykmentin," see #M2 and M3.	
44.		3 Marka, green. Agricultural symbol	1.25
45.		5 Marka, blue. Farmer plowing	1.50
46.		10 Marka, brown. Shepherd with horn, cow and sheep	
		a. "Kumme Marka" inserted in black border on reverse	2.50
		b. "Kumme Marka" without black border on reverse	2.50
47.		25 Marka, violet. Potato harvest	3.00

155 × 94

48.		100 Marka, brown. Woman spinning	5.00
49.	(1920–21)	500 Marka, violet on bluish paper. Eagle with arms on reverse. (Notes without series number, Series II and III (A and B) issued in 1920, series D in 1921)	11.00
50.		1,000 Marka, green and brown. "Birth of Freedom" on the reverse. (Notes without series letter issued 1920, series A and B issued 1921)	20.00
51.	1923	100 Marka, green and brown. Bank building (Notes without series letter issued 1923, series A issued 1927)	4.00
52.		500 Marka, brown, blue and yellow, Toompealoss Castle	10.00

Eesti Vabariigi Vahetustaht (Promissory Notes)

53.	1922	10 Marka, red brown	
		a. Watermarked with "E.V." without series letter	5.00
		b. Watermarked, with squares serial letter A (issued 1924)	6.50

145 × 78

54.		25 Marka, olive and violet (varieties without series letter and series A issued 1926)	10.00

Eesti Pank (Estonian Bank)

Bank notes in mark denominations

55.	1919	50 Marka, green. Globe on reverse	5.00

56.	1921	100	Marka, brown. Two blacksmiths	10.00
57.	(1921)	500	Marka, light green and grey	12.50
58.	1922	100	Marka, violet, brown and green. Sailing ship on reverse	4.00
59.	(1922)	1,000	Marka, rose, violet and green. City and harbor of Tallinn (Reval)	15.00
60.	1923	5,000	Marka, blue, brown and green. Bank building on reverse	R

Eesti Vabariigi Kassastaht (Treasury Notes)

Notes in kroon denominations

| 61. | (1928) | 1 | Kroon, green and brown. Same as #51 with overprint of new value | 4.00 |

Eesti Pank (Estonian Bank)

Bank notes in kroon denominations

62.	1928	10	Krooni, blue. Peasant woman in national costume	4.00
63.	1929	5	Krooni, red brown. Fisherman at rudder	2.00
64.		50	Krooni, brown. Steep coastline of Rannamoisa	4.00
65.	1932	20	Krooni, grey green. Shepherd with horn	3.00

181 × 102

66.	1935	100	Krooni, blue. Blacksmith at anvil	5.00
67.	1937	10	Krooni, blue. Type of #62 but different date and signature	7.50
68.	1940	10	Krooni, blue. Type of #67 (not issued)	RR

"Pohjan Pojat" (Finnish Regiment, Sons of the North)

Finnish and Estonian notes stamped "Pohjan Pojat Rykmentin Rahaston hoitaja"—paymaster of the regiment, Sons of the North—circulated in 1919 in southern Estonia and northern Latvia.

M1.		1	Mark. Same as Finland #19 but overprinted	RR
M2.		50	Penni. Same as Estonia #42 but overprinted	RR
M3.		1	Marka. Same as Estonia of #43 but overprinted	RR

FAROE ISLANDS (Faeroerne)

A group of islands in the North Atlantic Ocean that have been under Danish control since 1400.

1 Krone = 100 Ore

Faero Amt (Faroe Government Council)

1.	1904	5 Kroner	R
2.		10 Kroner	R

Danish notes with red overprint "Kun gyldig paa Faeroerne, Faero Amt, Juni 1940"

3.	June 1940	5 Kroner, blue. Denmark #30 with above overprint. Signature "Hilbert" handwritten	R
4.		10 Kroner, brown. Denmark #31 with above overprint. Signature "Hilbert" handwritten	R
5.		50 Kroner, blue. Denmark #32 with above overprint. Signature "Hilbert" handwritten	RR
6.		100 Kroner, brown. Denmark #33 with above overprint. Signature "Hilbert" handwritten	RR
7.		500 Kroner, grey blue. Denmark #34 with above overprint. Signature "Hilbert" handwritten	RRR
8.		5 Kroner, blue. Type of #3 but signature printed	$30.00

 130 × 78

9.		10 Kroner, brown. Type of #4 but signature printed	37.50
10.		50 Kroner, blue. Type of #5 but signature printed	50.00
11.		100 Kroner, brown. Type of #6 but signature printed	R
12.		500 Kroner, grey blue. Type of #7 but signature printed	RR

Faero Amt (Faroe Government Council)

Newly printed notes

13.	1.10.1940	10 Kronur, brown on light brown	50.00
14.		100 Kronur	R
15.	November 1940	1 Krona, blue and violet	5.00
16.		5 Kronur, green	15.00
17.		10 Kronur, lilac and green	20.00
18.		100 Kronur, green and brown	R
19.	12.4.1949	5 Kronur, green. Coins and sheep at left	—
20.		10 Kronur, orange. Arms and sheep at left	—

155 × 103

21.		100 Kronur, grey green	
		a. Trimmed edge	20.00
		b. Deckle edge left and right	22.50
22.	12.4.1949	100 Kronur, red. V.U. Hammershaimb at left (issued 1967)	—
23.	12.4.1949	50 Kronur, blue green. Nolsoyar Pall at left (issued 1968)	—

FINLAND (Suomi)

Under Swedish control until 1809, Finland was then made a Grand Duchy of Czarist Russia. After the collapse of the Russian Empire in 1917, Finland declared itself an independent republic.

1 Markka = 100 Pennia

Suomen Pankki—Finlands Bank (Bank of Finland)

Notes issued after 1909 are known with numerous signature variations.

Grand Duchy

1.	1897	5 Markkaa, blue. Woman's head in middle. On the reverse, the lower part of the arms shield is round	$4.00
2.		5 Markkaa, blue. Type of #1 but the arms shield on the reverse is pointed	6.50
3.	1898	10 Markkaa, violet. Standing woman at left. Revese printed in green	7.50
4.		10 Markkaa, violet. Type of #3 but reverse printed in brown	8.50
5.		20 Markkaa, dark green. Woman with youth and globe	10.00
6.		50 Markkaa, blue. Woman with writing tablet at left	22.50
7.		100 Markkaa, violet. Young couple at left	20.00

195 × 111

8.		500 Markkaa, blue. Woman with lion at left	45.00
9.	1909	5 Markkaa, blue. River and river boat on reverse (serial numbers to 19,397,000)	
		a. Watermarked with "FB SP"	1.00
		b. No watermark	1.25
10.		10 Markkaa, lilac. House and two cows on reverse	1.50

11.		20 Markkaa, orange brown. Stylized tree on reverse (serial numbers to 9,927,507)	
		a. Watermarked with "FB SP"	2.50
		b. No watermark	1.50
12.		50 Markkaa, blue. Lighthouse on reverse	5.00
13.		100 Markkaa, violet. Farmer plowing at left and right (serial numbers to 2,775,000)	4.50
14.		500 Markkaa, orange and brown. Two blacksmiths (serial numbers to 170,000)	12.50
15.		1,000 Markkaa, yellow and brown. Two men with caduceus	22.50
16.	1915	1 Markka, red	
		a. Without series letter	1.50
		b. With series letter "A"	.75
17.	1916	25 Penni, yellow brown (not issued)	R
18.		50 Penni, grey blue (not issued)	R
19.		1 Markka, dark brown on rose	1.00
		For note with overprint "Pohjan Pojat," see Estonia #M1.	

Soviet Issue, 1918

20.	1909	5 Markkaa, blue. Type of #9 but serial numbers 19,397,001-20,789,000 (issued 1918)	.75
21.		20 Markkaa, orange brown. Type of #11 but serial numbers 9,927,508–10,019,000 (issued 1918)	2.00

169 × 102

22.		100 Markkaa, violet. Type of #13 but serial numbers 2,775,001–2,983,000 (issued 1918)	4.00
23.		500 Markkaa, orange and brown. Type of #14 but serial numbers 170,001–262,000 (issued 1918)	8.50

Republic

24.	1909, "Litt. A" (issued 1918)	5 Markkaa, blue. Type of #9 but with "Litt. A"	
		a. Watermarked with "FB SP"	1.00
		b. No watermark	1.00
25.		10 Markkaa, red. Type of #10 but with "Litt. A"	1.25

26.		20 Markkaa, orange brown. Type of #1 but with "Litt. A"	2.00
27.		50 Markkaa, blue. Type of #12 but with "Litt. A"	4.00
28.		100 Markkaa, violet. Type of #13 but with "Litt. A"	5.00
29.		500 Markkaa, orange and brown. Type of #14 but with "Litt. A"	37.50
30.	1909, "Ser. II" (issued 1918)	5 Markkaa, green. Type of #9 but with "Ser. II"	1.00
31.		100 Markkaa, grey green. Type of #13 but with "Ser. II"	6.50
32.		500 Markkaa, yellow. Type of #14 but with "Ser. II"	15.00
33.	1918	25 Penni, dark brown and light brown	.50
34.		50 Penni, dark brown and blue	.75
35.		1 Markka, dark brown on rose. Type of #19	.75
36.		5 Markkaa, green. Type of #9	1.00
37.		10 Markkaa, lilac. Type of #10	1.25

140 × 83

38.		20 Markkaa, blue. Type of #11	1.50
39.		50 Markkaa. Type of #12	3.50
40.		100 Markkaa, light brown on grey. Type of #13	5.00
41.		1,000 Markkaa. Type of #15	30.00

Suomen Pankki (Finlands Bank)

42.	1922	5 Markkaa, green. Spruce tree in middle	.75
43.		10 Markkaa, brown. Pine tree in middle	1.00
44.		20 Markkaa, violet. Pine tree in middle (issued 1926)	1.25
45.		50 Markkaa, dark blue. Allegorical group of six figures	3.00
46.		100 Markkaa, dark brown. Type of #45 (issued 1923)	4.50
47.		500 Markkaa, brown on green. Allegorical group of 11 figures (issued 1924)	10.00
48.		1,000 Markkaa, brown. Allegorical group of 13 figures (issued 1923)	20.00

118 × 61

49.	1922, "Litt. A"	5 Markkaa, green. Type of #42 but with "Litt. A" (issued 1926)	.75
50.		10 Markkaa, brown. Type of #43 (issued 1926)	1.25
51.		20 Markkaa, violet. Type of #44 (issued 1927)	2.00
52.		50 Markkaa, dark blue. Type of #45 (issued 1925)	4.00
53.		100 Markkaa, dark brown. Type of #46 (issued 1923)	6.50
54.		500 Markkaa, brown on green. Type of #47 (issued 1930)	12.50
55.		1,000 Markkaa, brown. Type of #48 (issued 1929)	22.50
56.	1922, "Litt. B"	5 Markkaa, green. Type of #42 but with "Litt. B" (issued 1929)	2.50
57.		10 Markkaa, brown. Type of #43 (issued 1929)	4.00
58.		20 Markkaa, violet. Type of #44 (issued 1929)	5.00
59.		50 Markkaa, dark blue. Type of #45 (issued 1929)	7.50
60.		100 Markkaa, dark brown. Type of #46 (issued 1929)	12.50
61.	1922, "Litt. C"	5 Markkaa, green. Type of #42 but with "Litt. C" (issued 1930)	.75
62.		10 Markkaa, brown. Type of #43 (issued 1930)	1.25

#67

203 × 120

63.		20 Markkaa, red. Type of #44 (issued 1931)	2.00
64.		50 Markkaa, dark blue. Type of #45 (issued 1931)	4.00
65.		100 Markkaa, dark brown. Type of #46 (issued 1931)	6.50
66.		500 Markkaa, brown on green. Type of #47 (issued 1932)	10.00
67.		1,000 Markkaa, brown. Type of #48 (issued 1931)	15.00
68.	1922, "Litt. A"	5,000 Markkaa. Same as #47 with blue overprint (issued 1939)	RRR
69.	1939, "Litt. D"	5 Markkaa, green. Type of #42 (issued 1942)	.75
70.		10 Markkaa, brown. Type of #43 (issued 1939)	1.00
71.		20 Markkaa, violet. Type of #44 (issued 1939)	1.75
72.		50 Markkaa, dark blue. Type of #45 (issued 1939)	2.50
73.		100 Markkaa, dark brown. Type of #46 (issued 1940)	4.00
74.		1,000 Markkaa, brown. Type of #48 (issued 1939)	22.50
75.	1939	5,000 Markkaa, dark blue and violet. J. V. Snellmann at left	R

In 1946, some 500, 1,000 and 5,000 markkaa notes were cut in half. The right halves became a forced loan, the left halves were temporarily valued at half face value as legal tender as follows:

250 Markkaa (left halves of #47, #54 or #66)
500 Markkaa (left halves of #48, #55 or #67)
2,500 Markkaa (left half of #75)

76.	1945, "Litt. A" (issued 1946)	5 Markkaa, yellow. Spruce tree in middle	.75
77.		10 Markkaa, red. Pine tree in middle	1.25
78.		20 Markkaa, blue. Pine tree in middle	2.00
79.		50 Markkaa, brown. Young couple on reverse	2.50
80.		100 Markkaa, blue green. Woman with lion on reverse	4.00
81.		500 Markkaa, blue. Allegorical group of 11 figures	17.50
82.		1,000 Markkaa, blue violet. Allegorical group of 13 figures	22.50
83.		5,000 Markkaa, dark brown. Type of #75	R
84.	1945, "Litt. B" (issued 1948)	5 Markkaa, yellow. Type of #76	.75
85.		10 Markkaa, red. Type of #77	1.00
86.		20 Markkaa, blue. Type of #78	1.25
87.		50 Markkaa, brown. Type of #79	2.50

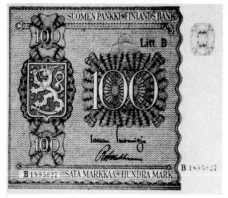

120 × 103

88.		100	Markkaa, blue green. Type of #80	4.00
89.		500	Markkaa, blue. Type of #81	7.50
90.		1,000	Markkaa, violet. Type of #82	12.50
91.	1955	100	Markkaa, brown on olive	5.00
92.		500	Markkaa, brown on blue. Conifer tree branch	7.50

140 × 70

93.		1,000	Markkaa, dark green. J. K. Paasikivi at left	5.00
94.		5,000	Markkaa, brown and lilac. K. J. Stahlberg at left	20.00
95.		10,000	Markkaa, lilac. J. V. Snellmann	32.50
96.	1956	500	Markkaa, blue. Conifer tree branch	2.00
97.	1957	100	Markkaa, lilac brown on yellow brown	.75

Currency Reform, 1963: *100 Old Markkaa = 1 New Markka*

98.	1963	1	Markka, lilac brown on yellow. Type of #97	—
99.		5	Markkaa, blue. Type of #96	—
100.		10	Markkaa, dark green. Type of #93	—
101.		50	Markkaa, brown. Type of #94	—
102.		100	Markkaa, violet. Type of #95	—
103.	1963, "Litt. A" (issued 1969)	10	Markkaa, dark green. Type of #100	—
104.		50	Markkaa, brown. Type of #101	—
105.		100	Markkaa, violet. Type of #101	—
106.	1963, "Litt. B"	50	Markkaa, brown. Type of #101	—

FIUME (Rijeka)

Following the Hungarian revolution of 1919, the Fiume area was occupied by the Italian, Gabriele d'Annunzio. The Treaty of Rapallo (12.11.1920) made Fiume temporarily independent. After World War II, the Fiume area was given to Yugoslavia.

The notes in use were those of the Austro-Hungarian Bank with one of the following stamps or overprints:

1. Round hand stamp "Citta di Fiume,"
2. Round machine stamp "Citta di Fiume,"
3. Square overprint "Instituto di Credito Consiglio Nacionale, Citta di Fiume," size 45 × 58 mm.

Notes with overprint #2 were not known until the 1950's. A large parcel of them was sold at auction, but the authenticity of these notes has not yet been established.

1.	1.12.1916 (issued 1920)	1 Krone, stamp #1	$7.50
2.		1 Krone, stamp #2	2.50
3.		1 Krone, overprint #3	RR
4.		1 Krone, stamp #1. Serial number above 7,000	12.50
5.		1 Krone, stamp #2. Serial number above 7,000	7.50
6.		1 Krone, overprint #3. Serial number above 7,000	RR
7.	5.8.1914 (issued 1920)	2 Kronen, stamp #1	15.00
8.		2 Kronen, stamp #2	7.50
9.		2 Kronen, overprint #3	RR
10.	1.3.1917 (issued 1920)	2 Kronen, stamp #1	7.50
11.		2 Kronen, stamp #2	2.50
12.		2 Kronen, overprint #3	RR
13.		2 Kronen, stamp #1. Serial number above 7,000	12.50
14.		2 Kronen, stamp #2. Serial number above 7,000	7.50
15.		2 Kronen, overprint #3	RR
16.		2 Kronen, with overprint "Deutsch Osterreich"	R
17.	2.1.1904 (issued 1920)	10 Kronen, stamp #1	37.50
18.		10 Kronen, stamp #2	15.00
19.		10 Kronen, overprint #3	RR

149 × 79

20.	2.1.1915 (issued 1920)	10 Kronen, stamp #1	12.50
21.		10 Kronen, stamp #2	4.00
22.		10 Kronen, overprint #3	RR
23.	2.1.1907 (issued 1920)	20 Kronen, stamp #1	R
24.		20 Kronen, stamp #2	25.00
25.	2.1.1913 (issued 1920)	20 Kronen, stamp #1	15.00
26.		20 Kronen, stamp #2	5.00
27.		20 Kronen, overprint #3	RR
28.		20 Kronen, "II issue," stamp #1	12.50
29.		20 Kronen, "II issue," stamp #2	4.00
30.		20 Kronen, "II issue," overprint #3	RR
31.	2.1.1902 (issued 1920)	50 Kronen, stamp #1	R
32.		50 Kronen, stamp #2	25.00
33.	2.1.1914 (issued 1920)	50 Kronen, stamp #1	17.50
34.		50 Kronen, stamp #2	5.00
35.		50 Kronen, overprint #3	RR
36.	2.1.1910 (issued 1920)	100 Kronen, stamp #1	R
37.		100 Kronen, stamp #2	R
38.	2.1.1912 (issued 1920)	100 Kronen, stamp #1	15.00
39.		100 Kronen, stamp #2	5.00
40.		100 Kronen, overprint #3	RR
41.	2.1.1902 (issued 1920)	1,000 Kronen, stamp #1	20.00
42.		1,000 Kronen, stamp #2	7.50
43.		1,000 Kronen, overprint #3	RR

FRANCE

France's Third Republic was established in 1871, following the Franco-Prussian War. It ended in 1940 when German troops occupied the country and set up the Vichy regime under the aged Marshal Petain. The Fourth Republic was set up in 1946, the Fifth, under General Charles De Gaulle, in 1958.

1 Franc = 100 Centimes

Most French bank notes carry the date of printing rather than a date of issue which gives rise to many varieties. The dates given in the listings below are the first and last dates of printing known for each type and the valuations given are for the commonest date and signature combinations. The listings below follow the *Catalogue des Billets de la Banque de France* by Maurice Muszynski which is considered authoritative.

Banque de France (Bank of France)

5 Franc notes

1.	1.12.1871–19. 1.1874	5 Francs, blue. Man at left, woman with sword at right. Three figures on reverse	$10.00

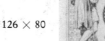 126 × 80

2.	2. 1.1912– 2. 2.1917	5 Francs, blue. Type of #1 but ornaments only on reverse	4.50
3.	1.12.1917–14. 9.1933	5 Francs, lilac. Helmeted woman's head at left, "Caissier Principal" (five signature varieties)	1.25
4.	13. 7.1939– 9. 1.1941	5 Francs, lilac. Type of #3 but "Caissier General"	.50
5.	2. 6.1943–30.10.1947	5 Francs, blue, green and multicolored. Pyrenees herdsman on reverse (two signature varieties)	.50

10 Franc notes

6.	3. 1.1916–25. 2.1937	10 Francs, blue. Minerva head at left, "Caissier Principal" (five signature varieties)	.75

7.	2. 2.1939– 5. 3.1942	10 Francs, blue. Type of #6 but "Caissier General"	.50
8.	11. 9.1941–30. 6.1949	10 Francs, multicolored. Miner at left (two signature varieties)	.50

20 Franc notes

9.	1. 7.1874–11. 1.1905	20 Francs, blue on ochre. Mercury seated at left, woman seated right. Denomination in black (two signature varieties)	12.50
10.	2. 1.1906–12. 2.1913	20 Francs. Type of #9 but denomination blue (two signature varieties)	8.50
11.	1. 7.1916–21. 2.1919	20 Francs. Head of Bayard at left	5.00
12.	7.12.1939– 8. 1.1942	20 Francs, multicolored. Man and woman (Science and Industry) at right	.75
13.	12. 2.1942– 9. 2.1950	20 Francs, multicolored. Breton fisherman (two signature varieties)	.50

50 Franc notes to 1945

14.	1. 8.1884– 4. 3.1889	50 Francs, blue. Woman's head at left and right, two cupids above (three signature varieties)	30.00

179 × 124

15.	1. 5.1889–25. 3.1927	50 Francs, blue on lilac. Type of #14 but five heads in medallions in middle (eight signature varieties)	5.00
16.	11. 2.1927–17. 7.1930	50 Francs, multicolored. Three angels, Mercury below. Artist's name, "Luc Olivier-Merson," at bottom on both sides	6.00
17.	24. 7.1930–16. 8.1934	50 Francs, multicolored. Type of #16 but without artist's name (two signature varieties)	2.00

18.	15.11.1934–30. 6.1937	50 Francs, multicolored. Ceres and park at Versailles, with "Caissier Principal"	.75
19.	5. 8.1937–13. 6.1940	50 Francs, multicolored. Type of #18 but "Caissier General" (two signature varieties)	.50
20.	13. 6.1940–15. 5.1942	50 Francs, multicolored. Jacques Coeur and underground palace in Bourges at left	.50

100 Franc notes to 1945

21.	2. 1.1882–11. 9.1888	100 Francs, blue. Two seated women (four signature varieties)	37.50
22.	12. 9.1888–29. 1.1909	100 Francs, blue on rose. Type of #21 but four women's heads in middle (five signature varieties)	6.00
23.	2. 1.1908–10. 5.1908	100 Francs, multicolored. Woman and child at left and right. Bundles of goods inscribed with "L.O.M. 02" at right	8.50
24.	11. 5.1909–29.11.1923	100 Francs, multicolored. Type of #23 but no "L.O.M. 02" (three signature varieties)	2.50
25.	30.11.1923–30. 6.1937	100 Francs, multicolored. Type of #24 but space in frame for serial number measures from 20 to 23 mm wide, with "Caissier Principal"	.65
26.	9. 9.1937–14. 9.1939	100 Francs, multicolored. Type of #25 but "Caissier General" (two signature varieties)	
		a. Thin paper	.75
		b. Thick paper	.75
27.	19. 4.1939–23. 4.1942	100 Francs, multicolored. Woman and child with view of Paris in background	.50

160 × 91

| 28. | 15. 5.1942–14.12.1944 | 100 Francs, multicolored. Descartes at right | 2.50 |

300 Franc note

29.	(1938)	300	Francs, multicolored. Ceres at left	6.50

500 Franc notes to 1945

30.	2.11.1888–10. 6.1937	500	Francs, blue on lilac. Woman's head at left, Mercury head at right, with "Caissier Principal" (13 signature varieties)	1.50
31.	5. 8.1937–18. 1.1940	500	Francs, blue on rose. Type of #30 but "Caissier General" (three signature varieties)	1.00
32.	4. 1.1940–19. 4.1945	500	Francs, multicolored. Woman with wreath at left (two signature varieties)	.75

1,000 Franc notes to 1945

33.	7.11.1889–16. 9.1926	1,000	Francs, blue on lilac. Mercury at left, woman's head in medallion and allegorical figures at right (11 signature varieties)	4.00
34.	11. 2.1927–26. 8.1937	1,000	Francs, ochre, blue and multicolored. Ceres head at left, Mercury at right, two cupids below, with "Caissier Principal" (three signature varieties)	2.50
35.	4.11.1937–25. 7.1940	1,000	Francs, ochre, blue and multicolored. Type of #34 but "Caissier General" (three signature varieties)	2.00

192 × 118

36.	24.10.1940–12.10.1944	1,000	Francs, multicolored. Two women's heads. Blacksmith and Mercury on reverse (two signature varieties)	2.50
37.	28. 5.1942– 6. 4.1944	1,000	Francs, multicolored. Ceres and Hercules. Mercury on reverse	1.50

5,000 Franc notes to 1947

38.	2. 1.1918–29 1.1918 (Issued 1938)	5,000	Francs, multicolored. Seated worker and Mercury at left, cupid and agricultural products at right. View of Paris on reverse	45.00
39.	8.11.1934–11. 7.1935	5,000	Francs, violet and multicolored. Woman with victory statuette and olive branch. Statuette in copper plate print on the reverse. With "Caissier Principal"	45.00
40.	15.10.1938	5,000	Francs, violet and multicolored. Type of #39 but "Caissier General"	R
41.	8.12.1938–27. 7.1944	5,000	Francs, violet and multicolored. Type of #40 but reverse not copper plate print	12.50
42.	5. 3.1942– 25.9.1947	5,000	Francs, multicolored. Woman with three natives (two signature varieties)	8.50

Tresor Central (State Notes)

Notes #43 and #46 through 48 were given out on Corsica.

155 × 99

43.	2.10.1943	100	Francs, blue on green and violet. Marianne head in middle (printed in England)	10.00
44.	(1944)	500	Francs, brown. Marianne head at left (printed in England)	12.50
45.		1,000	Francs, green. Marianne head in middle (printed in England, two control number varieties)	8.50
46.	(1945)	500	Francs, blue on green. Note of "Banque de l'Algerie" of October, 1943 overprinted "TRESOR"	R
47.		1,000	Francs, multicolored. Note of "Banque de l'Algerie" of 1942–1943 overprinted "TRESOR"	R
48.		5,000	Francs, brown violet on rose. Note of "Bank de l'Algerie" of 1943 overprinted "TRESOR"	RR

State notes, "Freedom Issue," American printing

First Issue—Obverse with "Emis de France," French flag on reverse

49.	1944	2 Francs, green	.40

50.		5 Francs, blue on green	.50
51.		10 Francs, lilac on green	.75
52.		50 Francs, lilac on green	2.00
53.		100 Francs, blue on green	2.50
54.		500 Francs, brown on green	12.50
55.		1,000 Francs, red on green	10.00
		5,000 Francs (trial note only)	

Second Issue—Obverse with "France" only, flag inscribed "France" on reverse

156 × 67

56.	1944	50 Francs, lilac on green	1.50
57.		100 Francs, blue on green	2.00
58.		1,000 Francs, red on green	8.50

Banque de France (Bank of France)

Notes issued after 1945 with values in old Francs (also see #5, #8, #13 and #42)

59.	14. 3.1946– 7. 6.1951	50 Francs, multicolored. Head of Leverrier (four signature varieties)	.50
60.	7.11.1945– 1. 4.1954	100 Francs, multicolored. Farmer with two oxen (four signature varieties)	.75
61.	19. 7.1945– 2. 7.1953	500 Francs, violet and multicolored. Chateaubriand (three signature varieties)	2.50
62.	7. 1.1954–12. 2.1959	500 Francs, multicolored. Victor Hugo at right (three signature varieties)	2.00
63.	12. 4.1945–29. 6.1950	1,000 Francs, multicolored. Minerva and Hercules (two signature varieties)	5.00
64.	2. 4.1953– 5. 9.1957	1,000 Francs, multicolored. Richelieu at right	3.00

#65
171 × 111

65.	10. 3.1949– 7.11.1957	5,000	Francs, multicolored. Allegorical figures of Land and Sea (four signature varieties)	25.00
66.	7. 2.1957– 5. 3.1959	5,000	Francs, multicolored. Henry IV in middle (two signature varieties)	12.50
67.	27.12.1945– 7. 6.1959	10,000	Francs, multicolored. Young girl with book and globe (four signature varieties)	50.00
68.	1.12.1955–30.10.1958	10,000	Francs, multicolored. Napoleon Bonaparte at right (two signature varieties)	25.00

Currency Reform 1960: *100 Francs = 1 New Franc*

Notes with values overprinted in new francs (NF.), various dates to 1959.

69.	(1960)	5 NF. overprinted on #62	3.00
70.		10 NF. overprinted on #64	5.00
71.		50 NF. overprinted on #66	20.00
72.		100 NF. overprinted on #68	37.50

Newly printed notes with denomination in new francs (NF.)

73.	5 NF., multicolored. Type of #62	2.00
74.	10 NF., multicolored. Type of #64	3.00
75.	50 NF., multicolored. Type of #66	12.50
76.	100 NF., multicolored. Type of #68	25.00
77.	500 NF., multicolored. Moliere	R

Notes with denominations in francs (new francs) issued from 1963

78.	5 Francs, multicolored. Louis Pasteur at left	—
79.	10 Francs, multicolored. Voltaire at right	—
80.	50 Francs, multicolored. Racine at right	—
81.	100 Francs, multicolored. Pierre Corneille in middle	—
82.	500 Francs, yellow brown and dark brown. Blaise Pascal in middle	—

Regie des Chemins de Fer des Territoires Occupes (Railroad Authority of the occupied territories)

Issued by the French and Belgian railroad administration during the occupation of German territories following the First World War. All notes show a locomotive above, a view of the Rheinland in the background.

R1.	(1923)	0.05	Franc, yellow brown background	.25
R2.		0.10	Franc, light blue background	.25
R3.		0.25	Franc, violet background	.35
R4.		0.50	Franc, green background	.35
R5.		1	Franc, green background	.50
R6.		5	Francs, grey background	1.00
R7.		10	Francs, grey green background	2.00
R8.		20	Francs, violet background	4.00

180 × 112

R9.	50	Francs, rose background	25.00
R10.	100	Francs, rose background	50.00

French Military Notes

All notes show a woman and child at left, a soldier and a dog at right. Undated, these notes were valid from 1917 until two years after the Armistice.

M1.	50	Centimes, blue	.25
M2.	1	Franc, brown	1.00
M3.	2	Francs, violet	1.25

Undated, these notes were valid from 1919 until four years after the Armistice.

M4.	50	Centimes, blue. Type of M1	.25
M5.	1	Franc, brown. Type of M2	.50

French Military Notes for German territories occupied after 1945

First Issue with "Tresor Francais"

M6.	(1947)	5	Francs, multicolored. Woman's head	.75
M7.		10	Francs, multicolored. Woman's head	1.00
M8.		50	Francs, multicolored. Mercury	1.25
M9.		100	Francs, multicolored. Mercury	1.75
M10.		1,000	Francs, multicolored. Mercury	45.00

Second Issue with "Tresor Public"

M11.	(1955)	100	Francs, multicolored. Type of M9	4.00
M12.		1,000	Francs, multicolored. Mercury facing right	30.00
M13.		5,000	Francs, multicolored. Young farm couple	RR

122 × 80

M14. (1960)   5 NF., overprinted on 500 francs, multicolored.
                   Mercury   37.50
                   The 500 franc note is not known without the
                   overprint
M15.   50 NF., multicolored. Same as M13 except for over-
                   print   RR

French Military Notes for the Suez War of 1956

M16. (1956)   50 Francs, multicolored. Same as M8 but overprinted
                   "Forces Francaises en Mediterranee Orientale"   R
M17.   100 Francs, multicolored. Same as M9 but overprinted
                   as M16   R
M18.   1,000 Francs, multicolored. Same as M10 but over-
                   printed as M16   RR

GERMANY (Deutschland)

In 1871, the German States united to form the German Empire (Deutsches Reich) under Wilhelm I of Prussia who ruled until 1888. His son, Emperor Frederick III, died after only 99 days of rule. He was followed by Emperor Wilhelm II (1888–1918). Following the First World War, a republic was formed under President Friedrich Ebert, after whose death Field Marshal Paul von Hindenburg was elected to the office. In 1933, von Hindenburg appointed Adolf Hitler as Reichs Chancellor, Hitler eventually rising to become the dictator of the National Socialist Party. After World War II, the Allied Control set up the four zones of occupation controlled by the Americans, British, French and Russians. In 1949 the Western Zone became the German Federal Republic, the East or Russian Zone became the Communist German Democratic Republic.

1 Taler = 30 Groschen
1 Gulden = 60 Kreuzer
1 Mark = 100 Pfennig (1874–1923)
1 Rentenmark = 100 Rentenpfennig (1923–48)
1 Reichsmark = 100 Reichspfennig (1924–48)
1 Deutsche Mark (West) = 100 Pfennig (since 1948)
1 Deutsche Mark (East) = 100 Deutsche Pfennig (since 1948)

On inflation currency:

1 Million = 1,000,000
1 Milliard = 1,000,000,000
1 Billiard = 1,000,000,000,000,000

Empire

Reichskassenscheine (Empire Treasury Bank Notes), 1874–1914

1.	11. 7.1874	5 Mark, dark blue and grey blue. Two cupids with oak leaf garland	$50.00
2.		20 Mark, green and yellow. Medieval herald	R
3.		50 Mark, dark violet, brown and green. Two winged figures (the Military and Agriculture)	RR
4.	10. 1.1882	5 Mark, dark blue. Knight in armour holding a long sword	32.50
5.		20 Mark, green. Two cupids holding fruit	50.00
6.		50 Mark, dark brown. Winged figure holding hour glass and caduceus	R

149 × 99

7.	5. 1.1899	50 Mark, dark green and brown olive. Seated figure of Germania at left	RR
8.	31.10.1904	5 Mark, blue and blue green. Germania with child and dove at left. Dragon guarding treasure on the reverse	.75
9.	6.10.1906	10 Mark, dark green and olive green. Woman with palm branch at right (Agriculture)	.50

Reichsbanknoten (Empire Bank Notes), 1875–1914

| 10. | 1. 1.1876 | 100 Mark, dark blue and grey blue. Head of Minerva within wreath at right. Two cupids on the reverse | RR |
| 11. | | 1,000 Mark, brown. Woman and two children on the reverse (Industry, Trade and Transportation) | RRR |

157 × 100

12.	3. 9.1883	100 Mark, blue. Germania head in medallion supported by two women (Industry and Agriculture) on reverse	R
13.	2. 1.1884	1,000 Mark, brown. Two female figures (Sailing and Agriculture) on the reverse	RRR
14.	1. 1.1891	1,000 Mark, brown. Type of #13	RR
15.	1. 5.1891	100 Mark, blue. Type of #12	50.00
16.	1. 3.1895	100 Mark, blue. Type of #12	50.00
17.		1,000 Mark, brown. Type of #13	50.00
18.	10. 4.1896	100 Mark, blue. Type of #12	22.50

19.		1,000 Mark, brown. Type of #13	R
20.	1. 7.1898	100 Mark, blue. Type of #12	3.00
21.		1,000 Mark, brown. Type of #13	6.50
22.	17. 4.1903	100 Mark, blue. Type of #12	1.00
23.	10.10.1903	1,000 Mark, brown. Type of #13	3.00
24.	18.12.1905	100 Mark, blue. Type of #12	1.25
25.	10. 3.1906	20 Mark, blue. German eagle at upper right	1.00
26.		50 Mark, green. Head of Germania in medallions at upper left and right	1.00

186 × 110

27.	26. 7.1906	1,000 Mark, brown. Type of #13	3.50
28.	8. 6.1907	20 Mark, blue. Type of #25	.75
29.		50 Mark, green. Type of #26	15.00
30.		100 Mark, blue. Type of #12	1.50
31.	7. 2.1908	20 Mark, blue. Type of #25	.50
32.		50 Mark, green. Type of #26	.50
33.		100 Mark, blue. Type of #12	
		a. Red serial numbers and seal, numbers 29 mm wide	.35
		b. Serial numbers 24 mm wide	1.00
34.		100 Mark, blue. Type of #12 but green control numbers and seal	.50

205 × 101

| 35. | | 100 Mark, blue. Mercury head at left, Ceres head at right. Long, narrow format. Germania and naval fleet on reverse | .50 |

36.		1,000 Mark, brown. Type of #13	4.00
37.	10. 9.1909	20 Mark, blue. Type of #25	.75
38.		100 Mark, blue. Type of #35	.75
39.		1,000 Mark, brown. Type of #13	2.00
40.	21. 4.1910	20 Mark, blue. Type of #25	
		a. No watermark	.25
		b. Watermarked "20"	1.50
41.		50 Mark, green. Type of #26	.25
42.		100 Mark, blue. Type of #35, red serial numbers and seal	.25
43.		100 Mark, blue. Type of #35, green serial numbers and seal	.35
44.		1,000 Mark, brown. Type of #13, red serial numbers and seal	
		a. Six digit serial numbers (to 1916)	1.25
		b. Seven digit serial numbers	.25
45.		1,000 Mark, brown. Type of #13, green serial numbers and seal	.50
46.	19. 2.1914	20 Mark, blue. Type of #25	.25

Darlehnskassenscheine (State Loan Office Treasury Bank Notes), 1914–22

47.	5. 8.1914	5 Mark, grey violet. Bust of Germania in medallions at left and right on reverse	.25
48.		20 Mark, brown and violet. Minerva head at upper left. Mercury head at upper right on reverse	.25
49.		50 Mark, lilac red on grey. Bust of Germania in medallions on reverse	.35
50.	12. 8.1914	1 Mark, light green and lilac. Without background color	.35
51.		1 Mark. Type of #50 but with background printing and red serial numbers and seal	.25
52.		1 Mark. Type of #51 but blue serial numbers and seal	.25
53.		2 Mark, carmine red. Without background color	.35

#54
139 × 90

54.		2 Mark. Type of #53 but with background printing and red serial numbers and seal	.25
55.		2 Mark. Type of #54 but blue serial numbers and seal	.25
56.	1. 8.1917	5 Mark, violet blue. Young girl's head at right	.25
57.	20. 2.1918	20 Mark, dark brown on carmine. Minerva head at left, Mercury head at right. Man and woman (War and Peace) on reverse	.25
58.	1. 3.1920	1 Mark, olive green and blue green	.25
59.		2 Mark, red. Brown serial numbers and seal	.25
60.		2 Mark, brown. Red serial numbers and seal	.25
61.	15. 9.1922	1 Mark, dark green on light green	
		a. Light green paper	.25
		b. Grey paper	10.00
62.		2 Mark, brown on rose	.25

Reichsbanknoten (Reichsbank Notes) 1915–24, with denominations in mark values

Among the inflation notes are many watermark and serial number varieties as well as different grades of paper. Counterfeits of many issues are common.

| 63. | 4.11.1915 | 20 Mark, violet and dark blue. Two men with cornucopias of money. Man and woman (Work and Rest) on reverse | .25 |

139 × 107

64.	20.10.1918	50 Mark, dark brown on grey violet. Dark border lines (known as the "mourning note")	
		a. Watermarked with wavy lines	30.00
		b. Watermarked with spades	35.00
65.	30.11.1918	50 Mark, olive brown. Broad ribbon frame with white oval in middle (known as the "picture frame" or "egg" note)	2.00
66.	24. 6.1919	50 Mark, green on light green. Woman's head in frame at upper right	.25
67.	6. 2.1920	10 Mark, dark green and olive green	.25

68.	23. 7.1920	50	Mark, dark green and green. Woman's head with flowers and fruit (Autumn) at right. Farmer and worker on reverse	.25
69.	1.11.1920	100	Mark, dark brown and blue green. Head of the Bamberg Knight at upper left and right	.25
70.	19. 1.1922	10,000	Mark, blue green on olive brown. Young man's head at right (from a painting by Albrecht Durer). Rectangular ornaments on reverse (210 × 125 mm)	.25
71.		10,000	Mark. Type of #70 but oval ornament on reverse	.25
72.		10,000	Mark. Type of #71 but smaller format (180 × 100 mm)	.25
73.	27. 3.1922	500	Mark, dark blue and olive green. Bust of a young noble landowner (Junker) at right	.25
74.	7. 7.1922	500	Mark, black on white	
			a. Red serial numbers	.35
			b. Green serial numbers	.25
75.	4. 8.1922	100	Mark, blue black on white	.25
76.	15. 9.1922	1,000	Mark, dark green on green and lilac	
			a. White paper watermarked with hook-pointed stars	.25
			b. Light blue paper watermarked with thorns	.25
			c. Light blue paper watermarked with irregular lines	.25
			d. White paper watermarked with C pattern	.25
			e. White paper watermarked with small quatrefoil design	.25
			f. White paper watermarked with latticework of figure eights	.25
			g. White paper watermarked with figure eight design	.25
			h. Light blue and white paper watermarked with waves	.25
77.	16. 9.1922	5,000	Mark, blue on grey and green. Portrait of Mintmaster Spinelli at right (from a painting by Memling)	1.00

#78
198 × 105

78.	19.11.1922	5,000 Mark, dark brown on brown. Portrait of Treasurer H. Urmiller at left (from a painting by an unknown artist)	.35
79.		50,000 Mark, black on white. At right, paper deep green. Burgomaster Brauweiler at left (from a painting by B. Bruyn)	.25
80.		50,000 Mark. Type of #79 but German eagle printed behind inscription	.25
81.	2.12.1922	5,000 Mark, brown on green and light brown. Portrait of the merchant Imhoff (from a painting by Albrecht Durer) at right	
		a. Watermarked with hook-pointed stars	.25
		b. Watermarked with latticework	.25
		c. Watermarked with thorns	.25
		d. Watermarked with C pattern	.25
		e. Watermarked with waves	.50
82.	15.12.1922	1,000 Mark, black on dark brown. Portrait of Mint-master Jorg Herz (from a painting by G. Penz) at left (not issued)	2.50
		For note overprinted "1 Milliarde," see #113.	
83.	1. 2.1923	100,000 Mark, dark brown on lilac. At right, paper deep lilac. Portrait of the merchant Gisze (from a painting by Hans Holbein) at left	.25
		Notes with "T" under illustration are several times scarcer.	
84.	3. 2.1923	10,000 Mark, dark blue on green and red (not issued)	10.00
85.	20. 2.1923	20,000 Mark, dark blue on rose and green	
		a. Watermarked with small crosses	.25
		b. Watermarked with hook-pointed stars	.25
		c. Watermarked with latticework of figure eights	.35
		d. Watermarked with thorns	.35
		e. Watermarked with C pattern	.50
		f. Watermarked with waves	.75
86.		1,000,000 Mark, dark brown on light brown and dark green	.25
87.	15. 3.1923	5,000 Mark, dark brown on olive brown. Portrait of Treasurer H. Urmiller at left (not issued)	20.00
		For note overprinted "500 Milliarden" see #124.	
88.	1. 5.1923	500,000 Mark, dark green, on lilac and green. Medallion portraits of a beared man wearing a liberty cap	.25
89.	1. 6.1923	5,000,000 Mark, brown on lilac and green. Woman's head in middle. Paper deep yellow at right edge	.25
90.	23. 7.1923	2,000,000 Mark, dark brown on rose and green. Portraits of the merchant Gisze (from a painting by Hans Holbein) at left and right	.25

91.	25. 7.1923	100,000 Mark, black on green	
		a. Greenish paper watermarked with hook-pointed stars	.25
		b. White paper, watermarked with waves	.35
92.		500,000 Mark, carmine red. Paper deep violet at right edge	.25
93.		1,000,000 Mark, blue on lilac and light brown. Value over printed on 20,000 Mark	.35
94.		1,000,000 Mark, black on white. Paper deep yellow at right edge. Reverse blank	.25
95.		5,000,000 Mark, black on white. Paper blue green at left edge	.25
96.		10,000,000 Mark, black and dark green. Paper yellow at right edge	.25
97.		20,000,000 Mark, black and light blue. Paper lilac at right edge	.25
98.		50,000,000 Mark, black and lilac brown. Paper lilac at right edge	.25
99.	9. 8.1923	50,000 Mark, black on light brown	.25
100.		200,000 Mark, black on grey	.25
101.		1,000,000 Mark, black on white. Paper green at right edge, watermarked with oak leaves	.25
102.		1,000,000 Mark, black and green. Paper green at right edge	
		a. Watermarked with hook-pointed stars	.25
		b. Watermarked with small crosses	.25
		c. Watermarked with lattice work of figure eights	.35
		d. Watermarked with waves	.35
103.		2,000,000 Mark, black on white paper. Paper lilac at right edge, watermarked with oak leaves	.25
104.		2,000,000 Mark, black and lilac. Lilac ornament at right	
		a. Watermarked with hook-pointed stars	.25
		b. Watermarked with small crosses	.25
		c. Watermarked with lattice work of figure eights	.35
		d. Watermarked with waves	.35
105.	20. 8.1923	5,000,000 Mark, black on grey green. Rose paper	.25

#106
125 × 80

106.	22. 8.1923	10,000,000 Mark, black on olive green and blue grey	
		a. Watermarked with hook-pointed stars	.25
		b. Watermarked with small crosses	.25
		c. Watermarked with lattice work of figure eights	.35
		d. Watermarked with waves	.35
107.		100,000,000 Mark, black on blue green and olive brown	
		a. Watermarked with oak leaves	.25
		b. Watermarked with small quatrefoils. Thread fibers in paper on reverse	.25
		c. Watermarked with small quatrefoils. No thread fibers in paper on reverse	.25
		d. Watermarked with hook-pointed stars	.25
		e. Watermarked with small crosses	.25
		f. Watermarked with stars and S	.50
		g. Watermarked with lozenge shapes	.40
108.	1. 9.1923	20,000,000 Mark, black on olive brown and green	
		a. Watermarked with small crosses	.25
		b. Watermarked with lozenge shapes	.50
		c. Watermarked with hook-pointed stars	.25
		d. Watermarked with waves	.25
		e. Watermarked with lattice work of figure eights	.25
		f. Watermarked with stars and S	5.00
109.		50,000,000 Mark, black on grey and lilac	
		a. Watermarked with small quatrefoils, grey paper	.25
		b. Watermarked with hook pointed stars, white paper	.25
		c. Watermarked with small crosses, white paper	.25
		d. Watermarked with lozenge shapes, white paper	.75
		e. Watermarked with stars and S, white paper	.40
		f. Watermarked with lattice work of figure eights, white paper	.25
110.		500,000,000 Mark, dark brown on light brown and lilac. With "500" at right edge	
		a. Watermarked with thistle leaves. Paper lilac at right edge	.25
		b. Watermarked with small quatrefoils	.25
		Error: "500" reading up	30.00
		c. Watermarked with hook-pointed stars	.25
		d. Watermarked with small crosses	.25
		e. Watermarked with stars and S	.35
		f. Watermarked with lozenge shapes	12.50
		g. Watermarked with lattice work of figure eights	1.00

| 111. | | 500 Milliard Mark, blue, lilac and green (unissued pattern, printed in Vienna) | R |

180 × 98

112.		1 Billiard Mark, violet and lilac (unissued pattern, printed in Vienna)	R
113.	(Sept. 1923)	1 Milliard Mark, black on dark brown. Same as #82 with red overprint	
		a. Watermarked with "1000." White paper with brown threads at right edge	.25
		Error: Overprint inverted	10.00
		Error: Overprint on reverse only	10.00
		b. Watermarked with small quatrefoils, brown paper	.25
		c. Watermarked with small quatrefoils, white paper	.75
114.	5. 9.1923	1 Milliard Mark, black on dark green, lilac and blue. Paper blue green at right edge	.25
115.	10. 9.1923	5 Milliard Mark, black on olive brown	
		a. Watermarked with oak leaves. Paper lilac at right edge	.25
		b. Watermarked with small quatrefoils	.35
116.	15. 9.1923	10 Milliard Mark, black on grey lilac and blue green	
		a. Watermarked with thistle leaves. Paper yellow at right edge	.25
		b. Watermarked with small quatrefoils	1.50
117.	1.10.1923	10 Milliard Mark, dark green on lilac and green	
		a. Watermarked with hook-pointed stars	.50
		b. Watermarked with small crosses	.50
		c. Watermarked with stars and S	1.00
		d. Watermarked with lozenge shapes	7.50
		e. Watermarked with lattice work of figure eights	.50
118.		20 Milliard Mark, dark green on blue and orange	
		a. Watermarked with hook-pointed stars	.75
		Error: "20 Milliarden" on left edge	8.50
		b. Watermarked with small crosses	.75
		Error: "20 Milliarden" on left edge	10.00
		c. Watermarked with lozenge shapes	1.75

118. (Cont.)		d. Watermarked with lattice work of figure eights	2.00
		e. Watermarked with stars and S	2.50
119.	10.10.1923	50 Milliard Mark, black on orange and blue	
		a. Watermarked with oak leaves. Paper green at right edge	.75
		b. Watermarked with small quatrefoils, white paper	.75
		c. Watermarked with small quatrefoils, grey paper (no serial numbers)	.40
120.		50 Milliard Mark, black on orange, blue and green. Type of #119, white paper, but green rectangles in background at right	
		a. Watermarked with hook-pointed stars	.50
		b. Watermarked with small crosses	.50
		c. Watermarked with stars and S	.50
121.	15.10.1923	200 Milliard Mark, black on violet and green	
		a. Watermarked with hook-pointed stars	1.50
		b. Watermarked with small crosses	2.00
		c. Watermarked with stars and S	5.00
		d. Watermarked with lattice work of figure eights	30.00
122.	20.10.1923	1 Milliard Mark, black on blue green	.25
123.		5 Milliard Mark, black on violet	.25
124.	(Oct. 1923)	500 Milliard Mark, dark brown on olive brown. Same as #87 but overprinted with new value	4.50
		Error: Overprint on reverse only	15.00
125.	26.10.1923	50 Milliard Mark, black on blue green	
		a. Grey paper	.25
		b. Green paper	.35
126.		100 Milliard Mark, dark blue on white. Paper blue at right edge	.50
127.		500 Milliard Mark, dark brown on white	
		a. Watermarked with oak leaves. Paper green at right edge	1.50
		b. Watermarked "500," paper blue or violet at right edge	1.25
128.		100 Billiard Mark, black on lilac and grey. Paper brown at right edge	50.00
129.	1.11.1923	1 Billiard Mark, brown violet. Paper lilac at right edge	4.00
130.		5 Billiard Mark, black on blue and rose	
		a. Watermarked with thistles, paper yellow at right edge	7.50
		b. Watermarked with small quatrefoils	20.00
131.		10 Billiard Mark, black on green and light brown (format 170 × 85 mm)	
		a. Watermarked with thistles, paper blue green at right edge	12.50
		b. Watermarked with small quatrefoils	22.50

132.		10 Billiard Mark, black on brown and blue green (format 120 × 82 mm)	
		a. Watermarked with hook-pointed stars	11.00
		b. Watermarked with small crosses	12.50
133.	5.11.1923	100 Milliard Mark, red brown on olive and blue green	.75
134.		1 Billiard Mark, black on violet and brown	4.50
135.		2 Billiard Mark, black on green and rose	
		a. Watermarked with hook-pointed stars	5.00
		b. Watermarked with small crosses	6.50
		c. Watermarked with stars and S	11.00
136.	7.11.1923	5 Billiard Mark, black on blue and rose	
		a. Watermarked with thistles, paper yellow at right edge	12.50
		b. Watermarked with small quatrefoils	R
		c. Watermarked with hook-pointed stars	50.00
		d. Watermarked with small crosses	15.00
137.	1. 2.1924	10 Billiard Mark, brown on green. Paper lilac at right edge	10.00
138.	5. 2.1924	20 Billiard Mark, blue green and violet. Portrait of a woman at right (from a painting by Albrecht Durer). Paper violet at right edge	20.00

175 × 95

139.	10. 2.1924	50 Billiard Mark, brown and olive. Portrait of Councilman J. Muffel (from a painting by Albrecht Durer) at right. Paper green at right edge	30.00
140.	15. 2.1924	100 Billiard Mark, red brown and blue. Portrait of Willibald Pirkheimer (from a painting by Albrecht Durer) at right. Paper light blue at right edge	50.00
141.	15. 3.1924	5 Billiard Mark, green and lilac	6.50

Zinskupons der Kriegsanleihen (Interest Coupons of War Loan Bonds)

In October, 1918, all interest coupons due on 2.1.1919 (letter q) were declared legal tender.

142.	Loan Year 1915, 1916, 1917, 1918	2.50 Mark	3.00

143.		5	Mark	5.00

100 × 48

144.	12.50	Mark	6.50
145.	25	Mark	7.50
146.	50	Mark	10.00
147.	125	Mark	15.00

Wertbestandige Anleihestucke (Fixed Value Loan Pieces)

In October, 1923, fractional notes of the Reichsbank issued against exchequer bonds, part pieces of exchequer bonds and whole bonds of the German Government were declared to be legal tender.

FRACTIONAL AND SMALL NOTES OF THE REICHSBANK

148.	23.10.1923	0.42 Goldmark = 1/10 Dollar	2.50
149.		1.05 Goldmark = $\frac{1}{4}$ Dollar. Watermarked "5," reverse blank	12.50
150.		1.05 Goldmark = $\frac{1}{4}$ Dollar. Watermarked "50," large letters on reverse	5.00
151.		2.10 Goldmark = $\frac{1}{2}$ Dollar	10.00

PART PIECES OF EXCHEQUER BONDS

152.	26.10.1923	0.42 Goldmark = 1/10 Dollar	4.00
153.		1.05 Goldmark = $\frac{1}{4}$ Dollar. Watermarked "5"	20.00
154.		1.05 Goldmark = $\frac{1}{4}$ Dollar. Watermarked "10"	10.00
155.		1.05 Goldmark = $\frac{1}{4}$ Dollar. Watermarked "50"	6.50
156.		2.10 Goldmark = $\frac{1}{2}$ Dollar. Watermarked "5"	20.00
157.		2.10 Goldmark = $\frac{1}{2}$ Dollar. Watermarked "20"	10.00

COMPLETE EXCHEQUER BONDS

158.	25. 8.1923	4.20 Goldmark = 1 Dollar	20.00
159.		8.40 Goldmark = 2 Dollar	25.00
160.		21.00 Goldmark = 5 Dollar	30.00

Rentenbankscheine (Land Value Bank Notes from 1923)

1 Billiard Mark = 1 Rentenmark

161.	1.11.1923	1 Rentenmark, olive green	2.00
162.		2 Rentenmark, red and green	3.50
163.		5 Rentenmark, blue green and violet	8.50
164.		10 Rentenmark, lilac and green	12.50
165.		50 Rentenmark, brown and violet	45.00
166.		100 Rentenmark, brown and blue green	R
167.		500 Rentenmark, blue grey and green	RRR

154 × 85

168.		1,000 Rentenmark, brown and light green	RRR
169.	20. 3.1925	50 Rentenmark, brown, green and lilac. Head of farmer at right	18.50
170.	3. 7.1925	10 Rentenmark, green and brown. Head of peasant woman at left	20.00
171.	2. 1.1926	5 Rentenmark, dark green and olive. Head of peasant girl at right	2.50
172.	6. 7.1934	50 Rentenmark, dark brown on olive green. Portrait of Baron von Stein at right	15.00
173.	30. 1.1937	1 Rentenmark, olive green	.25
174.		2 Rentenmark, brown	.25

Reichsbanknoten (Government Bank Notes), from 1924

1 Rentenmark = 1 Reichsmark

175.	11.10.1924	10 Reichsmark, dark green and red lilac. Portrait of merchant Diedrich Born (from a painting by Hans Holbein)	15.00

159 × 80

176.		20 Reichsmark, brown and red lilac. Portrait of a woman (from a painting by Hans Holbein)	30.00
177.		50 Reichsmark, brown and dark green. Portrait of a young man (from a painting by Hans Holbein)	30.00
178.		100 Reichsmark, brown and blue green. Portrait of an English Lady (from a painting by Hans Holbein)	15.00
179.		1,000 Reichsmark, brown and blue. Portrait of the nobleman Wedigh (from a painting by Hans Holbein)	30.00

180. 22. 1.1929 10 Reichsmark, green. Portrait of Albrecht Daniel Thaer at right. Female head (Agriculture) on reverse
 a. Watermarked at left with head of Thaer, letters in background .75
 b. Watermarked at left with ornament, no letters (issued 1945) 5.00
 Also see #188.

181. 20 Reichsmark, brown. Portrait of Werner von Siemens at right. Worker's head (Craftsmanship) on reverse
 a. Watermarked at left with head of von Siemens, letters in background 1.00
 b. Watermarked at left with ornament, no letters (issued 1945) 5.00

182. 30. 3.1933 50 Reichsmark, green. Portrait of David Hansemann at right. Mercury head on reverse
 a. Watermarked at left with head of Hansemann, letters in background 1.00
 b. Watermarked at left with ornament, no letters (issued 1945) 4.00
 Also see #189.

183. 24. 6.1935 100 Reichsmark, blue. Head of Justus von Liebig at right. Head and torch (Knowledge) on reverse
 a. Watermarked at left with head of von Liebig, letters in background 1.25
 b. Watermarked at left with ornament, no letters (issued 1945) 3.00
 Also see #190.

184. 22. 2.1936 1,000 Reichsmark, brown. Head of Karl Friedrich Schinkel at right. Head and protractor on reverse (Art) 15.00

160 × 79

185. 16. 6.1939 20 Reichsmark, brown. Young Austrian woman holding edelweiss flower. Mountain scene on reverse 1.00

186. 1. 8.1942 5 Reichsmark, red brown. Youth's head at right. Lion monument in Brunswick on reverse .50
 Error: Watermarked "S" inverted 20.00

After the Allied troops' entry into the Eupen-Malmedy district in 1944, the then current German bank notes plus some isolated issues of German Credit Account Notes were stamped by various Belgian communities. These stamped notes were only valid as legal tender in exchange for Belgian notes. Nearly all of these notes are scarce and seldom seen. The values range from $12.50 to more than $50.00.

Reichsbanknoten (National Bank Notes) Emergency Issue of 1944–45

ISSUES FOR THE SUDETENLAND AND LOWER SILESIA (REICHENBERG)

187.	28. 4.1945	20 Reichsmark, brown	2.00

ISSUES OF THE GERMAN NATIONAL BANK AUTHORITY IN GRAZ, LINZ AND SALZBURG

These notes were photo-mechanically reproduced from a specimen of the circulating notes. All notes of any one value have the same control numbers.

188.	22. 1.1929	10 Reichsmark, blue green. Type of #180 but poorly printed, serial number D02776733	20.00
189.	30. 3.1933	50 Reichsmark, green. Type of #182 but poorly printed, serial number E 06647727	17.50

177 × 95

190.	24. 6.1935	100 Reichsmark, blue. Type of #183 but poorly printed, serial number T 7396475	17.50

Alliierte Militarbehorde (Allied Military Administrative Authority)

The notes issued by the Western Allies show the initial "F" of the printer Forbes. Those of the Russian printing (printing plates acquired from the USA) are without this imprint. These circulated alongside the Reichsmark and Rentenmark issues.

191.	1944	½ Mark, green on light blue	.50
192.		1 Mark, blue on light blue	.75
193.		5 Mark, lilac on light blue	1.25
194.		10 Mark, blue on light blue	1.75
195.		20 Mark, red on light blue	2.50

155 × 68

196.		50 Mark, blue on light blue	4.00
197.		100 Mark, lilac on light blue	3.00
198.		1,000 Mark, green on light blue	37.50

GERMAN FEDERAL REPUBLIC (Bundesrepublik Deutschland)

Currency Reform, 1948: Deutsche Mark introduced 20.6.1948.

Bank notes of 1948

1.	1948	½ Deutsche Mark, green	1.00
2.		1 Deutsche Mark, blue	1.00
3.		2 Deutsche Mark, lilac. Seated female figure at left	1.25
4.		5 Deutsche Mark, brown. Seated man at right (Seafaring)	3.50
5.		10 Deutsche Mark, blue. Three figures (Labor, Justice, Building) in middle	11.50
6.		20 Deutsche Mark, green. Two figures (Industry and Agriculture) at left	15.00

150 × 67

7.		50 Deutsche Mark, violet. Female figure in middle	25.00
8.		100 Deutsche Mark, red brown. Woman reading in center	37.50
9.	(1948)	20 Deutsche Mark, blue. Woman's head in medallion at left.	20.00
10.		50 Deutsche Mark, green blue. Female head in middle (in circulation only a few days)	RR

Bank Deutscher Lander (Bank of the German Lands)

11.	(1948)	5 Pfennig, green	.50
12.		10 Pfennig, blue	.50
13.	9.12.1948	5 Deutsche Mark, black green and yellow. Europa being adbucted on the back of a winged bull	2.50
14.		50 Deutsche Mark, brown and yellow green. Portrait of the merchant Imhoff (from a painting by Albrecht Durer) at right. Imhoff and a medieval trading scene on reverse	17.50
15.		100 Deutsche Mark, light violet and rose on blue. Councilman J. Muffel (from a painting by Albrecht Durer) at right. Muffel and a view of medieval Nuremberg on reverse	30.00

#16
140 × 66

16.	22. 8.1949	10 Deutsche Mark, blue. Type of #5 but with name of bank	4.50
17.		20 Deutsche Mark, green. Type of #6 but with name of bank	7.50

Notes #1–10 and 13–17 are also known with a "B" stamp, "B" perforation, or both, as a control mark on currency used in West Berlin as legal tender. Their value is about 50% more than the normal notes.

Deutsche Bundesbank (German Government Bank)

18.	2. 1.1960	5 Deutsche Mark, green. Young Venetian girl (from a painting by Albrecht Durer). Oak leaf and acorns on the reverse	—
19.		10 Deutsche Mark, blue. Portrait of a man with long hair. Sailing ships on the reverse	—
20.		20 Deutsche Mark, green. Portrait of Elsbeth Tucher (from a painting by Albrecht Durer). Violin and clarinet on reverse	—
21.		50 Deutsche Mark, brown and green. Portrait of Treasurer H. Urmiller. View of the Holstentor in Lubeck on reverse	—
22.		100 Deutsche Mark, blue. Portrait of Master of Arts S. Munster (from a painting by Christian Amberger)	—
23.		500 Deutsche Mark, brown lilac. Man's head. View of Eltz on reverse	—
24.		1,000 Deutsche Mark, brown. Portrait of the astronomer Dr. Schoner (from a painting by Lucas Kranach the Elder). Limburg cathedral on reverse	—

GERMAN DEMOCRATIC REPUBLIC

Currency Reform, 1948: East German Mark introduced.

Provisional issue created by pasting gummed, perforated stamps on to old Rentenmark and Reichsbank notes. The stamps carry the date and value.

1.	1948	1 Deutsche Mark. Blue control stamp on #173 1 Rentenmark of 30.1.1937	$1.25
2.		2 Deutsche Mark. Green control stamp on #174, 2 Rentenmark of 30.1.1937	2.00
3.		5 Deutsche Mark. Brown control stamp on #186, 5 Reichsmark of 1.8.1942	2.50
4.		10 Deutsche Mark. Lilac control stamp on #180, 10 Reichsmark of 22.1.1929	4.00

160 × 80

5.	20 Deutsche Mark. Brown control stamp on #181, 20 Reichsmark of 22.1.1929, or #185, 20 Reichsmark of 16.6.1939	5.00
6.	50 Deutsche Mark. Blue control stamp on #182, 50 Reichsmark of 30.3.1933	12.50
7.	100 Deutsche Mark. Green blue control stamp on #183, 100 Reichsmark of 24.6.1935	20.00

Stamps are also found on 5 Rentenmark notes of 2.1.1926 (#171) and 50 Rentenmark notes of 6.7.1934 (#172). They were not, however, officially affixed.

Deutsche Notenbank (German Note Bank)

8.	1948	50 Deutsche Pfennig, blue	.50
9.		1 Deutsche Mark, olive	.75
10.		2 Deutsche Mark, brown	1.00
11.		5 Deutsche Mark, brown	1.25
12.		10 Deutsche Mark, green	1.25
13.		20 Deutsche Mark, brown	1.50
14.		50 Deutsche Mark, green	1.00
15.		100 Deutsche Mark, blue	3.00

191 × 97

16.		1,000	Deutsche Mark, brown	37.50
17.	1955	5	Deutsche Mark, grey blue	3.00
18.		10	Deutsche Mark, violet and lilac	5.00
19.		20	Deutsche Mark, blue violet	10.00
20.		50	Deutsche Mark, red brown	20.00
21.		100	Deutsche Mark, brown	30.00
22.	1964	5	Deutsche Mark, brown. Alexander von Humboldt at right	—
23.		10	Deutsche Mark, green. Friedrich von Schiller at right	—
24.		20	Deutsche Mark, red brown. Johann Wolfgang von Goethe at right	—
25.		50	Deutsche Mark, blue green. Friedrich Engels at right	—
26.		100	Deutsche Mark, blue. Karl Marx at right	—

GERMAN REGIONAL BANK NOTES

Of the numerous note-issuing banks of the old German States, only those mentioned below produced paper money after 1900. During the war of 1914–1918 and in the following years of inflation, many local banks and governments issued paper money most of which was not recognized as legal tender. The exceptions were the notes issued by the *Badischen Bank* (Baden), the *Bayerischen Notenbank* (Bavaria), the *Sachsischen Bank* (Saxony) and the *Wurttembergische Notenbank* (Wurttemberg) which did not lose their right to print paper money until 1935.

Baden

Badische Bank (Bank of Baden)

Notes R1 through R6 carry the same allegorical designs. On the obverse at left and right is a woman with two children; on the reverse is a river god (the Rhine) and a goddess (the Neckar).

R1.   1.12.1870   10 Gulden, black and green on grey brown   R

171 × 115

R2.	1. 7.1871	50 Gulden, black and blue on yellow brown	RR
R3.	1. 1.1874	100 Mark, black on blue and yellow brown	R
R4.	1. 1.1890	100 Mark	RRR
R5.	1.10.1902	100 Mark, black and blue on light blue	$3.50
R6.	1. 1.1907	100 Mark, black and blue on light blue	
		a. With printer's name	2.00
		b. Without printer's name	1.50
R7.	15.12.1918	100 Mark, blue and blue green	.75
R8.	1. 8.1922	500 Mark, violet on grey green	.25
R9.	1.12.1922	5,000 Mark, brown on violet and yellow	.25
R10.	1. 4.1923	10,000 Mark, brown, blue and green	.25
R11.	1. 8.1923	500,000 Mark, dark brown on grey brown and violet	.25
R12.	7. 8.1923	1 Million Mark, black on violet	.25
R13.	25. 9.1923	2 Milliard overprint on 20 Million Mark, dark brown on grey green. Red overprint	.25
R14.	30.10.1923	100 Milliard Mark, dark brown on brown violet and light blue	1.25
R15.	11.10.1923	50 Reichsmark. J. Peter Hebel	RR

The bank's right to issue paper money expired in 1935.

Bavaria

Bayerische Notenbank (Bavarian Note-issuing Bank)

R16.	3.11.1875	100 Mark, black on blue. Four allegorical figures	RRR
R17.	1. 1.1900	100 Mark, black on blue and brown. Type of R16	.50
R18.	1. 1.1922	100 Mark, multicolored	.25
R19.	1.10.1922	1,000 Mark, blue black on blue and brown	.25
R20.	1.12.1922	5,000 Mark, multicolored	.25
R21.	1. 3.1923	20,000 Mark, multicolored	.25
R22.	15. 3.1923	50,000 Mark, multicolored	.25
R23.	15. 6.1923	100,000 Mark, multicolored	.25
R24.	15. 8.1923	1,000,000 Mark, blue black on brown and blue	.25
R25.	18. 8.1923	500,000 Mark, violet and lilac	.35
R26.	20. 8.1923	1,000,000 Mark, dark brown on yellow and green	.35
R27.		5,000,000 Mark, dark brown on green and red brown	.35
R28.		25,000,000 Mark, blue and brown	.35
R29.		50,000,000 Mark, light olive and red brown	.35
R30.	1. 9.1923	10,000,000 Mark, blue and brown	.25
R31.	1.10.1923	1 Milliard Mark, dark brown and violet	.25
R32.	10.10.1923	5 Milliard Mark, lilac and grey blue	.35
R33.	24.10.1923	50 Milliard Mark, dark green	.50
R34.	Old date: 1. 8.1923	500 Milliard overprint on 100 milliard Mark, multicolored. Red-brown overprint	8.50
R35.	11.10.1924	50 Reichsmark	RR
R36.		100 Reichsmark	R

170 × 84

R37.	1. 9.1925	50 Reichsmark. H. Holzschuher (from a painting by Durer) at right	R

The bank's right to issue paper money expired in 1935.

Brunswick

Braunschweigische Bank (Brunswick Bank)

R38.	1. 5.1854	10 Taler	RR
R39.	1. 6.1856	10 Taler	RRR
R40.	1. 1.1869	10 Taler, black on brown. Bank building	50.00
R41.	1. 7.1874	100 Mark	R

The bank relinquished its right to print paper money
in 1905.

Frankfurt

Frankfurter Bank (Bank of Frankfurt)

R42.	1. 1.1855	5	Gulden, brown and blue. Crowned female bust at left and right	45.00
R43.		10	Gulden. Type of R42	50.00
R44.		35	Gulden. Type of R42	R
R45.		50	Gulden. Type of R42	RR
R46.		100	Gulden. Type of R42	RR
R47.		500	Gulden. Type of R42	RR
R48.	25. 7.1870	500	Gulden (deposit note)	RRR
R49.	1. 1.1874	100	Mark, brown and blue. Crowned female bust at left and right	R
R50.		500	Mark. Type of R49	R

214 × 137

R51.		1,000	Mark. Type of R49	RR
R52.	1. 8.1890	100	Mark. Type of R49	45.00
R53.		1,000	Mark, dark brown and brown. Type of R49	50.00

The bank relinquished its right to print paper money in 1901.

Hesse

Bank fur Suddeutschland (Bank for South Germany)

R54.	1. 7.1856	10	Gulden	RR
R55.		10	Taler	RRR
R56.	1.12.1856	25	Gulden	RRR
R57.		50	Gulden	RRR
R58.		100	Gulden	RRR
R59.		25	Taler	RRR
R60.		50	Taler	RRR
R61.		100	Taler	RRR
R62.	20. 3.1857	10	Taler	RRR
R63.	2. 1.1870	10	Gulden, black on green	RR

R64.		25 Gulden	RRR
R65.	1. 1.1874	100 Mark	RR

The bank relinquished its right to print paper money in 1902.

Saxony

Landstandische Bank des kgl. Sachs. Markgraftums Oberlausitz (People's Bank of the Kingdom of Saxony and the Margraviate of Oberlausitz) in Bautzen

R66.	1860	5 Taler	RRR
R67.	1861	10 Taler	RRR
R68.	10.10.1868	10 Taler	RR
R69.	1. 1.1875	100 Mark, green and red	RR

The bank relinquished its right to print paper money in 1906.

Sachsische Bank (Bank of Saxony) in Dresden

R70.	15. 1.1866	10 Taler	RRR
R71.		20 Taler	RRR
R72.		50 Taler	RRR
R73.		100 Taler	RRR

171 × 102

R74.	1. 1.1874	100 Mark, black on green. Woman's head at left, Mercury head at right	20.00
R75.		500 Mark	RRR
R76.	15. 6.1890	100 Mark, black on blue and brown. Type of R74	3.50
R77.		500 Mark, black on red brown and blue. Type of R74	6.50
R78.	2. 1.1911	100 Mark. Type of R76	1.00
R79.		500 Mark. Type of R77	1.50
R80.	1. 7.1922	500 Mark. Type of R77	.50
R81.	12. 9.1922	500 Mark, blue on yellow	.50
R82.		1,000 Mark, dark olive on light olive	.75
R83.	1. 3.1923	10,000 Mark, green and rose	.25
R84.	12. 3.1923	5,000 Mark, green blue on green	.25
R85.	2. 7.1923	100,000 Mark, green and rose	.25

R86.	25. 7.1923	50,000 Mark, blue on green and brown	.25
R87.	12. 8.1923	5,000,000 Mark, dark brown and grey green	.25
R88.	15. 8.1923	500,000 Mark, black on green and violet	.25
R89.	18. 8.1923	1,000,000 Mark, brown and light blue	.25
R90.	1. 9.1923	2,000,000 Mark, brown olive	.25
R91.	1.10.1923	100,000,000 Mark, multicolored	.25
R92.	20.10.1923	20 Milliard Mark, brown violet and green	1.25
R93.		100 Milliard Mark, brown violet and light brown	3.00
R.94	15.11.1923	1 Billiard Mark, green and olive	11.50
R95.		10 Billiard Mark, lilac and blue	15.00
R96.	11.10.1924	50 Reichsmark. Leibniz	RR
R97.		100 Reichsmark, dark blue and brown. Lessing at left	RR

The bank's right to print paper money expired in 1935.

Wurttemberg

Wurttembergische Notenbank (Wurttemberg Note-issuing Bank)

Notes R98–R101 display three cupids at right and left.

R98.	15.11.1871	10 Gulden	RR

159 × 107

R99.		35 Gulden	RR
R100.	1. 1.1874	100 Mark, dark brown on light brown and blue	R
R101.	1. 1.1875	100 Mark, blue and light brown	45.00
R102.	1. 1.1890	100 Mark. Type of R101	37.50
R103.	1. 1.1902	100 Mark. Type of R101	20.00
R104.	1. 1.1911	100 Mark. Type of R101 (two signature varieties)	1.25
R105.	1. 9.1922	1,000 Mark, blue on grey violet	1.00
R106.	20. 2.1923	10,000 Mark, dark blue and yellow brown	.25
R107.	10. 6.1923	50,000 Mark, green and red brown on lilac	.25
R108.	15. 6.1923	20,000 Mark, dark green and red on light brown	.25
R109.		100,000 Mark, dark green and blue on brown	.15
R110.		1 Million Mark, blue and red brown on brown	.15
R111.	1. 8.1923	1 Million Mark, red and blue on orange. Man's head in middle	.15

R112.		5 Million Mark, carmine	.20
R113.		100 Million Mark, dark blue	.30
R114.	15.10.1923	10 Milliard Mark	1.50
R115.	Old date:		
	15.12.1918	50 Milliard Mark on 100 Million Mark	2.50
R116.	20.11.1923	500 Milliard Mark	8.75
R117.	11.10.1924	50 Reichsmark	R
R118.		100 Reichsmark	RR
R119.	1. 8.1925	50 Reichsmark. Schubart	RR

The bank's right to print paper money expired in 1935.

NOTES FOR GERMAN OCCUPIED TERRITORIES

Ostbank fur Handel und Gewerbe, Darlehnskasse Ost (Eastern Bank for Trade and Industry, Eastern State Loan Office) in Posen

Notes circulating in Lithuania from 1919

R120.	17. 4.1916	20 Kopecks, blue green	$0.25
R121.		50 Kopecks, red brown and blue green	
		a. Small letters in reverse text, reads "Aiſdewu" at right	.50
		b. Larger letters in reverse text	.75
		c. As R121a but text at right reads "Aiſdewu"	.25
		d. As R121b but text at right reads "Aiſdewu"	.35
R122.		1 Ruble, blue and brown	
		a. Reverse as R121a	.50
		b. Reverse as R121b	.50
		c. Reverse as R121c	.35
		d. Reverse as R121d	.35
R123.		3 Rubles, brown on green	
		a. Reverse text reads "Aiſdewu . . ." at right	1.50
		b. Reverse text reads "Aiſdewu . . ." at right	1.25
R124.		10 Rubles, red brown and green	2.00
R125.		25 Rubles, blue and lilac	4.00

R126

171 × 107

R126.	100 Rubles, blue. Woman's head at left, helmeted man's head at right	6.50

Darlehnskasse Ost (Eastern State Loan Office) in Kowno

As R120–R126, the following notes circulated in Lithuania from 1919.

R127.	½ Mark, lilac and light brown	.50
R128.	1 Mark, brown and green	.75
R129.	2 Mark, red brown and lilac	1.25
R130.	5 Mark, brown and blue	1.50
R131.	20 Mark, red brown on green and rose	2.50
R132.	50 Mark, dark blue on grey violet	4.50
R133.	100 Mark, brown. Woman's head at left, helmeted man's head at right	6.50
R134.	1,000 Mark, green. Mercury and youth in armor at right	5.00

Reichskreditkassenscheine (German Government Loan Office Notes)

Established as legal tender in the various countries occupied by German troops during World War II.

R135. (1939–45)	50 Reichspfennig, green	1.00
R136.	1 Reichsmark, brown	
	a. With embossing	1.00
	b. Without embossing (starting with "Series 481"	.50
R137.	2 Reichsmark, dark green and brown	
	a. With embossing (seven digit serial number)	.75
	b. Without embossing (eight digit serial number)	.25
R138.	5 Reichsmark, dark blue. Man's head at left and right	
	a. With embossing (seven digit serial number)	1.00
	b. Without embossing (eight digit serial number)	.50
R139.	20 Reichsmark, brown on red brown and olive. "Der Baumeister" ("The Master Builder" from a painting by Durer)	1.25
R140.	50 Reichsmark, dark blue on violet. Reverse Farmer's wife at right	2.25

At the end of World War II, the 5, 20 and 50 reichsmark notes of the government loan office issues were declared legal tender in the British Zone of Occupation when officially stamped by an office of the Reichsbank. All notes bearing any of the various stamps on them are quite scarce and seldom seen. Values range upward from $25.00.

German Military Notes

Etappen Inspektion I

Notes stamped to indicate control check by communications commander of the First Army. Issued for use in occupied French territories. All have "1915" printed, balance of date handwritten.

M1.	1915	50 Centimes	12.50
M2.		1 Franc	12.50
M3.		2 Francs	12.50
M4.		5 Francs	12.50

Etappen Kommandantur

Notes stamped to indicate control check by the communications command. Issued for use in occupied French territories.

M5.	1915	50 Centimes. Type of M1	12.50
M6.		1 Franc	12.50
M7.		2 Francs	12.50
M8.		5 Francs	12.50

Etappen Inspektion 2

Notes stamped to indicate control check by communications command of the Second Army. Issued for use in occupied French territories. These are the so-called "Deichmann-Bons" notes with stamps of various French communities.

M9.	1914–15	5 Francs	25.00
M10.		10 Francs	25.00
M11.		20 Francs	25.00

174 × 100

M12.	50 Francs	25.00
M13.	100 Francs	25.00

Etappen Kommandantur

Issued in occupied French territories, "Deichmann-Bons" issue

M14.	1914–15	5 Francs. Type of M9	25.00

M15.		10 Francs	25.00
M16.		20 Francs	25.00
M17.		50 Francs	25.00
M18.		100 Francs	25.00

Etappen Inspektion 3

Control check by communications command of Third Army. Issued for use in occupied French territories.

M19.	1915	1 Franc	12.50
M20.		2 Francs	12.50
M21.		3 Francs	12.50
M22.		5 Francs	12.50
M23.		10 Francs	12.50
M24.		25 Francs	12.50
M25.		50 Francs	12.50
M26.		100 Francs	12.50

Reichsmarine des Ostseebereichs (German Navy, Eastern Sea Command) in Kiel

M27.	27.10.1923	1 Milliard Mark	5.00
M28.		5 Milliard Mark	7.50
M29.		20 Milliard Mark	2.00
M30.		50 Milliard Mark	2.50

Behelfszahlungsmittel fur die Deutsche Wehrmacht (Auxiliary Payment Certificates for use by the German Army)

During World War II, currency was the responsibility of the military. The face value of the following notes was only 1/10 of their actual value. A 1 pfennig note thus had the purchasing power of 10 pfennig.

100 × 50

M31.	(1940)	1 Reichspfennig, lilac brown. Swastika in middle background	10.00
M32.	(1942)	1 Reichspfennig, blue. Small swastika and eagle in background	.75
M33.		5 Reichspfennig, red	1.00
M34.		10 Reichspfennig, green	1.25
M35.		50 Reichpfennig, red	1.50
M36.		1 Reichsmark, ochre	2.50
M37.		2 Reichsmark, lilac	8.50

Also see Greece M20–M22.

Verrechnungsscheine fur die Deutsche Wehrmacht (Accounting Notes for the German Army)

Near the end of 1944, the actual value of the military paper money was about the same as the face value stated on the note as legal tender.

M38.	15.9.1944	1 Reichsmark, green	.50
M39.		5 Reichsmark, blue	.75
M40.		10 Reichsmark, red	1.25
M41.		50 Reichsmark, lilac brown	2.00

GIBRALTAR

A peninsula on the southern coast of Spain, Gibraltar has been under British control since 1704.

1 Pound = 20 Shillings

Government notes with the embossed seal of the "Anglo-Egyptian Bank, Ltd. Gibraltar"

1.	5.8.1914, Series A	2 Shillings, red	$15.00
2.		10 Shillings, blue	25.00
3.		1 Pound, black on yellowish paper	37.50
4.		5 Pounds, black on bluish paper	R
5.		50 Pounds, black on bluish paper	RR
6.	6.8.1914, Series B	2 Shillings, green on rose	15.00
7.		10 Shillings, lilac on rose	25.00
8.		1 Pound, blue on green	37.50
9.		5 Pounds, brown on green	R
10.		50 Pounds, rose on green	RR

2 Shilling notes with the date 3.8.1938 (Series C) were printed but not issued. They were destroyed in 1968.

Government of Gibraltar, "Currency Note Ordinance 1927"

11.	1.10.1927	10 Shillings, blue on yellow brown. Cliffs of Gibraltar at right	12.50
12.		1 Pound, green on yellow brown. Cliffs of Gibraltar in middle	20.00
13.		5 Pounds, brown. Cliffs of Gibraltar in middle	30.00

Government of Gibraltar, "Currency Note Ordinance of 1934"

Printed by Waterlow and Sons Ltd. Various date varieties

14.	10 Shillings, blue on yellow brown. Type of #11. (two control number and four signature varieties)	—

145 × 94

15.	1 Pound, green on yellow brown. Type of #12 (two control number and five signature varieties)	—

| 16. | | 5 Pounds, brown. Type of #13 (two control number and four signature varieties) | — |

Printed by Thomas de la Rue & Co. Ltd.

17.	1.5.1965	10 Shillings. Type of #11	—
18.		1 Pound. Type of #12	—
19.		5 Pounds. Type of #13	—

GREAT BRITAIN

The kingdom of Great Britain is composed of England, Wales, Scotland with its off-shore islands, the Isle of Man, the Channel Islands of Jersey and Guernsey and Northern Ireland. Queen Victoria ruled from 1837 to 1901 followed by King Edward VII, 1901–10; George V, 1910–36; Edward VIII, January to December, 1936; George VI, 1936–52; and Elizabeth II, from 1952.

1 Pound = 20 Shillings = 100 New Pence
1 Shilling = 12 Pence

Bank of England

The note type introduced in 1870 has black printing on only one side of watermarked paper. Each note carries two control or serial numbers. A third small control number below the signature was added in 1903. All types have various date and signature (Chief Cashier) varieties. Through 1939, notes were issued at various cities besides London.

1.	London, dates to 1945	5 Pounds, black. Paper without silver thread	$30.00
2.	1945–48	5 Pounds. Type of #1 but thick paper with silver thread	37.50
3.	1948–57	5 Pounds. Type of #2 but thinner paper	30.00
4.	dates to 1943	10 Pounds, black	50.00
5.	dates to 1943	20 Pounds, black	R

210 × 132

6.	dates to 1943	50 Pounds, black	RR
7.	dates to 1943	100 Pounds, black	RRR
8.	dates to 1928	200 Pounds, black	RRR

9.	dates to 1943	500 Pounds, black	RRR
10.		1,000 Pounds, black	RRR
11.	Birmingham, dates to 1939	5 Pounds. Type of #1	R
12.		10 Pounds, black	R
13.		20 Pounds, black	RR
14.		50 Pounds, black	RR
15.		100 Pounds, black	RRR
16.		500 Pounds, black	RRR
17.		1,000 Pounds, black	RRR
18.	dates to 1928	200 Pounds, black	RRR
19.	Bristol, dates to 1939	5 Pounds. Type of #1	R
20.		10 Pounds, black	R
21.		20 Pounds, black	RR
22.		50 Pounds, black	RR
23.		100 Pounds, black	RRR
24.		500 Pounds, black	RRR
25.		1,000 Pounds, black	RRR
26.	dates to 1928	200 Pounds, black	RRR
27.	Hull, dates to 1939	5 Pounds. Type of #1	R
28.		10 Pounds, black	R
29.		20 Pounds, black	RR
30.		50 Pounds, black	RR
31.		100 Pounds, black	RRR
32.		500 Pounds, black	RRR
33.		1,000 Pounds, black	RRR
34.	dates to 1928	200 Pounds, black	RRR
35.	Leeds, dates to 1939	5 Pounds. Type of #1	R
36.		10 Pounds, black	R
37.		20 Pounds, black	RR
38.		50 Pounds, black	RR
39.		100 Pounds, black	RRR
40.		500 Pounds, black	RRR
41.		1,000 Pounds, black	RRR
42.	dates to 1928	200 Pounds, black	RRR
43.	Liverpool, dates to 1939	5 Pounds. Type of #1	R
44.		10 Pounds, black	R
45.		20 Pounds, black	RR
46.		50 Pounds, black	RR
47.		100 Pounds, black	RRR
48.		500 Pounds, black	RRR
49.		1,000 Pounds, black	RRR
50.	dates to 1928	200 Pounds, black	RRR
51.	Manchester, dates to 1939	5 Pounds. Type of #1	R
52.		10 Pounds, black	R
53.		20 Pounds, black	RR
54.		50 Pounds, black	RR
55.		100 Pounds, black	RRR
56.		500 Pounds, black	RRR
57.		1,000 Pounds, black	RRR
58.	dates to 1928	200 Pounds, black	RRR

59.	Newcastle-on-Tyne, dates to 1939	5 Pounds. Type of #1	R
60.		10 Pounds, black	R
61.		20 Pounds, black	RR
62.		50 Pounds, black	RR
63.		100 Pounds, black	RRR
64.		500 Pounds, black	RRR
65.		1,000 Pounds, black	RRR
66.	dates to 1928	200 Pounds, black	RRR
67.	Plymouth, dates to 1939	5 Pounds. Type of #1	R
68.		10 Pounds, black	R
69.		20 Pounds, black	RR
70.		50 Pounds, black	RR
71.		100 Pounds, black	RRR
72.		500 Pounds, black	RRR
73.		1,000 Pounds, black	RRR
74.	dates to 1928	200 Pounds, black	RRR
75.	Portsmouth, dates to 1939	5 Pounds. Type of #1	R
76.		10 Pounds, black	R
77.		20 Pounds, black	RR
78.		50 Pounds, black	RR
79.		100 Pounds, black	RRR
80.		500 Pounds, black	RRR
81.		1,000 Pounds, black	RRR
82.	dates to 1928	200 Pounds, black	RRR

Treasury Notes

130 × 63

83.	(August 1914)	10 Shillings, red. Head of George V at left (format 130 × 63 mm)	10.00
84.		1 Pound, black. Head of George V at left (format 130 × 63 mm)	20.00
85.	(January 1915)	10 Shillings, red. Head of George V at left, St. George at right (format 138 × 80 mm)	7.50
86.	(October 1914)	1 Pound, black. Head of George V at left, St. George at right (format 140 × 80 mm)	15.00
87.	(1915)	1 Shilling (not released, entire printing destroyed)	
88.		2 Shillings 6 Pence (2/6) (not released, entire printing destroyed)	
89.		5 Shillings (issue withdrawn after two days)	RRR
90.	(1918–19)	10 Shillings, green. Britannia at left, head of George V at right. Inscribed "United Kingdom of Great Britain and Ireland" (two signature varieties)	12.50

91.	(1917–19)	1 Pound, brown. St. George and dragon at left, head of George V at right. Inscribed "United Kingdom of Great Britain and Ireland" (two signature varieties)	
		a. Watermarked "One Pound" in two lines	7.50
		b. Watermarked "One Pound" in one line	7.50
92.	(1928)	10 Shillings, green. Type of #90 but inscribed "United Kingdom of Great Britain and Northern Ireland"	10.00
93.		1 Pound, brown. Type of #91 but inscribed "United Kingdom of Great Britain and Northern Ireland"	6.50

Bank of England

All notes are without dates, signatures of Chief Cashiers change

94.	(1928–40)	10 Shillings, brown. Britannia at left. Paper without metallic thread (three signature varieties)	3.00
95.		1 Pound, green. Britannia at left. Paper without metallic thread (three signature varieties)	5.00
96.	(1940–48)	10 Shillings, violet. Britannia at left. Paper with metallic thread	5.00

150 × 85

97.		1 Pound, blue. Britannia at left. Paper with metallic thread	6.50
98.	(1948–60)	10 Shillings, brown. Type of #94 but paper with metallic thread (three signature varieties)	2.00
99.		1 Pound, green. Type of #95 but paper with metallic thread (three signature varieties)	4.50
100.	(1957–61)	5 Pounds, blue and multicolored. Britannia head at left, St. George and dragon in middle. Value "£5" in blue on reverse	—
101.	(1961–63)	5 Pounds, blue and multicolored. Type of #100 but reverse value in white outline figure	17.50
102.	(dates from 1961)	10 Shillings, brown. Queen Elizabeth at right (three signature varieties)	—

103.	(dates from 1960)	1 Pound, green. Queen Elizabeth at right (three signature varieties)	—
104.	(dates from 1963)	5 Pounds, dark blue. Queen Elizabeth at right (two signature varieties)	—
105.	(dates from 1964)	10 Pounds, dark brown. Queen Elizabeth at right (two signature varieties)	—
106.	(dates from 1970)	20 Pounds, lilac and multicolored. Queen Elizabeth at right, St. George and dragon in middle	—

Postal Orders

In 1914, Post Office and bank money orders with imprinted values were declared legal tender. The most popular denominations were 10 and 20 shillings but 2/6 and 5 shilling orders were also used. All of these money orders which carry the head of George V in three-quarter profile are very rare (RR). Postal money orders were also declared legal tender during the period 1939–41.

Local Bank Issues

Many local banks in Britain once had the right to issue paper money. The Bank Charter Act of 1844 drastically reduced their number.

Notes of the following banks were in circulation in 1900 and later:

Ashford Bank, Pomfret, Burra & Co. (until 1902)
Aylesbury Old Bank, Cobb Bartlett & Co. (until 1902)
Banbury Bank, Gillet & Co. (until 1918)
Banbury Old Bank, T. R. Cobb & Sons (until 1902)
Bank of Whitehaven Ltd. (until 1916)
Bedford Bank, Thomas Barnard & Co. (until 1915)
Bicester & Oxfordshire Bank—Tibb & Co. (until 1920)
Bradford Banking Co. Ltd. (until 1910)
Bradford Commercial Banking Co. Ltd. (until 1904)
Buckingham Bank—Bartlett & Co. (until 1902)
Cambridge & Cambridgeshire Bank Ltd.—Fosters (until 1904)
Canterbury Bank, Hammand, Plumptre, Hilton, McMaster & Furley (until 1903)
Carlisle & Cumberland Banking Co. Ltd. (until 1911)
City Bank, Exeter—Milford, Snow & Co. (until 1901)
Cumberland Union Banking Co. Ltd. (until 1901)
Derby Bank, Samuel Smith & Co. (until 1902)
East Riding Bank, Beckett & Co., York (until 1920)
Exeter Bank—Sanders & Co. (until 1901)
Faversham Bank, Hilton, Rigden & Rigden (until 1902)
Halifax Commercial Bank Ltd. (until 1919)
Halifax & Huddersfield Union Bank Ltd. (until 1910)
Hull & Kingston-upon-Hull, Samuel Smith (until 1902)
Ipswich Bank, Bacon Cobbold & Co. (until 1904)
Kington & Radnorshire Bank Ltd.—Davies Bank & Co. (until 1910)
Knaresborough & Claro Banking Co. Ltd. (until 1903)
Lancaster Banking Co. Ltd. (until 1907)
Leeds Bank, Beckett & Co. Leeds (until 1920)

Leeds Union Bank, William Williams, Brown & Co. (until 1900)
Leicestershire Banking Co. Ltd. (until 1900)
Lincoln Bank, Smith, Ellison & Co. (until 1902)
Lincoln & Lindsey Banking Co. Ltd. (until 1913)
Llandovery & Llandilo Bank—David Jones & Co. (until 1909)
Moore & Robinsons, Notts Banking Co. Ltd. (until 1901)
Naval Bank, Plymouth, Harris, Bulteel & Co. (until 1914)
Newark Bank, Samuel Smith & Co. (until 1902)
Newark & Sleaford Bank, Peacock, Wilson & Co. (until 1912)
Newmarket Bank, Hammand & Co. (until 1905)
North & South Wales Bank Ltd. (until 1908)
Nottingham Bank, Samuel Smith & Co. (until 1902)
Nottingham and Nottinghamshire Banking Co. Ltd. (until 1919)
Oxford Old Bank, Parsons Thomson & Co. (until 1900)
Oxfordshire Witney Bank, Gillett & Co. (until 1918)
Pares' Leicestershire Banking Co. Ltd. (until 1902)
Reading Bank, Simonds & Co. (until 1913)
Richmond Bank, Yorkshire, Roper & Priestman (until 1902)
Sheffield Banking Co. Ltd. (until 1905)
Sheffield & Hallamshire Bank, Ltd. (until 1913)
Sheffield & Rotherham Joint Stock Banking Co. Ltd. (until 1907)
Stamford, Spalding & Boston Banking Co. Ltd. (until 1907)
Stuckeys Banking Co. Ltd. (until 1909)
Tring Bank & Chesham Bank, Thomas Butcher & Sons (until 1900)
Uxbridge Old Bank—Woodbridge, Lacy, Hartland, Hibbert & Co. (until 1900)
Wakefield & Barnsley Union Bank Ltd. (until 1906)
Wallingford Bank, Hedges Wells & Co. (until 1905)
Wellington, Somerset Bank, Fox, Fowler & Co. (until 1920)
West Riding Bank, Leathem Tew & Co. (until 1906)
West Riding Union Banking Co. Ltd.(until 1902)
West Yorkshire Banking Co. Ltd. (until 1919)
Whitehaven Joint Stock Banking Co. Ltd. (until 1908)
Wilts & Dorset Banking Co. Ltd. (until 1914)
Worcester Old Bank, Berwick Lechmere & Co. (until 1905)
Yarmouth, Norfolk & Suffolk Bank Ltd.—Lancons, Youell & Kemp (until 1901)
York City & County Banking Co. Ltd. (until 1909)
Yorkshire Banking Co. Ltd. (until 1901)
York Union Banking Co. Ltd. (until 1902)

Scotland

All notes are known with various dates and signatures. The dates in parenthesis are examples from notes actually observed. The following local banks had the right to print paper money:

Aberdeen Town and County Bank (until 1903)
Caledonian Banking Company, Inverness (until 1903)

Bank of Scotland

1.	dates from 1900	1 Pound	R
2.		5 Pounds	R
3.		10 Pounds	RR

4.		20 Pounds	RR
5.		50 Pounds	RRR
6.		100 Pounds	RRR
7.	dates from 1929	1 Pound, grey blue and yellow brown. Arms at left, date and city below. Smaller format than #1 (22.1.1929)	20.00
8.	dates from 1945	1 Pound, grey blue and light brown. No arms, city and date below. Two women on reverse (format 150 × 85 mm) (5.1.1951; 16.10.1953)	8.50
9.		5 Pounds, grey and light brown. Arms on reverse (format 177 × 102 mm) (18.1.1951)	20.00

150 × 85

10.	dates from 1954	1 Pound, blue and light brown. Type of #8 but ship on reverse (format 150 × 85 mm) (1.3.1955; 1.12.1959)	6.50
11.		5 Pounds, blue and light brown. Type of #9 but ship and arms on reverse. Double line numeral of value (format 139 × 84 mm) (14.9.1961)	17.50
12.	dates from 1961	1 Pound, blue and light brown. Type of #10 but format 150 × 71 mm. Date below (16.11.1961; 20.11.1961)	4.50
13.		1 Pound, blue and light brown. Type of #12 but date in middle at right side (format 150 × 71 mm) (1.6.1966)	4.00
14.		1 Pound, blue and light brown. Type of #13 but with dark stripes on reverse for mechanical sorting (format 150 × 71 mm) (3.3.1967)	4.50
15.		5 Pounds, blue and light brown. Type of #11 but solid numeral of value (format 139 × 84 mm) (1.2.1967)	15.00
16.	dates from 1968	1 Pound, multicolored. Arms and two women (format 135 × 66 mm) (17.7.1968)	—
17.		5 Pounds, multicolored. Type of #16 but format 145 × 77 mm	—

The British Linen Bank (until 1906, the British Linen Co.). The dominant color of all notes is blue.

18.	dates from 1900	1 Pound, blue and red	R

19.		5 Pounds	R
20.		10 Pounds	RR
21.		20 Pounds	RRR
22.		100 Pounds	RRR
23.	dates from 1906	1 Pound, blue and red. Type of #18 but new bank name. Blank reverse	R
24.		5 Pounds	R
25.		10 Pounds	RR
26.		20 Pounds	RR
27.		100 Pounds	RRR
28.	dates from 1914	1 Pound. Printed reverse	R
29.	dates from 1915	5 Pounds. Printed reverse	R
30.		10 Pounds	RR
31.		20 Pounds	RR
32.		100 Pounds	RRR
33.	dates from 1935	1 Pound. Arms of the bank	20.00
34.		5 Pounds	R
35.		10 Pounds	RR
36.		20 Pounds	RR
37.		100 Pounds	RRR
38.	dates from 1944	5 Pounds. Smaller format 184 × 99 mm	R

#39b

150 × 84

39.	dates from 1945	1 Pound. Printed signature of the General Manager.	
		a. Printed by Waterlow (5.8.1950; 28.8.1958)	5.00
		b. Printed by De La Rue (30.9.1961)	5.00
40.		5 Pounds	20.00
41.		10 Pounds	R
42.		20 Pounds	R
43.		100 Pounds	RR
44.	dates from 1961	1 Pound. Type of #39 but format 150 × 72 mm (31.2.1962; 4.5.1964)	5.00
45.		5 Pounds. Type of #40 but format 159 × 90 mm (2.1.1961)	R
46.	dates from 1962	5 Pounds. Sir Walter Scott at right (format 140 × 85 mm) (21.9.1962)	25.00
47.	dates from 1967	1 Pound. Type of #44 but different design on reverse, with stripes for mechanical sorting (format 150 × 72 mm) (13.6.1967)	7.50

| 48. | dates from 1968 | 1 Pound. Sir Walter Scott at left (format 135 × 67 mm) (29.2.1968) | — |
| 49. | | 5 Pounds. Type of #46 but different format (145 × 78 mm) (22.3.1968) | — |

Clydesdale Bank Ltd. (United with North of Scotland Bank in 1950)

50.	dates from 1900	1 Pound	R
51.		5 Pounds	R
52.		20 Pounds	RR
53.		100 Pounds	RRR
54.	dates from 1922	1 Pound	R
55.		5 Pounds	R
56.		20 Pounds	RR
57.		100 Pounds	RRR
58.	dates from 1927	1 Pound. Smaller format	25.00

151 × 85

59.	dates from 1950	1 Pound, blue. Inscribed "Clydesdale & North of Scotland Bank." Landscape on reverse (format 151 × 85 mm) (1.11.1956; 1.11.1960)	7.50
60.		5 Pounds, violet. Arms on reverse (format 180 × 97 mm) (2.5.1951)	22.50
61.		20 Pounds	—
62.		100 Pounds	—
63.	dates from 1961	1 Pound, green. Harbor scene on reverse (format 152 × 71 mm)	5.00
64.		5 Pounds, blue and violet. Buildings on reverse (format 140 × 85 mm)	20.00
65.	dates from 1963	1 Pound. Type of #63 but bank name "Clydesdale Bank Ltd" (2.9.1963)	4.50
66.		5 Pounds, blue and violet. Type of #64 but bank name "Clydesdale Bank Ltd" (format 140 × 85 mm) (2.9.1963)	—
67.		10 Pounds, brown. Inscribed "Clydesdale Bank Ltd" (20.4.1964)	—
68.		20 Pounds, carmine red. Inscribed "Clydesdale Bank Ltd" (19.11.1964)	—
69.		100 Pounds, violet. Inscribed "Clydesdale Bank Ltd"	—

| 70. | dates from 1967 | 1 Pound, greenish. Type of #65 but stripes for mechanical sorting on reverse (format 152 × 71 mm) | — |
| 71. | | 5 Pounds, blue and violet. Type of #66 but with stripes for mechanical sorting on reverse (format 140 × 85 mm) (1.5.1967) | — |

Commercial Bank of Scotland (merged with the National Bank of Scotland in 1959)

72.	dates from 1900	1 Pound	R
73.		5 Pounds	R
74.		20 Pounds	RR
75.		100 Pounds	RRR
76.	dates from 1907	1 Pound	R
77.		5 Pounds	R
78.		20 Pounds	RR
79.		100 Pounds	RRR
80.	dates from 1924	1 Pound	R
81.		5 Pounds	R
82.		20 Pounds	RR
83.		100 Pounds	RRR
84.	dates from 1927	1 Pound. Smaller format	R
85.	dates from 1947	1 Pound (2.1.1951)	50.00
86.		5 Pounds	R
87.		20 Pounds	R
88.		100 Pounds	RRR

150 × 85

| 89. | dates from 1954 | 1 Pound, blue (format 150 × 85 mm) (2.1.1958) | 15.00 |

National Bank of Scotland (merged with the Commercial Bank of Scotland in 1959 under the new name of National Commercial Bank of Scotland)

90.	dates from 1900	1 Pound	R
91.		5 Pounds	R
92.		20 Pounds	RR
93.		100 Pounds	RRR
94.	dates from 1907	1 Pound	R
95.		5 Pounds	R
96.		20 Pounds	RR

97.		100 Pounds	RRR
98.	dates from 1927	1 Pound, black, red and yellow. Smaller format (150 × 85 mm) (1.11.1947; 4.1.1951)	15.00
99.	dates from 1957	5 Pounds, green. Bridge on reverse (format 179 × 102 mm) (1.11.1957)	25.00
100.		20 Pounds, red. Bridge on reverse (format 179 × 101 mm) (1.11.1957)	—
101.		100 Pounds, blue. Bridge on reverse (format 179 × 102 mm) (1.11.1957)	—
102.	dates from 1959	1 Pound, blue. Bridge. New name "National Commercial Bank of Scotland" (format 152 × 85 mm) (16.9.1959)	10.00
103.		5 Pounds, green. Bridge on reverse. New name "National Commercial Bank of Scotland" (format 179 × 102 mm) (16.9.1959)	—
104.		20 Pounds, red. Type of #103	—
105.		100 Pounds, violet. Type of #103	—
106.	dates from 1961	1 Pound, green. Type of #102 but smaller format (151 × 77 mm) (1.11.1961; 1.8.1963)	4.50
107.		5 Pounds, green. Type of #103 but smaller format (179 × 102 mm) (3.1.1961)	—
108.	dates from 1963	5 Pounds, blue. Landscape with buildings on reverse (2.1.1963)	—
109.	dates from 1966	10 Pounds, brown. Bridge on reverse (format 151 × 94 mm) (16.8.1966)	—

150 × 72

110.	dates from 1967	1 Pound, green. Type of #106 but stripes for mechanical sorting on reverse (format 150 × 72 mm) (4.1.1967)	7.50
111.	dates from 1968	1 Pound, green. As #110 but slightly different design and smaller format: 136 × 67 mm (4.1.1968)	—

North of Scotland Bank (united with Clydesdale Bank in 1950)

112.	dates from 1900 to 1950	1 Pound, blue and yellow (format 152 × 87 mm)	11.50
113.		5 Pounds	45.00

114.		10 Pounds	R
115.		20 Pounds	R
116.		100 Pounds	RRR

Royal Bank of Scotland

117.	dates from 1900	1 Pound	R
118.		5 Pounds	R
119.		10 Pounds	RR
120.		20 Pounds	RR
121.		100 Pounds	RRR

151 × 85

122.	dates from 1927	1 Pound, dark blue, brown and yellow. Small format (151 × 85 mm) (18.7.1951; 2.9.1963)	4.50
123.	dates from 1964	1 Pound, dark blue, brown and yellow. Type of #122 but smaller format (150 × 70 mm) (1.8.1964; 2.8.1965)	4.00
124.		5 Pounds, dark blue, brown and yellow. Type of #118 but smaller format (140 × 85 mm) (2.11.1964; 2.8.1965)	20.00
125.	dates from 1966	1 Pound, green. Head of David Dale at left (1.9.1967)	3.50
126.		5 Pounds, blue. Head of David Dale at left (1.11.1966)	—
127.	dates from 1969	1 Pound, green. Bridge (19.3.1969)	—
128.		5 Pounds, blue. Arms at left (19.3.1969)	—
129.		20 Pounds, violet. Bridge on reverse (19.3.1969)	—

Union Bank of Scotland (merged with the Bank of Scotland in 1955)

#130

150 × 84

130.	dates to 1945	1 Pound, blue and red orange. Equestrian statue at left and right (1.8.1940)	20.00
131.		5 Pounds	R
132.		10 Pounds	R
133.		20 Pounds	RR
134.		100 Pounds	RRR
135.	dates from 1946	1 Pound, blue and red orange. Arms at left, ship at right (17.10.1949)	15.00
136.		5 Pounds, blue and red orange. Arms at left, ship at right (5.6.1951)	50,00
137.		20 Pounds, blue and red orange. Arms at left, ship at right (1.9.1950)	R
138.		100 Pounds, blue and red orange. Arms at left, ship at right (9.10.1950)	RRR

Northern Ireland

Until 1928, the notes of private banks circulated throughout all of Ireland. After the founding of the Irish Free State (see separate listing under "Ireland"), the private notes were only valid in Northern Ireland. The Irish notes all have date and signature varieties.

Bank of Ireland

1.	dates from 1900	1 Pound	R
2.		5 Pounds	R
3.		10 Pounds	RR
4.		20 Pounds	RRR

152 × 82

5.	dates from 1928	1 Pound, light blue and green. Woman's head in middle (24.8.1942)	$6.50
6.		5 Pounds, red and ochre. Type of #5 (20.12.1946)	20.00
7.		10 Pounds, blue and green. Type of #5 (20.1.1942)	R
8.		20 Pounds, brown and green. Type of #5 (9.5.1929)	R
9.	(from 1966)	1 Pound, brown lilac. Woman's head at left	—
10.		5 Pounds, blue violet. Type of #9	—
11.		10 Pounds, brown and yellow. Type of #9	—
12.		20 Pounds. Type of #9	—

Belfast Banking Company

13.	dates from 1900	1 Pound. So-called "Blue-black Issue"	R
14.		5 Pounds	R
15.		10 Pounds	R
16.		20 Pounds	RR
17.		50 Pounds	RR
18.		100 Pounds	RRR
19.	dates from 1922	1 Pound	R
20.		5 Pounds	R
21.		10 Pounds	R
22.		20 Pounds	RR
23.		50 Pounds	RR
24.		100 Pounds	RRR
25.	dates from 1928	1 Pound	6.50
26.		5 Pounds	—
27.		10 Pounds	—
28.		20 Pounds	—
29.		50 Pounds	—
30.		100 Pounds	—

National Bank Ltd.

31.	dates from 1900	1 Pound	R
32.		5 Pounds	R
33.		10 Pounds	RR
34.		20 Pounds	RRR
35.	dates from 1928	1 Pound, black on green. Arms in middle (1.8.1933)	10.00
36.		5 Pounds, blue on brown. Type of #35 (6.5.1929)	20.00
37.		10 Pounds, green on brown. Type of #35 (6.5.1929)	30.00
38.		20 Pounds, brown on blue. Arms in Type of #35 (6.5.1929)	R
39.	dates from 1937	1 Pound, black and green. Woman with harp (2.10.1939)	6.50
40.		5 Pounds, blue and brown. Type of #39 (2.5.1949)	—
41.		10 Pounds, green and light brown. Type of #39 (1.8.1942)	—
42.		20 Pounds, brown and green. Type of #39 (1.1.1949)	—

Northern Bank Ltd.

43.	dates from 1900	1 Pound	R
44.		5 Pounds	R
45.		10 Pounds	R
46.		20 Pounds	RR
47.		50 Pounds	RR
48.		100 Pounds	RRR

150 × 81

49.	dates from 1928	1 Pound	7.50
50.		5 Pounds	—
51.		10 Pounds	—
52.		20 Pounds	—
53.		50 Pounds	—
54.		100 Pounds	—

Provincial Bank of Ireland

55.	dates from 1900	1 Pound	R
56.		5 Pounds	R
57.		10 Pounds	R
58.		20 Pounds	RR
59.		50 Pounds	RR
60.		100 Pounds	RRR
61.	dates from 1928	1 Pound	R
62.		5 Pounds	R
63.		10 Pounds	RR
64.		20 Pounds	RRR
65.	dates from 1952	1 Pound	17.50
66.		5 Pounds	R
67.	dates from 1954	1 Pound. Woman's head in middle (format 150 × 84 mm)	
		a. Printed by Waterlow (1.10.1954)	8.50
		b. Printed by De La Rue (1.12.1965)	7.50
68.		5 Pounds. Type of #67	20.00
69.	dates from 1966	1 Pound. Type of #67 but smaller format (150 × 71 mm)	5.00
70.		5 Pounds. Type of #68 but smaller format (139 × 84 mm)	15.00

Ulster Bank

71.	dates from 1900	1 Pound	R
72.		5 Pounds	R
73.		10 Pounds	R
74.		20 Pounds	RR
75.		50 Pounds	RR
76.		100 Pounds	RRR

77.	dates from 1928	1 Pound	15.00
78.		5 Pounds	25.00
79.		10 Pounds	R
80.		20 Pounds	RR
81.		50 Pounds	RR
82.		100 Pounds	RRR
83.	dates from 1966	1 Pound. Smaller format (150 × 72 mm) (4.10.1966)	5.00
84.		5 Pounds. Smaller format (138 × 84 mm) (4.10.1966)	15.00

Isle of Man

All Manx bank notes have date and signature varieties. Treasury bills issued after 1961 are undated.

Barclays Bank Ltd.

1.	dates from 1919	1 Pound, brown (16.4.1935)	12.50

Isle of Man Bank Ltd. (The Isle of Man Banking Co. Ltd. prior to 1926)

2.	dates from 1900	1 Pound, black and grey. Printed by Johnston	R
3.		5 Pounds	RR
4.	dates from 1928	1 Pound, blue green. Printed by Waterlow (2.12.1935)	15.00
5.		5 Pounds, blue green. Printed by Waterlow (1.12.1936)	37.50

Lloyds Bank Ltd.

6.	dates from 1919	1 Pound, black on violet and green	30.00

Martins Bank Ltd.

7.	1 Pound, black. Bird on dark field in shield of arms at left (1.8.1934)	37.50

151 × 84

8.	1 Pound, black. Bird on light field in shield of arms at left (1.5.1953; 1.2.1957)	6.50

Westminster Bank Ltd.

9.	dates from 1900	1 Pound	R
10.	dates from 1923	1 Pound, black on light yellow. Smaller format (150 × 85 mm). Printed by Waterlow (3.3.1959)	6.50

Government Notes

11.	(from 1961)	10 Shillings, red. Queen Elizabeth at right	—
12.		1 Pound, violet. Type of #12	—
13.		5 Pounds, green and blue. Type of #12	—
14.	(from 1969)	50 New Pence, blue. Type of #12	—

Guernsey

Notes #1, #2, #10–16 and #42–46 have date and signature varieties.

The States of Guernsey, Government Notes

1.	dates from 1900	1 Pound	RRR
2.		5 Pounds	RRR
3.	5. 8.1914	5 Shillings	RR
4.		10 Shillings	RR
5.	1. 9.1914	5 Shillings = 6 Francs	RR
6.		10 Shillings = 12 Francs	RR
7.		1 Pound	RRR
8.	(1921)	5 Shillings. Same as #5 but overprinted "British"	RRR
9.		10 Shillings. Same as #6 but overprinted "British"	RRR
10.	1. 3.1921– 19.11.1932	10 Shillings, black and grey. No numerals in middle (17.5.1924)	R
11.	1. 3.1921– 6.12.1926	1 Pound, black and grey on orange. No numerals in middle (17.5.1924)	RR
12.	22. 7.1927– 2.12.1932	1 Pound, black and grey on red. Value "£1" in middle (6.12.1927)	RR
13.	3. 1.1933– 18.11.1933	10 Shillings, light blue and brown. Value "10/–" in middle. One signature only. English text on reverse (18.11.1933)	37.50
14.		1 Pound, grey on red. Type of #12 but only one signature. English text on reverse	R
15.	from 29.3.1934	10 Shillings, light blue and brown. Type of #13 but text "s'BALLIVIE INSULE DEGERNEREYE" on reverse	25.00
16.		1 Pound, grey. Type of #14 but reverse text as #15	50.00
17.	March 1940	1 Pound	30.00
18.	25. 3.1941	2 Shillings 6 Pence (2/6), blue and orange	20.00
19.		5 Shillings, black and red	22.50
20.	17. 5.1941	2 Shillings 6 Pence (2/6)	20.00
21.		5 Shillings	20.00
22.	16.10.1941	6 Pence (6d), violet and rose	20.00
23.		1 Shilling 3 Pence (1/3), black and yellow	20.00
24.	1. 1.1942	6 Pence (6d)	20.00
25.		1 Shilling 3 Pence (1/3)	22.50
26.	18. 7.1942	1 Shilling 3 Pence (1/3)	22.50
27.		1 Shilling overprinted on 1 Shilling 3 Pence. Same as #26 with overprint	30.00
28.	1. 1.1943	1 Shilling overprinted on 6 pence. Same as #24 with overprint	37.50
29.		1 Shilling overprinted on 1 Shilling 3 Pence. Same as #26 with overprint	37.50
30.		2 Shillings 6 Pence (2/6)	30.00
31.		5 Shillings (5/–)	30.00
32.		10 Shillings (10/–), blue	30.00

149 × 88

33.		1 Pound, black	37.50

Notes #18–33 were issued during the German occupation in World War II.

34.	1. 1.1945	5 Shillings. Text reads "Backed by Guernsey Notes." Printed on French paper	RR
35.		10 Shillings	RR
36.		1 Pound	RR
37.		5 Pounds	RR
38.		5 Shillings. Text reads "Backed by British Notes"	RR
39.		10 Shillings	RR
40.		1 Pound	RR
41.		5 Pounds	RR
42.	dates from 1945	10 Shillings, lilac and light green (1.8.1945; 1.1.1950; 1.5.1953; 1.6.1959)	2.50
43.		1 Pound, violet and green (1.8.1945; 1.1.1950; 1.5.1953; 1.2.1955)	6.50
44.		5 Pounds, green and blue (1.12.1956)	15.00
45.	(1969)	1 Pound, olive and yellow	—
46.		5 Pounds, violet and light brown	—

Guernsey Banking Co. Ltd.

R1.	dates to 1914	1 Pound	RRR

The bank's right to print paper money expired in 1914 but the notes continued to circulate until the bank's merger with the National Provincial Bank in 1923.

Guernsey Commercial Banking Co. Ltd.

R2.	dates to 1914	1 Pound	RRR

The bank's right to print paper money expired in 1914 but the notes continued to circulate until the bank's merger with the Westminster Bank Ltd. in 1923.

Jersey

The States of Jersey, Government Notes

1.	(1941–42)	6 Pence, dark brown and carmine	7.50
2.		1 Shilling, dark brown and blue	10.00
3.		2 Shillings, blue and light brown. Picture on reverse	12.50
4.		2 Shillings, violet and light brown. No picture on reverse	11.50

128 × 84

| 5. | | 10 Shillings, green | 12.50 |
| 6. | | 1 Pound, violet and green | 15.00 |

Notes #1–6 were issued during the German occupation in World War II.

7.	(1963)	10 Shillings, brown. Queen Elizabeth	—
8.		1 Pound, green. Queen Elizabeth	—
9.		5 Pounds, dark red. Queen Elizabeth	—

Private bank notes of 1 pound denomination were issued by the Banque Massoit Cie., Barclays Bank, Ltd., Capital and Countries Bank, Lloyds Bank Ltd., Midland Bank Ltd. and the National Provincial Bank.

Military Notes

British Military Authority

Issued 1943–45 for use in North Africa and Greece, all notes show the British lion and crown.

M1.	(1943–45)	6 Pence (6d), lilac brown	1.50
M2.		1 Shilling, grey on violet	1.00
M3.		2 Shillings 6 Pence (2/6), green on rose	1.25
M4.		5 Shillings, brown on blue and green	2.00
M5.		10 Shillings, blue on olive and lilac	3.50
M6.		1 Pound, violet on light brown	7.50

British Armed Forces Special Vouchers

Issued for the British troops in Germany and Austria. All are multicolored and only the dominant color is listed below.

M7.	(1945–46)	$\frac{1}{2}$ Pence ($\frac{1}{2}$d). Round, imprinted disc of brown plastic	2.50
M8.		1 Pence (1d). Type of M7	2.50
M9.		3 Pence (3d), lilac	.50
M10.		6 Pence (6d), brown	.75
M11.		1 Shilling, grey blue	1.00
M12.		2 Shillings 6 Pence (2/6), red	1.50
M13.		5 Shillings, green	3.00
M14.		10 Shillings, violet	4.50

139 × 70

M15.		1 Pound, blue	7.50
M16.	(1950) "2nd Series"	3 Pence (3d), brown	.75
M17.		6 Pence (6d), blue	1.00
M18.		1 Shilling, grey blue	1.25
M19.		2 Shillings 6 Pence (2/6), lilac brown	1.50
M20.		5 Shillings, violet	2.50
M21.		10 Shillings, green	3.50
M22.		1 Pound, lilac	6.50
M23.		5 Pounds, dark blue	20.00

GREECE

From 1456 until the beginning of the 19th century, Greece was under Turkish control. An independent kingdom was set up in 1822 and was ruled in turn by Otto I, 1832–62; George I, 1863–1913; Constantine I, 1913–17, 1920–22; Alexander, 1917–20; and George II, 1922–23. Greece was declared a republic in 1924 but King George II was returned to the throne in 1935. During World War II, German and Italian troops occupied the nation and, after their retreat, a civil war raged until 1949. Greece became a kingdom once again in 1947 under Paul I, followed by his son, Constantine II in 1964.

1 Drachma = 100 Lepta

All banknotes issued until 1932 display the portrait of the first Bank Governor, Georgios Stavros. The single type note carries various dates and different issues can be distinguished by an inscription in Greek letters on the reverse. The number of the issue can be determined by referring to the table below. The cardinal numeral follows "*EKΔOΣIΣ*," the Greek word for "issue." The dates in parenthesis are examples taken from notes actually observed.

1st   = *ΠΡΩΤΗ*
2nd = *ΔΕΥΤΕΡΑ*
3rd = *ΤΡΙΤΗ*
4th = *ΤΕΤΑΡΤΗ*
5th = *ΠΕΜΠΤΗ*
6th = *ΕΚΤΗ*
7th = *ΕΒΔΟΜΗ*
8th = *ΟΓΔΟΗ*
9th = *ΕΝΑΤΗ*
10th = *ΔΕΚΑΤΗ*
11th = *ΕΝΔΕΚΑΤΗ*
12th = *ΔΩΔΕΚΑΤΗ*
13th = *ΔΕΚΑΤΗ ΤΡΙΤΗ*
14th = *ΔΕΚΑΤΗ ΤΕΤΑΡΤΗ*

(National Bank of Greece) *ΕΘΝΙΚΗ ΤΡΑΓΕΖΑ ΤΗΣ ΕΛΛΑΔΟ*

Notes to 1922

1.	5 Drachmai, 1st issue (designation not on note). Printed by Bradbury (2.10.1897; 12.12.1897)	$10.00
2.	5 Drachmai, 2nd issue. Printed by American Bank Note Company (many dates between 1905 and 1919)	6.50
3.	10 Drachmai, 2nd issue (1st issue of this denomination not issued). Printed by American Bank Note Company	15.00
4.	10 Drachmai, 3rd issue	15.00

5.	10 Drachmai, 4th issue	15.00
6.	10 Drachmai, 5th issue	15.00
7.	10 Drachmai, 6th issue (designation not on note). Printed by Bradbury (1.6.1900)	10.00
8.	10 Drachmai, 7th issue (dates to 1907)	10.00
9.	10 Drachmai, 8th issue (designation not on note). Printed by American Bank Note Company	10.00
10.	10 Drachmai, 9th issue. Printed by American Bank Note Company (1.10.1912; 20.3.1913; 8.1.1914; 15.4.1914)	6.50
11.	25 Drachmai, 1st issue (designation not on note). Printed by Bradbury	25.00
12.	25 Drachmai, 2nd issue. Printed by American Bank Note Company	20.00
13.	25 Drachmai, 3rd issue	20.00
14.	25 Drachmai, 4th issue	20.00
15.	25 Drachmai, 5th issue	20.00
16.	25 Drachmai, 6th issue (designation not on note). Printed by Bradbury	20.00
17.	25 Drachmai, 7th issue (dates to 1909)	20.00
18.	24 Drachmai, 8th issue (designation not on note). Printed by American Bank Note Company (3.8.1903)	12.50

167 × 87

19.	25 Drachmai, 9th issue. Printed by American Bank Note Company (10.3.1912; 1.9.1913; 15.7.1917; 10.8.1917)	10.00
20.	50 Drachmai, 1st issue (designation not on note). Printed by Bradbury	30.00
21.	50 Drachmai, 2nd issue. Printed by American Bank Note Company (dates to 1907)	25.00
22.	100 Drachmai, 1st issue (designation not on note). Printed by Bradbury	37.50
23.	100 Drachmai, 2nd issue. Printed by American Bank Note Company	30.00
24.	100 Drachmai, 3rd issue	30.00
25.	100 Drachmai, 4th issue	30.00
26.	100 Drachmai, 5th issue	30.00
27.	100 Drachmai, 6th issue (designation not on note). Printed by Bradbury	25.00
28.	100 Drachmai, 7th issue (dates to 1907)	25.00

29.	100 Drachmai, 8th issue. Printed by American Bank Note Company (dates to 1926)	25.00
30.	100 Drachmai, 9th issue. Printed by American Bank Note Company (7.1.1912; 12.11.1917; 25.2.1918)	15.00
31.	100 Drachmai, 10th issue. Printed by American Bank Note Company (date to 1926)	15.00
32.	500 Drachmai, 1st issue (designation not on note). Printed by Bradbury	50.00
33.	500 Drachmai, 2nd issue. Printed by American Bank Note Company (dates to 1907)	45.00
34.	500 Drachmai, 5th issue (dates to 1917)	37.50

Third and fourth issues of this denomination not issued.

35.	500 Drachmai, 6th issue (designation not on note). Printed by Bradbury	37.50
36.	500 Drachmai, 7th issue	37.50
37.	1,000 Drachmai, 8th issue (designation not on note)	R

The law of 25.3.1922 decreed a forced loan to the government, based on the bank-notes then in circulation. The notes were cut into halves with the left part continuing to circulate as legal tender at half the former face value (until 1927). The right part had to be held as a loan certificate, also for half of the note's former par-value. The following issues are known to have been halved:

```
    5 Drachmai, 2nd issue
   10 Drachmai, 6th, 8th and 9th issues
   25 Drachmai, 8th and 9th issues
  100 Drachmai, 8th, 9th and 10th issues
  500 Drachmai, 6th and 7th issues
1,000 Drachmai, 1st issue
```

(State Notes of the Finance Ministry) *ΒΑΣΙΛΕΙΟΝ ΤΗΣ ΕΛΛΑΔΟΣ*

38.	1917	1 Drachma, blue and brown (old date 21.12.1885). Head of Athene at left. Printed by Bradbury. Brown overprint *ΝΟΜΟΣ* 991 and *ΤΟΥ* 1917	2.50
39.		2 Drachmai, blue and brown (old date 21.12.1885). Hermes head at right. Printed by Bradbury. Brown overprint as #38	4.00
40.	27.10.1917	1 Drachma, brown. Seated Hermes in middle. Printed by Aspiotis Freres	1.00

66 × 40

41.		1 Drachma, violet and green. Head of Homer in middle. Printed by Bradbury	1.25
42.		1 Drachma, blue on lilac and olive. Seated Hermes at right. Printed by Bradbury	1.50

43.		2 Drachmai, blue green and brown. Type of #40. Printed by Aspiotis Freres	1.75
44.		2 Drachmai, blue on rose and light blue. Statue of Zeus at left. Printed by Bradbury	1.25
45.		2 Drachmai, red brown. Lyre player in middle. Printed by Bradbury	1.75
46.	(1918)	1 Drachma, brown. Pericles at right. Printed by Aspiotis Freres	2.00
47.		2 Drachmai, light blue and yellow. Pericles at left. Printed by Aspiotis Freres	2.50
48.	(1920)	10 Lepta, brown. Hermes head. Postage stamp of 1911–1921 issue printed on cardboard (Scott #202, Michel #162)	
		a. Dark brown, punched	1.50
		b. Light brown, perforated	2.50
49.		50 Lepta, blue. Standing Athena in middle. Printed by Aspiotis Freres	1.00

(National Bank of Greece) *ΕΘΝΙΚΗ ΤΡΑΓΕΖΑ ΤΗΣ ΕΛΛΑΔΟΣ*

Notes issued from March 1922 to 1926 without overprint

50.	5 Drachmai, 3rd issue	15.00
51.	5 Drachmai, green, 4th issue. Printed by Bradbury (24.3.1923)	10.00
52.	5 Drachmai, black on rose and multicolored, 5th issue. Printed by American Bank Note Company (26.4.1923)	8.50
53.	10 Drachmai, blue, 10th issue. Printed by American Bank Note Company (15.7.1926)	10.00
54.	25 Drachmai, 10th issue	12.50
55.	50 Drachmai, 3rd issue	15.00
56.	100 Drachmai, 11th issue	15.00
57.	500 Drachmai, 8th issue	25.00
58.	1,000 Drachmai, 2nd issue	R

(National Bank of Greece) *ΕΘΝΙΚΗ ΤΡΑΓΕΖΑ ΤΗΣ ΕΛΛΑΔΟΣ*

Issue of 1926–27

By the law of 23.1.1926, older notes of denominations higher than 25 Drachmai were divided into a three-quarter left side piece and one-quarter right side piece. The left-hand parts were worth three-quarters of their reduced ($\frac{3}{4}$) value toward bank notes and one-quarter of their lowered value toward obligations of the Forced Loan exchange. The right quarter of the original note was likewise exchangeable toward the loan obligations.

The following notes have been encountered as three-quarter pieces:

    50 Drachmai, 4th issue
   100 Drachmai, 8th, 9th, 10th and 12th issues
   500 Drachmai, 6th, 7th and 9th issues
 1,000 Drachmai, 1st, 3rd and 4th issues

The following notes have been encountered as three-quarter pieces with a red overprint "Neon" (new):

> 50 Drachmai, 3rd and 4th issues
> 100 Drachmai, 11th and 12th issues
> 500 Drachmai, 8th and 9th issues
> 1,000 Drachmai, 3rd and 4th issues

The following notes are only known divided into parts:

59.	50 Drachmai, 4th issue
60.	100 Drachmai, 12th issue
61.	500 Drachmai, 9th issue
62.	1,000 Drachmai, 3rd issue
63.	1,000 Drachmai, 4th issue

New issue without overprint

64.	25 Drachmai, 11th issue. Printed by Bradbury (5.3.1923)	12.50

New printing of undivided notes with red overprint "Neon 1926" (some carry dates prior to 1926)

65.	5 Drachmai, red brown, 6th issue. Printed by American Bank Note Company (17.12.1926)	7.50
66.	50 Drachmai, rose and green, 5th issue. Printed by Bradbury (6.5.1923)	8.50

157 × 77

67.	100 Drachmai, green. 13th issue. Printed by Bradbury (20.4.1923)	10.00
68.	500 Drachmai, brown, 10th issue. Printed by Bradbury (12.4.1923)	20.00
69.	1,000 Drachmai, 2nd issue	37.50

(Bank of Greece) *ΤΡΑΠΕΖΑ ΤΗΣ ΕΛΛΑΔΟΣ*

Provisional issues from 1928

Notes inscribed with the old bank name and dates, without the overprint "Neon" and with no overprint of the new bank name (Reprints of #51, #52, #53 and #64 were also released at this time)

70.	5 Drachmai, 6th issue. Printed by the American Bank Note Company (24.5.1927)	5.00
71.	25 Drachmai, multicolored 12th issue. Printed by American Bank Note Company (15.4.1923)	6.50

72.	100 Drachmai, green on violet and brown, 14th issue. Printed by American Bank Note Company (26.5.1927)	5.00
73.	500 Drachmai, violet, 11th issue. Printed by American Bank Note Company (12.11.1926)	15.00

Notes with the old bank name and dates overprinted "Neon"

74.	5 Drachmai, multicolored, 3rd issue. Printed by American Bank Note Company (29.7.1918; 26.8.1918; 20.10.1918; 23.10.1918)	4.00
75.	25 Drachmai, 10th issue (10.1.1918; 25.1.1919)	6.50

Notes overprinted with the new bank name but not "Neon"

76.	5 Drachmai, brown and multicolored, 6th issue. Printed by American Bank Note Company (17.9.1926; 17.12.1926)	3.00
77.	20 Drachmai, brown, 1st issue. Printed by American Bank Note Company (19.10.1926)	4.00
78.	25 Drachmai, brown, 11th issue. Printed by Bradbury (5.3.1923)	6.50
79.	25 Drachmai, 12th issue. Printed by American Bank Note Company (15.4.1923)	10.00
80.	50 Drachmai, 3rd issue	15.00
81.	50 Drachmai, rose and green, 5th issue. Printed by Bradbury	12.50
82.	50 Drachmai, olive green, 6th issue. Printed by American Bank Note Company (30.4.1927; 13.5.1927; 24,5,1927)	5.00
83.	100 Drachmai, green, 14th issue. Printed by American Bank Note Company (6.1.1927; 14.6.1927; 25.5.1927)	5.00
84.	1,000 Drachmai, green, 5th issue. Printed by American Bank Note Company (15.10.1926; 4.11.1926)	4.00
85.	5,000 Drachmai, brown, 1st issue. Printed by American Bank Note Company (5.10.1926)	37.50

Note overprinted with the new bank name and "Neon"

86.	50 Drachmai, 3rd issue	12.50

Notes with the old bank name overprinted "Neon 1926" (Reprints of re-issue of #66 and #67 were also released at this time)

87.	25 Drachmai, 11th issue	6.50
88.	25 Drachmai, 12th issue	7.50
89.	500 Drachmai, 11th issue	20.00

Notes overprinted with the new bank name and "Neon 1926"

90.	25 Drachmai, 11th issue	10.00
91.	25 Drachmai, 12th issue	12.50
92.	50 Drachmai, brown, 5th issue. Printed by Bradbury (6.5.1923)	7.50
93.	100 Drachmai, 13th issue. Printed by Bradbury	7.50
94.	500 Drachmai, 11th issue	20.00

95.   1. 9.1932   5,000 Drachmai, brown. Athena in middle. Printed by American Bank Note Company   4.00

96.   1.10.1932   500 Drachmai, multicolored. Athena in middle. Printed by American Bank Note Company   2.50

204 × 100

97.   1. 5.1935   1,000 Drachmai, multicolored. Young girl in costume holding jug (French printing)   6.00

98.   1. 9.1935   50 Drachmai, multicolored. Young girl with sheaf at left (French printing)   3.00

99.   100 Drachmai, multicolored. Mercury in middle (French printing)   4.00

100.   1. 1.1939   50 Drachmai, green. The poet Hesiod   .50

101.   100 Drachmai, green and yellow. Two peasant women   10.00

102.   500 Drachmai, blue violet and lilac. Woman in costume at left   1.50

103.   1,000 Drachmai, green. Woman in costume at right   2.00

104.   1,000 Drachmai on 100 Drachmai, green. Same as #101 but overprinted with new value   1.00
For 50 drachmai note dated 1.1.1941, see #134.

105.   10. 7.1941   100 Drachmai, brown. Reverse Kapnikarea church   .50

106.   1.10.1941   1,000 Drachmai, blue and brown. Coin of Alexander the Great
a. Picture name in illustration   2.50
b. Picture name in field   .75

107.   20. 6.1942   5,000 Drachmai, brown, red and green. Statue of Victory of Samothrace   .75

108.   21. 8.1942   1,000 Drachmai, blue and brown. Head of young girl of Thasos   .50

109.   29.12.1942   10,000 Drachmai, brown. Young peasant couple from Delphi
a. Picture name in illustration on reverse   2.50
b. Picture name in field on reverse   .75

110.   1. 2.1943   50 Drachmai, brown. Young girl   .35

111.	19. 7.1943	5,000 Drachmai, green, blue and brown. Head of Athena	.50
112.	12. 8.1943	25,000 Drachmai, brown and green. The nymph Deidamia	.50
113.	14. 1.1944	50,000 Drachmai, blue. Athlete's head	.75
114.	21. 1.1944	100,000 Drachmai, green and brown. Ancient Greek coins at left and right	.50
115.	20. 3.1944	500,000 Drachmai, brown. The Zeus of Mylasa	.40
116.	29. 6.1944	1,000,000 Drachmai, green and brown. Youth of Antikythera	.40
117.	20. 7.1944	5,000,000 Drachmai, green and brown. Head of Arethusa on an ancient coin	.25
118.	29. 7.1944	10,000,000 Drachmai, brown	.25
119.	10. 8.1944	25,000,000 Drachmai, green. Ancient Greek coins at left and right	.40
120.	9. 9.1944	200,000,000 Drachmai, brown and red brown. Section of Parthenon frieze	.25
121.	1.10.1944	500,000,000 Drachmai, blue. The Apollo of Olympia	.75
122.	11.10.1944	2,000,000,000 Drachmai, green. Section of Parthenon frieze	.40
123.	20.10.1944	10,000,000,000 Drachmai, blue and brown. Head of Arethusa on an ancient coin	1.00
124.	3.11.1944	100,000,000,000 Drachmai, brown. The Nymph Deidamia	4.50

(Treasury bills of the branch office at Patras) *ΥΠΟΚΑΤΑΣΤΗΜΑ ΠΑΤΡΩΝ*

125.	7.10.1944	100,000,000 Drachmai, brown. Ancient Greek coin at left	10.00
126.		500,000,000 Drachmai, blue. Ancient Greek coin in middle	12.50

(Treasury bills of the branch office at Kerkyras) *ΥΠΟΚΑΤΑΣΤΗΜΑ ΚΕΡΚΥΡΑΣ*

139 × 69

127.	7.10.1944	100,000,000 Drachmai, green and olive	20.00

(Government Notes, Kingdom of Greece) *ΒΑΣΙΛΕΙΟΝ ΤΗΣ ΕΛΛΑΔΟΣ*

128.	6. 4.1940	10 Drachmai, blue, brown and green. Head of Demeter at left	.25
129.		20 Drachmai, green and brown. Head of Poseidon on coin	.25

(Greek State Notes) *ΕΛΛΗΝΙΚΗ ΠΟΛΙΤΕΙΑ*

130.	18. 6.1941	50 Lepta, red and light green. Statue of Victory of Samothrace	.75
131.		1 Drachma, lilac and blue. Statue of Aristotle	.25
132.		2 Drachmai, blue and grey brown. Coin of Alexander the Great	.25
133.		5 Drachmai, brown lilac. Three women (from a wall fresco)	.25

(Bank of Greece) *ΤΡΑΠΕΖΑ ΤΗΣ ΕΛΛΑΔΟΣ*

Currency reform, notes in new values issued from November 1944 to 1953

134.	1. 1.1941 (issued 1944)	50 Drachmai, red brown. Type of #100	.75
135.	9.11.1944	50 Drachmai, light brown and blue. Statue of Victory of Samothrace	7.50
136.		100 Drachmai, blue. Canaris	3.00
137.		500 Drachmai, green. Count Capo D'Istria (president of 1828–31 republic) at left	4.00
138.		1,000 Drachmai, brown. Freedom fighter Kolokotronis at left (format 161 × 80 mm)	4.00
139.		5,000 Drachmai, red. Woman with children in middle (format 170 × 84 mm)	5.00
140.		5,000 Drachmai, red. Type of #139 but smaller format (153 × 80 mm)	6.50
141.		5,000 Drachmai, blue. Type of #139 but larger format (180 × 90 mm)	6.50
142.		5,000 Drachmai, violet. Type of #140 (format 153 × 80 mm)	7.50
143.		5,000 Drachmai, brown. Type of #140 (format 153 × 80 mm)	6.50
144.		10,000 Drachmai, orange. Head of old man at left (format 180 × 90 mm)	7.50

179 × 89

145.	10,000 Drachmai, blue. Type of #144	7.50

146.		10,000 Drachmai, orange. Type of #144 but smaller format (153 × 80 mm)	7.50
147.		20,000 Drachmai, dark green. Athena (format 180 × 90 mm)	8.50
148.		20,000 Drachmai, dark green. Type of #147 but smaller format (153 × 80 mm)	5.00
149.	9. 1.1947	1,000 Drachmai, brown. Freedom fighter Kolokotronis. Type of #138 but smaller format (145 × 75 mm)	2.00
150.	14.11.1947	1,000 Drachmai, brown. Type of #149	2.50
151.	29.12.1947	10,000 Drachmai, orange. Head of old man at left. Type of #144 but smaller format (150 × 79 mm)	4.50
152.	29.12.1949	20,000 Drachmai, blue. Athena at left. Type of #146 but smaller format (147 × 78 mm)	5.00
153.	28.10.1950	5,000 Drachmai, orange	12.50
154.		5,000 Drachmai, brown. Rev. Battle of Missolonghi (format 151 × 78 mm)	5.00
155.		10,000 Drachmai, dark green	12.50
156.	2.11.1950	20,000 Drachmai, dark green (format 154 × 81 mm)	10.00
157.	1.12.1950	50,000 Drachmai, multicolored. Woman's head at left (format 152 × 80 mm)	10.00

(State Notes, Kingdom of Greece) *ΒΑΣΙΛΕΙΟΝ ΤΗΣ ΕΛΛΑΔΟΣ*

New values from November, 1944

158.	9.11.1944	1 Drachma, blue	4.00
159.		10 Drachmai, brown and green	10.00

 87 × 62

160.		20 Drachmai, blue	10.00
161.	15. 1.1945	5 Drachmai, brown	6.50
162.	10. 7.1950	100 Drachmai, blue. Man's head in middle	1.00
163.		500 Drachmai, green. Ancient Greek coins at left and right	1.25
164.		1,000 Drachmai, brown. Type of #163	1.00
165.	1.11.1953	100 Drachmai, blue. Type of #162	1.00
166.		500 Drachmai, green. Type of #163	1.25
167.		1,000 Drachmai, brown. Type of #164	2.00

(Bank of Greece) *ΤΡΑΠΕΖΑ ΤΗΣ ΕΛΛΑΔΟΣ*

Notes in new values from 1954

168.	15. 1.1954	10 Drachmai, orange. Head of old man at left	2.50

169.		20 Drachmai, blue. Head of Athena at left	4.00
170.		50 Drachmai, multicolored. Woman's head at left	5.00
171.	31. 3.1954	100 Drachmai, dark red. Themistocles at left	5.00
172.	15. 5.1954	10 Drachmai, orange. King Paul at left	1.50
173.	1. 3.1955	10 Drachmai, orange. Type of #172	2.00
174.		20 Drachmai, blue. Democritos at left	2.00
175.		50 Drachmai, dark green. Pericles in center	2.50
176.	1. 7.1955	100 Drachmai, dark red. Type of #170	4.50
177.	8. 8.1955	500 Drachmai, green. Socrates in center	—
178.	16. 4.1956	1,000 Drachmai, brown. Alexander the Great at left	—
179.	1.10.1964	50 Drachmai, blue and green. Head of Arethusa	—
180.	1. 7.1966	100 Drachmai, brown. Democritos at left	—
181.	1.10.1967	100 Drachmai, brown. Type of #180	—
182.	1.11.1968	500 Drachmai, olive. Relief of Eleusis	—
183.	1.11.1970	1,000 Drachmai, brown. Head of Zeus at left	—

Regional Banks

(Epirus-Thessaly Bank) *ΤΡΑΠΕΖΑ ΗΠΕΙΡΟ — ΘΕΣΣΑΛΙΑΣ*

R1.	dates to 1905	10 Drachmai	RRR
R2.		25 Drachmai	RRR
R3.		100 Drachmai	RRR

The Epirus-Thessaly Bank was taken over by the National Bank in 1899 but its notes continued to circulate until 1905.

(Ionian Bank) *ΙΟΝΙΚΗ ΤΡΑΠΕΖΑ*

R4.	dates to 1920	10 Drachmai	RRR
R5.		25 Drachmai	RRR
R6.		100 Drachmai	RRR

The Bank's right to issue paper money expired in 1920.

(Bank of Crete)

R7.	dates to 1929	10 Drachmai	RRR
R8.		25 Drachmai	RRR
R9.		100 Drachmai	RRR

The Bank of Crete was founded in 1899. Its right to issue paper money expired in 1929.

Occupation Issues

Cassa Mediterranea di Credito per la Grecia (World War II Italian issues for Greece)

M1.	(1940)	5 Dracme, green	3.00
M2.		10 Dracme, red	4.00
M3.		50 Dracme, blue	5.00
M4.		100 Dracme, brown	5.00
M5.		500 Dracme, dark green	7.50
M6.		1,000 Dracme, light brown	10.00
M7.		5,000 Dracme, lilac	15.00
M8.		10,000 Dracme, grey	20.00

195 × 93

M9.	20,000 Dracme, blue	25.00
M10.	50,000 Dracme, dark green	37.50

Credito Mediterraneo

M11.	5 Dracme, green	RRR

Biglietti a corso legale per le Isole Ionie (Italian issue for the Ionian Islands)

M12.	(1940)	1 Dracma, dark green	2.50
M13.		5 Dracme, red	5.00
M14.		10 Dracme, green	5.00
M15.		50 Dracme, brown	4.00
M16.		100 Dracme, blue	4.00
M17.		500 Dracme, lilac	10.00
M18.		1,000 Dracme, brown	12.50
M19.		5,000 Dracme, blue	6.50

Notes R17–R19 are also known bearing Greek military stamps.

Behelfszahlungsmittel fur die Deutsche Wehrmacht (Emergency Currency for the German Army)

German notes with a German stamp "Saloniki-Agais" and a Greek stamp on the reverse

M20.	1 Pfennig, blue. Same as Germany M32 but stamped	4.00
M21.	5 Pfennig, red. Same as Germany M33 but stamped	5.00
M22.	10 Pfennig, green. Same as Germany M34 but stamped	10.00

(Civil Union for National Freedom) *ΠΟΛΙΤΙΚΗ ΕΠΙΤΡΟΠΗ ΕΘΝΙΚΗΣ ΑΠΕΛΕΥΘΕΡΩΣΗΣ*

Notes of the Markos Partisans in northern Greece

M23.	5. 6.1944	5 Drachmai, green and light brown. Soldier in middle, burning houses at left, peasants at right	15.00
M24.		25 Drachmai, green and light brown. Type of M23	30.00

M23 is also known with various stampings. It is quite likely that there were issues of 100 and 500 Drachmai denomination.

GREENLAND (Gronland)

The world's largest island, Greenland is an integral part of Denmark.

1 Krone = 100 Ore

Government notes with Copenhagen as place of issue

1.	1888	50 Ore, brown	$25.00
2.	1892	25 Ore, black	20.00
3.	1897	1 Krone, blue	30.00

102 × 68

4.	1905	25 Ore, red	15.00
5.		1 Krone, blue	25.00
6.	(1911)	1 Krone, blue. Note #5 overprinted "Den Kgl. Gronlandske Handel"	R

Styrelsen af Koloniere i Gronland (Government of the Colony of Greenland)

7.	(from 1912)	25 Ore, red. Bird	2.00
8.		50 Ore, brown. Sea lion	2.50
9.		1 Krone, blue	4.00

Gronlands Styrelse (Government of Greenland)

#10
125 × 85

10.   (from 1912)   5 Kroner, green. Polar bear
                        a. Paper unwatermarked   5.00
                        b. Paper watermarked with wavy lines   5.00

132 × 85

11.   10 Kroner, brown. Whale
                        a. Paper unwatermarked   10.00
                        b. Paper watermarked with wavy lines   10.00
12.   50 Kroner, lilac. Sailing ship
                        a. Paper unwatermarked   20.00
                        b. Paper watermarked with wavy lines   20.00

Den Kongelige Gronlandske Handel (Royal Greenland Commerce)

13.   (from 1938)   5 Kroner, green. Type of #10   3.00
14.   10 Kroner, brown. Type of #11   5.00
15.   50 Kroner, lilac. Type of #12   12.50
16.   16. 1.1953   100 Kroner, orange and green blue. K. Rasmussen at
                        left   25.00

Since 1968, only regular Danish notes have been in circulation.

Greenland Administration, Trade Certificates

Notes issued for use by American troops stationed in Greenland during World
War II.

Notes M1–M4 are perforated narrow pieces of cardboard with "Grl. Adm" and
value.

M1.   1 Ore, brown   5.00
M2.   2 Ore, yellow   5.00
M3.   5 Ore, violet   7.50
M4.   10 Ore, white   10.00
M5.   (1941)   1 Skilling, red. Embossed stamp at left   37.50
M6.   5 Skilling, blue. Embossed stamp at left   30.00
M7.   20 Skilling, green. Embossed stamp at left   37.50
M8.   (1942)   1 Skilling, red. Type of M5 but black stamp at left   20.00
M9.   5 Skilling, blue. Type of M6 but black stamp at left 20.00
M10.   20 Skilling, green. Type of M7 but black stamp at
                        left   17.50

HUNGARY (Magyarorszag)

In 1867, Hungary became a partner in the dual monarchy of the Austro-Hungarian Empire which collapsed at the end of World War I. A republic formed in 1918 was taken over by a communist regime in 1919. In 1920 the kingdom was re-established under the control of a regent. Following World War II, Hungary became a Peoples Republic.

1 Korona = 100 Filler (to 1926)
1 Pengo = 100 Filler (1926–46)
1 Forint = 100 Filler (from 1946)

Except for the special issues of 1914–18 listed below, the paper money used in Hungary was that of Austria-Hungary catalogued under Austria.

Magyar Kiralyi Hadi Kolcsonpenztar-jegy (Kingdom of Hungary, War Loan Office)

1.	27. 9.1914	250 Korona	$20.00
2.		2,000 Korona	20.00
3.		10,000 Korona	20.00

Osztrak-Magyar Bank (Austro-Hungarian Bank)

Non-interest bearing treasury notes of Hungarian branches. Text is printed in Hungarian and there are many date varieties (ended in 1918).

4.	Kolozsvar	1,000 Korona	RRR
5.		5,000 Korona	RRR
6.		10,000 Korona	RRR
7.	Szatmarnemet	1,000 Korona	RRR
8.		5,000 Korona	RRR
9.		10,000 Korona	RRR

Osterreich-Ungarische Bank (Austro-Hungarian Bank)

Notes printed in Budapest in 1919 are variations of the issues regularly printed in Austria.

10.	(1919)	1 Korona, red. Same as Austria #20 but serial number over 7,000. Note dated 1.12.1916	.75
11.	(1919)	2 Korona, red. Same as Austria #21 but serial number over 7,000. Note dated 1.3.1917	.75
		Error: Reads "Gene*n*alsekretar"	15.00
12.	(1919)	25 Korona, blue and light brown. Same as Austria #23 but serial number over 3,000. Note dated 27.10.1918. Reverse blank (two control number varieties)	2.50
13.		25 Korona, blue and light brown. Type of #12 but with wavy lines on reverse (three control number varieties)	3.00
14.		200 Korona, green on red brown. Same as Austria #24 but serial numbers to A 2,000	4.00

15.	200 Korona, green on red brown. Type of #14 but serial numbers over A 2,000. Reverse blank	2.00
16.	200 Korona, green on red brown. Type of #15 but with wavy lines on reverse	2.00

Österreich-Ungarische Bank, Treasury Note of the Budapest Branch

17.	3.11.1918 200 Korona, Hungarian text (known only as specimens)	R

Osztrak-Magyar Bank (Austro-Hungarian Bank)

Notes with a red, stamp-like overprint reading "Magyarorszag" around the Hungarian coat-of-arms were issued as state notes. The seal is upright or turned to the left (less scarce on the 1,000 and 10,000 Korona notes). Notes with seal turned to the right are R.

18.	2.1.1904 (1920)	10 Korona. Dated 2.1.1904. Austria #9 with overprint	5.00
19.		10 Korona. Dated 2.1.1915. Austria #19 with overprint	1.00
20.		20 Korona. Dated 2.1.1913. Austria #13 with overprint	1.00
21.		20 Korona. Dated 2.1.1913, "II Auflage." Austria #14 with overprint	1.00
22.		25 Korona. Dated 27.10.1918. Serial numbers to 3,000. Austria #23 with overprint	7.50
23.		25 Korona. Dated 27.10.1918. Serial numbers over 3,000. Note #12 with overprint	10.00
24.		50 Korona. Dated 2.1.1902. Austria #6 with overprint	R
25.		50 Korona. Dated 2.1.1914. Austria #15 with overprint	1.00

163 × 109

26.	100 Korona. Dated 2.1.1910. Austria #11 with overprint	RR
27.	100 Korona. Dated 2.1.1912. Austria #12 with overprint	1.00
28.	200 Korona. Dated 27.10.1918. Serial numbers over A 2,000. Note #15 with overprint	37.50

29.		200 Korona. Dated 27.10.1918. Serial letter B. Austria #24 with overprint	R
30.		200 Korona. Dated 27.10.1918. Six digit serial number	R
31.		1,000 Korona. Dated 2.1.1902. Austria #8 with overprint	1.50
32.		10,000 Korona. Dated 2.11.1918. Austria #25 with overprint	7.50

Notes #18–32 are known with additional South Slavic or Rumanian stamps. Notes with an unofficial overprint of a Balkan cross in black (#18–23, #25, #27–32) and a Hungarian text stamp of the State Printing Office (#26, #31, #32) are also known.

Magyar Postatakarekpenztar (Hungarian Postal Savings Notes)

33.	1. 5.1919	5 Korona (specimen, not issued)	RR
34.	15. 5.1919	5 Korona, blue on green. Man sowing seeds at right. Text reads "Az Osztrak—Magyar Bank Bankjegyeire"	1.00
35.		5 Korona, blue on green. Type of #34 but text reads "Mas Torrenyes Penznemekre"	.75
36.		10 Korona (specimen, not issued)	RR
37.	15.7.1919	10 Korona, blue on green blue. Woman with cap	1.00
38.		20 Korona, dark blue on olive. Woman's head and two cupids in middle (two control number varieties)	1.00
39.		100 Korona (specimen, not issued)	RR
40.	9. 8.1919	5 Korona (specimen, not issued)	RR
41.		10 Korona, grey blue on brown. Head of woman without cap (three control number varieties)	1.25

143 × 90

42.		20 Korona, dark blue on green and rose. Woman's head and two cupids in middle	1.25
43.	2.10.1920	20 Filler, brown	.25
44.		50 Filler, blue	.25
45.	1. 5.1921	10,000,000 Korona (specimen, not issued)	RR

Magyar Nemzeti Bank (Hungarian National Bank)

Unissued specimen notes

46.	15. 3.1919	50 Korona	RR
47.		1,000 Korona	RR
48.	2. 5.1919	25 Korona	RR
49.	2. 6.1919	2 Korona	RR
50.		20 Korona	RR
51.	1. 8.1919	10 Korona	RR
52.	15. 8.1919	100 Korona	RR
53.		1,000 Korona	RR

Penzugyminiszterium (State Notes of the Finance Ministry)

54.	1920	50 Filler. Round format (unissued proof)	RR
55.		1 Korona. Type of #54	RR
56.		2 Korona. Type of #54	RR
57.	1. 1.1920	1 Korona, blue. Woman's head at right	.25
58.		2 Korona, red. Peasant mowing at right (two control number varieties)	.25
59.		5 Korona (unissued proof)	RR
60.		10 Korona, brown and green. Bridge with city view in middle	.25
61.		20 Korona, green and brown. Church at right (two control number varieties)	.25
62.		50 Korona, brown on yellow brown. Franz Rakoczy at right	.25
63.		100 Korona, brown on light brown. Laureate head of man at right. Format 155 × 100 mm.	.25
64.		100 Korona. Format 119 × 70 mm. (unissued proof)	RR
65.		500 Korona, dark green on olive brown. Helmeted head of man at right	.35
66.		1,000 Korona, dark brown on brown. Head of bearded man at right	.50
67.		5,000 Korona, dark brown on green and grey. Crowned head of woman at right	1.00
68.		10,000 Korona, dark green and violet. "Patrona Hungariae" at right	1.25
69.	15. 8.1922	25,000 Korona, violet. "Patrona Hungariae" at right	
		a. Paper without silk thread	6.50
		b. Paper with silk thread	25.00
70.		50,000 Korona (unissued proof)	RR
71.	1. 5.1923	50,000 Korona, red. Young man's head at right	
		a. Printed by Orell Fussli	7.50
		b. No printer's imprint	9.00
72.		100,000 Korona, dark blue. Young man's head at right	
		a. Printed by Orell Fussli	15.00
		b. Printed by Magyar Penzjegynyomda	20.00
73.	1. 7.1923	100 Korona, brown. Laureate head of man at right	

#69
212 × 144

73. (Cont.)		a. Printed by Magyar Penzjegynyomda	.50
		b. No printer's imprint	.25
74.	500	Korona, green. Helmeted head of man at right	
		a. Printed by Magyar Penzjegynyomda	.75
		b. No printer's imprint	.50
75.	1,000	Korona, dark brown. Head of bearded man at right	
		a. Printed by Magyar Penzjegynyomda	.50
		b. No printer's imprint	.50
76.	5,000	Korona, dark brown. Crowned head of woman at right	
		a. Printed by Magyar Penzjegynyomda	1.00
		b. No printer's imprint	.75
77.	10,000	Korona, dark green. "Patrona Hungariae" at right	
		a. Printed by Magyar Penzjegynyomda	1.00
		b. No printer's imprint	.75
		c. Printed by Orell Fussli	1.25
78.	25,000	Korona, violet. Crowned head of man	5.00
79.	500,000	Korona, violet on brown. Wreathed head of woman at right	
		a. Printed by Magyar Penzjegynyomda	37.50
		b. Printed by Orell Fussli	50.00

#80
184 × 84

80.   4. 9.1923   1,000,000 Korona, blue on green. Wreathed head of
woman at right
- a. Printed by Magyar Penzjegynyomda   R
- b. No printer's imprint   R

A series of notes are believed to have been printed by the authority of the State Bond Division (5, 10, 50 and 100 million kronen, dated 14.7.1923) but none has ever been seen.

Currency Reform, 1925: *12,500 old Korona = 1 Pengo*

Notes overprinted with new values

81.   8 Filler on 1,000 Korona. Note #75 overprinted with new
value
- a. Printed by Magyar Penzjegynyomda   5.00
- b. No printer's imprint   3.00

82.   40 Filler on 5,000 Korona. Note #76 overprinted with new
value
- a. Printed by Magyar Penzjegynyomda   6.50
- b. No printer's imprint   4.00

83.   80 Filler on 10,000 Korona. Note #77 overprinted with new
value
- a. Printed by Magyar Penzjegynyomda   7.50
- b. No printer's imprint   7.50
- c. Printed by Orell Fussli   10.00

84.   2 Pengo on 25,000 Korona. Note #78 overprinted with new
value   15.00

85.   4 Pengo on 50,000 Korona. Note #71 overprinted with new
value
- a. Printed by Orell Fussli   25.00
- b. No printer's imprint   25.00

86.   8 Pengo on 100,000 Korona. Note #72 overprinted with new
value
- a. Printed by Orell Fussli   37.50
- b. Printed by Magyar Penzjegynyomda   30.00

87.   40 Pengo on 500,000 Korona. Note #79 overprinted with new
value
- a. Printed by Magyar Penzjegynyomda   50.00
- b. No printer's imprint   50.00

88.   80 Pengo on 1,000,000 Korona #80
- a. Printed by Magyar Penzjegynyomda   R
- b. No printer's imprint   R

Magyar Nemzeti Bank (Hungarian National Bank)

89.   1. 3.1926   5 Pengo, brown. Count Stephan Szechenyi at
right   10.00

90.   10 Pengo, green. Franz Deak at right   12.50

91.		20 Pengo, brown on green. Lajos Kossuth at right	15.00
92.		50 Pengo, blue. Franz Rakoczi at right	20.00
93.		100 Pengo, brown lilac. King Mathias at right	30.00

192 × 111

94.	1. 7.1927	1,000 Pengo, blue, green and red. Head of Hungaria at right	50.00
95.	1. 8.1928	5 Pengo, blue. Count Stephan Szechenyi at right	7.50
96.	1. 2.1929	10 Pengo, green. Franz Deak at right	7.50
97.	2. 1.1930	20 Pengo, dark blue. Lajos Kossuth at right	2.00
98.	1. 7.1930	100 Pengo, lilac. King Mathias at right, serial number without *	1.00
99.	1.10.1932	50 Pengo, red brown. Alexander Petofi at right	1.00
100.	22.12.1936	10 Pengo, green. Madonna with Christ child at left, girl's head at right, serial number without *	.50
101.	15. 1.1938	50 Filler (unissued proof)	RR
102.		1 Pengo, blue on brown. Girl's head at right, serial number without *	1.00
103.		2 Pengo (specimen, not issued)	11.50
104.		5 Pengo, brown on green. Girl's head at right	7.50
105.		20 Pengo on 50 Filler (specimen, not issued)	RR
106.	25.10.1939	5 Pengo, brown. Girl's head at right	1.50
107.		100 Pengo on 5 Pengo (specimen, not issued)	RR
108.	15. 7.1940	2 Pengo, green. Girl's head at right	2.00
109.	15. 1.1941	20 Pengo, blue. Girl in national costume at right	.50
110.	5. 4.1945	50 Pengo, brown on green. Franz Rakoczy at right	1.00
111.		100 Pengo, lilac. King Mathias at right	1.00

Magyar Nemzeti Bank (Hungarian National Bank)

Issues of the Szalasi regime in Veszprem (1944–45)

112.	1. 7.1930	100 Pengo, lilac. Type of #98 with * in serial number	1.25

160 × 80

113.	22.12.1936	10 Pengo, green. Type of #100 with * in serial number	
			2.50
114.	15. 1.1938	1 Pengo, blue on brown. Type of #102 with * in serial number	4.00
115.	24. 2.1943	100 Pengo, lilac brown on light brown. Young man with fruit and pigeons at left, girl's head at right	
		a. Both sides printed	15.00
		b. Printed on reverse only	7.50
116.		1,000 Pengo, lilac brown. Head of Hungaria at right	1.50

Magyar Nemzeti Bank (Hungarian National Bank)

Post-war notes in pengo values

117.	15. 5.1945	500 Pengo, blue. Wreathed head of woman at right	
			.75
		Error: in reverse text ИЯТЬСОТ	2.50
118.	15. 7.1945	1,000 Pengo, dark green on red brown. Head of woman with flowers at right	
		a. No stamp attached	.75
		b. With red adhesive stamp attached	.75
119.		10,000 Pengo, lilac brown on green. Woman's head at right	
		a. No stamp attached	.50
		b. With brown adhesive stamp attached	.75

#121

177 × 79

120.	23.10.1945	100,000 Pengo, brown on green blue. Woman in costume at right	
121.		100,000 Pengo, blue. Type of #120	
		a. No stamp attached	37.50
		b. With green adhesive stamp attached	45.00
122.	16.11.1945	1,000,000 Pengo, blue. Lajos Kossuth at right	.50
123.		10,000,000 Pengo, dark green. Lajos Kossuth at right	.50
124.	18. 3.1946	100,000,000 Pengo, brown and green. Woman's head with scarf at right	.50
125.		1,000,000,000 Pengo, lilac and brown. Girl's head at right	.50

1 Milpengo = 1 Million Pengo

126.	29. 4.1946	10,000 Milpengo, dark blue. Girl's head at right	.75
127.		100,000 Milpengo, dark green. Woman in costume at right	.75
128.	24. 5.1946	1,000,000 Milpengo, brown on yellow. Lajos Kossuth at right	.50
129.		10,000,000 Milpengo, brown on blue. Lajos Kossuth at right	.50
130.	3. 6.1946	100,000,000 Milpengo, green. Woman's head with cover-cloth at right	.75
131.		1,000,000,000 Milpengo, blue. Girl's head at right	1.00

1 B.-Pengo = 1,000,000,000 Pengo

132.		10,000 B.-Pengo, brown on lilac. Woman's head at right	.75
133.		100,000 B.-Pengo, red brown. Woman in costume at right	1.00
134.		1,000,000 B.-Pengo, dark brown. Lajos Kossuth at right	1.50
135.		10,000,000 B.-Pengo, violet. Lajos Kossuth at right	2.00
136.		100,000,000 B.-Pengo, blue. Woman's head with cover cloth at right	4.00
137.		1,000,000,000 B.-Pengo, green. Girl's head at right	30.00

Finance Ministry Notes

1 Adopengo = 2 trillion Pengo (2,000,000,000,000)

138.	25. 5.1946	50,000 (otvenezer) Adopengo, green	
		a. Grey paper with watermark and control numbers	1.25
		b. Grey paper with watermark but no control numbers	1.50
		c. White paper without watermark or control numbers	1.25

139.   500,000 (otszazezer) Adopengo, dark blue
- a. Grey paper with watermark and control numbers   1.25
- b. White paper without watermark or control numbers   1.25

140.   1 Million (egymillio) Adopengo, red on grey
- a. Grey paper with watermark and control numbers   1.25
- b. As #140a but arms in background inverted (cross at left)   2.50
- c. White paper without watermark or control numbers   1.25

141.   10 Million (tizmillio) Adopengo, blue on yellow
- a. White paper without watermark or control numbers   2.00
- b. As #141a but arms in background inverted (cross at left)   5.00
- c. Grey paper with watermark but without control numbers. Arms in background inverted (cross at left)   5.00

134 × 82

142.   100 Million (szazmillio) Adopengo, grey blue on rose
- a. White paper without watermark or control numbers   2.00
- b. As #142a but arms in background inverted (cross at left)   5.00

143. 28. 5.1946 10,000 (tizezer) Adopengo, brown
- a. Grey paper with watermark and control numbers. Reverse inscribed "5970/1946 M.E."   1.25
- b. Grey paper with watermark but no control number   1.25
- c. White paper without watermark or control numbers. Reverse inscribed "5600/1946 M.E."   10.00

144.		100,000 (egyszazezer) Adopengo, brown lilac	
		a. Grey paper with watermark and control numbers. Reverse inscribed "5970/1946 M.E."	1.25
		b. Grey paper with watermark but no control numbers	1.25
		c. As #144a but arms in background inverted (cross at left)	10.00
		d. Grey paper with watermark and control numbers. Reverse inscribed "5600/1946 M.E."	10.00
		e. White paper without watermark or control numbers. Reverse inscribed "5600/1946 M.E."	4.00

The Finance Ministry decreed that the stamps used on various promissory notes, tax credits, duties, deeds, judgements, accounts etc. were to circulate as legal tender.

Magyar Nemzeti Bank (Hungarian National Bank)

Notes in forint values

145.	3. 6.1946	10 Forint, green. Young man with hammer at left	37.50
146.		100 Forint, blue. Young woman with sickle and sheaf at left	50.00
147.	27. 2.1947	10 Forint, green. A. Petofi at right	7.50
148.		20 Forint, lilac. G. Dozsa at right	10.00
149.		100 Forint, red brown. Lajos Kossuth at right	6.50
150.	24.10.1949	10 Forint, green. Type of #147 but arms with a star	4.00
151.		20 Forint, blue. Type of #148 but arms with a star	5.00
152.		100 Forint, red brown. Type of #149 but arms with a star	4.00
153.	1. 9.1951	50 Forint, brown. Franz Rakoczy at right	—
154.	23.5.1957	10 Forint, green. Type of #150 but arms without hammer and sheaf	1.50
155.		20 Forint, blue. Type of #151 but arms without hammer and sheaf	2.00
156.		100 Forint, red brown. Type of #152 but arms without hammer and sheaf	—
157.	24. 8.1960	10 Forint, green. Type of #154 but different signature	—
158.		20 Forint, blue. Type of #155 but different signature	—
159.		100 Forint, red brown. Type of #156 but different signature	—

160.	12.10.1962	10 Forint, green. Type of #157 but different signature	—
161.		20 Forint, blue. Type of #158 but different signature	—
162.		100 Forint, red-brown. Type of #159 but different signature	—
163.	3. 9.1965	20 Forint, blue. Type of #161 but different signatures	—
164.		50 Forint. Type of #153 but different arms	—
165.	24.10.1968	100 Forint, red brown. Type of #162 but different signatures	—

Russian Red Army occupation issues of World War II. Many variations of the printing colors exist.

M1.	1944	1 Pengo, blue on brown. Printed area on date side 106 × 49 mm.	
		a. Horizontal waves in background	.65
		b. Vertical waves in background	.65

129 × 67

M2.		1 Pengo, blue on brown. Printed area on date side 118 × 54 mm.	
		a. Without control numbers, horizontal waves	.50
		b. Without control numbers, vertical waves	.50
		c. With control numbers	15.00
M3.		2 Pengo, blue on green	.75
M4.		5 Pengo, lilac on light blue	.75
M5.		10 Pengo, green and lilac	1.00
M6.		20 Pengo, grey	
		a. Without control numbers	15.00
		b. With control numbers (two varieties)	1.00
M7.		50 Pengo, olive (two control number varieties)	1.15
M8.		100 Pengo, dark brown (two control number varieties)	1.15
M9.		1,000 Pengo, red	10.00

ICELAND (Island)

Norwegian refugees settled the island in the 9th century. With the separation of Norway from Denmark in 1814, Iceland elected to remain with Denmark. In 1918 it became a free state under the personal direction of the Danish king. Iceland became an independent republic in 1944.

1 Krone = 100 Aurar

Landssjodur Islands

1.	18. 9.1885	5 Kronur, grey. Profile head of King Christian IX at left	$37.50
2.		10 Kronur, blue. Type of #1	50.00
3.		50 Kronur, grey green and light brown. Type of #1	R

120 × 72

4.	18. 9.1885–12. 1.1900	5 Kronur, brown and grey. Facing head of King Christian IX at left	25.00
5.		10 Kronur, blue and brown. Type of #4	37.50
6.		50 Kronur, grey green and light brown. Head of King Frederick VIII at left	50.00
7.		5 Kronur, brown and grey green. Head of King Christian X at left, facing left	20.00
8.		10 Kronur, blue and brown. Type of #7	25.00
9.		50 Kronur, grey green and light brown. Type of #7	37.50

Islands Banki (Bank of Iceland)

10.	1904	5 Kronur, grey on lilac. King Christian IX at left	15.00
11.		10 Kronur, dark blue. Type of #10	20.00
12.		50 Kronur, blue and grey. Type of #10	30.00
13.		100 Kronur	R
14.	1919	100 Kronur, printed on reverse of 5 kronur (#1), blue and grey	RRR

#11
121 × 70

15.	1920	5 Kronur, grey on lilac. Geyser at left	12.50
16.		10 Kronur, dark blue. Landscape and river at left	20.00

Rikissjodur Islands (Government Notes)

17.	18. 9.1885–12. 1.1900	1 Krona, dark blue. Background of circles	6.50
18.		1 Krona, dark blue. Background of double circles	6.50
19.		5 Kronur, brown on green. Type of #7 but with "Fyrir Rikissjod Islands"	15.00
20.		10 Kronur, dark green on green. Type of #8 but with "Fyrir Rikissjod Islands"	20.00
21.		50 Kronur, grey green and light brown. Type of #9 but with "Fyrir Rikissjod Islands"	30.00
22.	1941	1 Krona	
		a. Green on greenish paper	2.50
		b. Blue green on white paper	2.50
		c. Blue on white paper	2.50
		d. Blue on yellowish paper	2.50
		e. Light blue on white paper	2.50
		f. Blue violet on white paper	2.50
		g. Brown to dark brown	2.50

Landsbanki Islands (National Bank of Iceland)

All notes have varieties of the signature at right.

23.	15. 4.1928 (Issued 1929)	5 Kronur, brown on green. Type of #19 but with "Landsbanki Islands"	12.50
24.		10 Kronur, dark blue on light blue. Type of #20 but with "Landsbanki Islands"	15.00
25.		50 Kronur, grey green on light brown. Type of #21 but with "Landsbanki Islands"	25.00
26.		100 Kronur, grey blue on grey. King Christian X at left	50.00
27.	15. 4.1928 (Issued 1935)	5 Kronur, brown and lilac. Jon Eriksson at left	1.25

164 • **Iceland**

| 28. | | 10 Kronur, blue. Jon Sigurdsson at left | 1.50 |
| 29. | | 50 Kronur, violet. Type of # 27 | 7.50 |

151 × 99

30.		100 Kronur, red. Type of #28	12.50
31.		500 Kronur, green. Type of #28	30.00
32.	15. 4.1928 (Issued 1945)	5 Kronur, green. Type of #27	.75

120 × 70

33.		10 Kronur, red. Type of #28	1.00
34.		50 Kronur, green. Type of #29	3.50
35.		100 Kronur, blue. Type of #30	6.50
36.		500 Kronur, brown. Type of #31	15.00

Landsbanki Islands—Sedlabankinn

37.	21. 6.1957	5 Kronur, red brown. Viking Ingolfur Arnason at left	—
38.		10 Kronur, violet brown and green. Jon Eriksson at left	—
39.		25 Kronur, violet. Magnus Stephensen at left	—
40.		100 Kronur, green blue. Tryggvi Gunnarsson at left	—
41.		1,000 Kronur, blue and green. Jon Sigurdsson at right	—

Sedlabanki Islands

42.	29. 3.1961	10 Kronur, violet brown and green. Type of #38	—
43.		25 Kronur, violet. Type of #39	—
44.		100 Kronur, green blue. Type of #40	—
45.		500 Kronur, green. Hannes Hafstein at left	—
46.		1,000 Kronur, blue and green. Type of #41	—

IRELAND (Eire)

A free state, the Irish Republic was formed in 1921. Northern Ireland remained a part of the United Kingdom.

1 Pound (Punt) = 20 Shillings (Scilling)

Currency Commission—*Coimisiun Airgid Reatha*

All notes show a young Irish girl at the left, with various printing dates from 10.9.1928 to 1942.

1.	10 Shillings, red orange	$15.00

151 × 84

2.	1 Pound, green	25.00
3.	5 Pounds, brown	R
4.	10 Pounds, blue	RR
5.	20 Pounds, red	RRR
6.	50 Pounds, violet	RRR
7.	100 Pounds, green	RRR

Currency Commission, Consolidated Bank Notes

A standardized design appears on the notes of all eight "shareholding banks." Only the bank names and signatures vary. All notes show a farmer with a plough and horses. The reverse scenes are different on the various denominations. The issue dates are from 1927 to 1942. The notes circulated until 1953.

Bank of Ireland

8.	1 Pound	10.00
9.	5 Pounds	25.00
10.	10 Pounds	50.00
11.	20 Pounds	R
12.	50 Pounds	RR
13.	100 Pounds	RRR

Hibernian Bank

14.	1 Pound	10.00
15.	5 Pounds	25.00
16.	10 Pounds	50.00
17.	20 Pounds	R
18.	50 Pounds	RR
19.	100 Pounds	RRR

Munster and Leinster Bank

151 × 83

20.	1 Pound	10.00
21.	5 Pounds	25.00
22.	10 Pounds	50.00
23.	20 Pounds	R
24.	50 Pounds	RR
25.	100 Pounds	RRR

National Bank

26.	1 Pound	10.00
27.	5 Pounds	25.00
28.	10 Pounds	50.00
29.	20 Pounds	R
30.	50 Pounds	RR
31.	100 Pounds	RRR

Northern Bank

32.	1 Pound	10.00
33.	5 Pounds	25.00
34.	10 Pounds	50.00
35.	20 Pounds	R
36.	50 Pounds	RR
37.	100 Pounds	RRR

Provincial Bank of Ireland

38.	1 Pound	10.00

39.	5 Pounds	25.00
40.	10 Pounds	50.00
41.	20 Pounds	R
42.	50 Pounds	RR
43.	100 Pounds	RRR

Royal Bank of Ireland

44.	1 Pound	10.00
45.	5 Pounds	25.00
46.	10 Pounds	50.00
47.	20 Pounds	R
48.	50 Pounds	RR
49.	100 Pounds	RRR

Ulster Bank

50.	1 Pound	10.00
51.	5 Pounds	25.00
52.	10 Pounds	50.00
53.	20 Pounds	R
54.	50 Pounds	RR
55.	100 Pounds	RRR

Central Bank of Ireland—*Banc Ceannais Na Eireann*

Notes are the same as those of the Currency Commission (#1–7) but with "Central Bank of Ireland." Panel at bottom reads "Payable to bearer on demand in London."

138 × 78

56.	dates from 1943	10 Shillings, red orange	4.00
57.		1 Pound, green	6.50
58.		5 Pounds, brown	—
59.		10 Pounds, blue	—
60.		20 Pounds, red	—
61.		50 Pounds, violet	—
62.		100 Pounds, green	—

Notes #63–69 are similar to #56–62 but do not read "Payable in London."

63.	dates from 1962	10 Shillings, red orange	—
64.		1 Pound, green	—
65.		5 Pounds, brown	—
66.		10 Pounds, blue	—
67.		20 Pounds, red	—
68.		50 Pounds, violet	—
69.		100 Pounds, green	—

ITALY (Italia)

King Victor Emmanuel II became king of a unified Italy in 1861. He was followed by Humbert I in 1878 and Victor Emmanuel III who ruled from 1900 until 1946 when Italy became a republic.

1 Lira = 100 Centesimi

Banca d'Italia (Bank of Italy)

The classification of Italian paper money is difficult since several dates appear on most notes—authorization date, dates of various decrees and the actual issue date (the most recent of those on the note). Since arrangement by dates is confusing, the notes have been divided by denomination. Individual listings are based on design differences and variations in the national emblem. The first and last known issue dates are indicated for each type. The following abbreviations refer to the national emblem:

E1.   Without national emblem. Reverse text reads "Decreto . . . " (until 18.5.1926).
E.2.   With fasces emblem (19.5.1926 to 6.8.1943).
E.3   With "B.I." (from 7.8.1943).
E4.   With head of Italia emblem.
E5.   With Medusa head emblem (from 14.8.1947).

The Italian notes are also differentiated by the names of the printing firms, the place of issue "Roma" or "L'Aquila" (1942–44) and the watermarks in the paper. The valuations are for the commonest date and signature variety of each listing.

25 Lire Notes

1.   24. 9.1918–12. 5.1919

25 Lire, brown. Head of Italia at right with eagle above. Paper watermarked with head of Minerva (two signature varieties) $7.50

50 Lire Notes

2.   12. 9.1896– 5. 8.1926

50 Lire, green. Type I with edge imprint, large "L" and woman with three children at left. Female figure on reverse, E1 (five signature varieties)   2.00

Some Italian notes were arranged in sheets with a tall, thin design imprint between pairs of notes. As the notes were separated, the imprint was cut through with a portion remaining on one edge of each note (see left edge of illustration of note #3). The term for this edge imprint is "talon" in German, "matrice" in Italian.

172 × 110

3.	8. 4.1926–17. 3.1936	50 Lire, green. As #2 but reverse E2 (three signature varieties) 1.50
4.	31. 3.1943	50 Lire, green. Type I without edge imprint, large "L" and woman with three children at left. Head of Italia on reverse, E2 1.00
5.	11. 8.1943–30.11.1944	50 Lire, green. As #4 but reverse E3 1.25
6.	16. 6.1915– 4. 1.1920	50 Lire. Type II, seated Italia at right. Farmer with oxen on reverse, E1. Paper watermarked with head of Dante Alighieri (two signature varieties) 4.00
7.	11.10.1933–18. 7.1942	50 Lire, blue violet and yellow brown. Type III, she wolf with Romulus and Remus at right. "Roma" on reverse, E2. Paper watermarked with head of Caesar (two signature varieties) .75
8.	28. 2.1942– 6. 8.1943	50 Lire, blue violet and yellow brown. As #7 but with "L'Aquila" on reverse .75
9.	23. 8.1943– 1. 2.1944	50 Lire, blue violet and yellow brown. As #7 but reverse E3 1.00
10.	10.12.1944 and 20.4.1946	50 Lire, green. Type IV, head of Italia at left. Paper watermarked with "50" (two signature varieties) .25

100 Lire Notes

11.	30.10.1897– 6. 3.1926	100 Lire, brown and rose. Type I with edge imprint, large "B" and woman with cupids at left. Reverse E1. Paper watermarked with head of Mercury (four signature varieties) 2.00
12.	18. 6.1926–17.11.1930	100 Lire, brown and rose. As #11 but reverse E2 1.00

13.	2. 2.1926– 4. 5.1926	100 Lire, blue. Type I without edge imprint, large "B" and woman with cupids at left. Reverse E1. Paper watermarked with head of Italia	4.00
14.	8. 8.1926–17.10.1934	100 Lire, blue. As #13 but reverse E2	2.50
15.	9.12.1942–15. 3.1943	100 Lire, brown and rose. As #14 except color	.75
16.	23. 8.1943–20.12.1944	100 Lire, yellow. As #13 but reverse E3 (two signature varieties)	.75

185 × 109

17.	5.10.1931–11. 6.1942	100 Lire, olive green and brown. Type II, Roma and she-wolf. "Roma" on reverse, E2. Paper watermarked with heads of Italia and Dante (two signature varieties)	.25
18.	28. 8.1942–17. 5.1943	100 Lire, olive green and brown. As #17 but with "L'Aquila" on reverse	.50
19.	23. 8.1943– 8.10.1943	100 Lire, olive green and brown. As #18 but reverse E.3	1.25
20.	10.12.1944 and 20.4.1946	100 Lire, red. Type III, head of Italia at left. Paper watermarked with "100" (two signature varieties)	.25

500 Lire Notes

21.	25.10.1898–Feb. 1921	500 Lire, rose brown. Type I with edge imprint, oval ornaments with allegorical figures. Reverse E1. Paper watermarked with head of Roma (three signature varieties)	4.50
22.	31. 3.1943	500 Lire, red. Type I without edge imprint, oval ornaments with allegorical figures. Reverse E2	2.50
23.	23. 8.1943–19. 2.1947	500 Lire, red. As #22 but reverse E3 (three signature varieties)	1.00

24.	14.11.1950	500 Lire, red. As #22 but reverse E5	2.00
25.	16. 7.1919–13. 4.1926	500 Lire, lilac and olive brown. Type II, peasant woman with sickle and sheaf at right. Reverse E1. Paper watermarked with head of Leonardo da Vinci	4.00
26.	6.12.1926–23. 3.1942	500 Lire, lilac and olive brown. As #25 but reverse E2 and "Roma" (four signature varieties)	2.00
27.	21.10.1942–17. 5.1943	500 Lire, lilac and olive brown. As #25 but with "L'Aquila" on reverse	2.50
28.	23. 8.1943– 8.10.1943	500 Lire, lilac and olive brown. As #25 but reverse E3	3.00
29.	20. 3.1947–23. 3.1961	500 Lire, lilac and brown. Type III, bust of Italia at left. Paper watermarked with head of Italia (two signature varieties)	1.25

1,000 Lire Notes

30.	6.12.1897–August 1920	1,000 Lire, lilac brown and brown. Type I with edge imprint, large "M" at left. Reverse E1. Paper watermarked with head of Italia at right, "1000" at left (four signature varieties)	10.00
31.	19. 8.1921–13. 4.1926	1,000 Lire, lilac brown and brown. Type I without edge imprint, large "M" at left. Reverse E1. Paper watermarked with head of Italia at right, Banca d'Italia at left	5.00

#32
244
×
148

32.	29. 6.1926– 6. 2.1943	1,000 Lire, lilac brown and brown. As #31 but reverse E2 (four signature varieties)	4.00
33.	11. 8.1943–12. 7.1947	1,000 Lire, lilac brown and brown. As #31 but reverse E3 (three signature varieties)	1.25
34.	22.11.1947–14.11.1950	1,000 Lire, lilac brown and brown. As #31 but reverse E5 (two signature varieties)	2.00
35.	7. 7.1930–15. 3.1943	1,000 Lire, blue and brown. Type II, two seated women (Venice and Genoa). Reverse E2 with "Roma." Paper watermarked with head of Columbus at right, head of Italia at left (three signature varieties)	1.50
36.	17. 5.1943– 6. 8.1943	1,000 Lire, blue and brown. As #35 but with "L'Aquila" on reverse	2.00
37.	23. 8.1943– 8.10.1943	1,000 Lire, blue and brown. As #36 but reverse E3	4.00
38.	20. 3.1947	1,000 Lire, violet and brown. Type III, head of Italia at left, E3. Paper watermarked with head of Italia	1.75
39.	1948–25.12.1961	1,000 Lire, violet and brown. As #38 but E5 on obverse	1.75

5,000 Lire Notes

40.	4. 8.1945–12. 7.1947	5,000 Lire, blue. Type I, head of Italia at left and right, "Titoli Provvisori" in background, E4. Paper watermarked with head of Italia	4.00
41.	8. 9.1947–22.11.1949	5,000 Lire, blue. As #40 but E5 on obverse (two signature varieties)	2.50
42.	17. 1.1947	5,000 Lire, green and brown. Type II, two seated women (Venice and Genoa) E4. Paper watermarked with head of Dante at left, head of Italia at right	10.00
43.	1948– 7. 1.1963	5,000 Lire, green and brown. As #42 but E5 on obverse	8.50

10,000 Lire Notes

44.	4. 8.1945–12. 7.1947	10,000 Lire, red brown. Type I, head of Italia at left and right "Titoli Provvisori" in background, E4. Paper watermarked with head of Italia	6.50
45.	8. 9.1947–12. 6.1950	10,000 Lire, red brown. As #44 but E5 on obverse (two signature varieties)	4.00

245
×
125

| 46. | 1948–24. 3.1962 | 10,000 Lire, brown and orange. Type II, two seated women (Venice and Genoa), E5. Paper watermarked with head of Verdi at left, head of Galileo at right | 20.00 |

Biglietti di Stato (State Notes)

47.	17.12.1882	5 Lire, blue. King Umberto I at left (three signature varieties)	3.00
48.	11. 3.1883	10 Lire, blue. King Umberto I at left on obverse and reverse	7.50
49.	5-17.2.1888	10 Lire, blue and light brown. King Umberto I. Numerals only on the reverse (eight signature varieties)	2.50
50.	9–17.5.1895	25 Lire, blue and green. Bust of Italia at left	20.00
51.	23.3–9.4.1902	25 Lire, blue. King Victor Emmanuel III at left	17.50
52.	7–19.10.1904	5 Lire, blue and light brown. King Victor Emmanuel III at right (six signature varieties)	1.00

150 × 98

| 53. | 20. 8.1923 | 25 Lire, brown. Head of Italia at right with eagle above (as #1) | 8.50 |

54.	18. 6.1935	10 Lire, blue. King Victor Emmanuel III at left. On bottom edge:	
		a. 1935	.25
		b. 1938	.25
		c. 1939	.25
		d. 1944	.25
55.	27.10.1939	5 Lire, lilac brown. King Victor Emmanuel III at left. On bottom edge:	
		a. 1940	.25
		b. 1944	.25
56.	14.11.1939	1 Lira, brown. Statue of Caesar Augustus on reverse	.25
57.		2 Lire, blue violet. Statue of Julius Caesar on reverse	.25
58.	23.11.1944	1 Lira, lilac brown. Head of Italia at left (three signature varieties)	.25
59.		2 Lire, green and yellow. Head of Italia at left (three signature varieties)	.25
60.		5 Lire, lilac brown. Helmeted female head at left (three signature varieties)	.25
61.		10 Lire, blue. Head of Jupiter at left (three signature varieties)	.25
62.	31.12.1951	50 Lire, green. Bust of Italia at left (two signature varieties)	.25
63.		100 Lire, lilac brown. Bust of Italia at left (two signature varieties)	.25
64.	31. 3.1966–20. 6.1966	500 Lire, blue and brown. Eagle with serpent at left, head of Arethusa at right	—

Buoni di Cassa (State Notes)

65.	4. 8.1893 (15 or 16.9.1893 on reverse)	1 Lira, brown and green. Head of King Umberto I at left	1.00
66.	21. 2.1894 (22 or 23.2.1894 on reverse)	2 Lire, blue and brown. Head of King Umberto I at left	1.50
67.	22. 7.1894 (15 or 16.9.1893 on reverse)	1 Lira, brown and green. Head of King Umberto I at left	2.00
68.	18. 8.1914 (19 or 20.8.1914 on reverse)	1 Lira, brown on blue. Head of King Victor Emmanuel at left (three signature varieties)	.75

69
82 × 46

69.		2 Lire, brown on light brown. Head of King Victor Emmanuel at left (three signature varieties)	1.00

Allied Military Currency

70.	1943	1 Lira, blue and brown	.25
71.		2 Lire, lilac and brown	.25
72.		5 Lire, green and brown	.25
73.		10 Lire, black and brown	.75
74.		50 Lire, blue	1.25
75.		100 Lire, lilac and blue	1.50
76.		500 Lire, green and blue	5.00
77.		1,000 Lire, black and blue	12.50

Notes # 70—77 exist both with and without "F" for the Forbes printing firm.

78.	1943A	5 Lire, green and brown	.40
79.		10 Lire, black and brown	.50
80.		50 Lire, blue	.75
81.		100 Lire, lilac and blue	1.00

155 × 66

82.		500 Lire, green and blue	3.50
83.		1,000 Lire, black and blue	7.50

Banca d'Italia (Bank of Italy new types)

84.	3. 7.1962–12. 4.1962	10,000 Lire, brown, violet and lilac. Head of Michaelangelo at right	—
85.	14. 7.1962–28. 6.1962	1,000 Lire, blue, red and brown. Head of Giuseppe Verdi at right	—
86.	3. 9.1964–20. 8.1964	5,000 Lire, green and red. Head of Christopher Columbus at right	—
87.	3. 7.1967–27. 6.1967	50,000 Lire, brown and green. Head of Leonardo da Vinci at right	—
88.		100,000 Lire, brown. Head of Alessandro Manzoni at right	—
89.	25. 3.1969–26. 2.1969	1,000 Lire, blue and lilac. Head of Giuseppe Verdi at right. Paper with metallic fibres	—

Austrian occupation of Venice, 1918

Cassa Veneta dei Prestiti, Buoni di Cassa (Treasury Bills)

M1.	2. 1.1918	5 Centesimi, blue	.25
M2.		10 Centesimi, light brown	.25
M3.		50 Centesimi, red	.25
M4.		1 Lira, lilac (two control number varieties)	.25
M5.		2 Lire, green (three control number varieties)	.50
M6.		10 Lire, blue (two control number varieties)	1.00
M7.		20 Lire, carmine (two control number varieties)	1.25

151 × 104

M8.		100 Lire, brown and green	4.00
M9.		1,000 Lire, brown	30.00

Banco di Napoli (Bank of Naples)

All notes read "Legge 10. Agosto 1893"

173 × 95

R1.	15. 7.1896	50 Lire, green. Woman with Mercury staff and book (Industry) at right (also with date 22.10.1903)	30.00
R2.	30. 6.1896	100 Lire, red brown. Woman with sickle and produce (Agriculture) at right (also with date 20.10.1903)	45.00

R3.	15. 6.1896	500	Lire, grey green and violet. Head of Leonardo da Vinci at left (also with dates 22.10.1903 and 20.7.1906)	R
R4.	1–2.3.1896	1,000	Lire, brown and blue. Head of Galileo Galilei at left (also with date 22.10.1903)	RRR
R5.	17. 8.1918	25	Lire, grey. Arms at left (also with date 4.6.1919)	30.00
R6.	30.12.1909	50	Lire, black and brown. Head of Salvator Rosa at left (also with dates 23.2.1911; 13.12.1914; 31.5.1915; 24.12.1917 and 16.8.1921)	7.50
R7.	10.11.1908	100	Lire, dark blue. Head of Torquato Tasso at left (also with dates 23.2.1911; 13.12.1914; 31.5.1915; 24.12.1917; 7.9.1918; 15.1.1921 and 16.8.1921)	7.50
R8.	7.12.1909	500	Lire, black on olive. Head of Gaetano Filangeri at left (also with dates 23.2.1911; 13.12.1914; 31.5.1915; 14.8.1917; 24.12.1917; 7.9.1918; 1.5.1919; 30.1.1920; 15.1.1921 and 16.8.1921)	15.00
R9.	7.12.1909	1,000	Lire. Head of Giambattista Vico at left (also with dates 23.2.1911; 13.12.1914; 31.5.1915; 14.8.1917; 24.12.1917; 24.12.1917; 7.9.1918; 1.5.1919; 30.1.1920; 15.1.1921 and 16.8.1921)	35.00

The bank's right to print paper money expired in 1926.

Banco di Sicilia (Bank of Sicily)

All notes read "Legge 10. Agosto 1893"

| R10. | 21. 2.1918 | 25 | Lire, grey green. Statue of "Palermo" at left (also with date 6.8.1918) | 20.00 |

R12
204 × 115

R11. 27. 4.1897   50 Lire, violet and brown. Statue of "Palermo" at
                      left (also with dates 8.12.1898; 18.12.1901;
                      27.12.1909; 16.12.1911; 24.12.1913; 18.5.1915;
                      22.6.1915;   24.12.1917;   30.5.1919   and
                      19.4.1920)   7.50
R12. 30.12.1896   100 Lire, blue. Statue of "Palermo" at left (also
                      with dates 18.12.1901; 27.12.1909; 24.12.1913;
                      18.5.1915; 22.6.1915; 24.12.1917; 30.5.1919
                      and 19.4.1920)   17.50
R13. 24.12.1897   500 Lire, red and blue. Statue of "Palermo" at
                      left (also with dates 18.12.1901; 27.12.1909;
                      24.12.1913; 18.5.1915; 22.6.1915; 24.12.1917;
                      22.3.1918; 30.5.1919; 19.4.1920; 23.5.1921)   35.00
R14. 15. 9.1897 1,000 Lire, brown and red. Statue of "Palermo" at
                      left (also with dates 18.12.1901; 27.12.1909;
                      24.12.1913; 18.5.1915; 22.6.1915; 24.12.1917;
                      30.5.1919; 12.4.1920; 19.4.1920 and 23.5.1921)   50.00

The bank's right to print paper money expired in 1926.

During the period 1943–45, many notes were issued by partisan groups such as the
Garibaldi Brigade, Osoppo Brigade, Comitato Liberazione Ligure, etc. All of these
notes are RRR and seldom seen.

LATVIA (Latvija)

Latvia was under Russian control from 1772 until 1918 when it became an independent republic. In 1940 Latvia became part of the Union of Soviet Socialist Republics. During World War II, the country was first occupied by Russian troops, then by the Germans and finally retaken by the Russians.

1 Ruble = 100 Kapeikas
1 Lats = 100 Santimu

Notes of the western Volunteer Army of Col. Avalov-Bermondt circulated in Latvia during 1919 (see Russia R97 through R101).

Latwijas Walstskases Sihmes (State Bank Notes)

Notes in ruble values, many control number varieties

1.	1919	1 Ruble, blue and brown. Paper watermarked with waves	$1.75
2.		1 Ruble, light and dark green	
		a. Paper watermarked with waves	1.00
		b. Paper watermarked with light lines	.75
3.		5 Rubles, light and dark blue. Woman's head in middle	
		a. Paper watermarked with waves	2.00
		b. Paper watermarked with light lines (three signature varieties)	2.50

129 × 82

4.	1919	10 Rubles, red brown and green. Sailing ship in middle	
		a. Paper watermarked with waves	3.00
		b. Paper watermarked with light lines (three signature varieties)	2.00
5.		25 Rubles, brown. Three stylized sheafs of produce on reverse	
		a. Paper watermarked with multiple waves	20.00
		b. Paper watermarked with stars	5.00
		c. Paper watermarked with light lines (two signature varieties)	4.00

6.		50 Rubles, green on grey	7.50

Excellent Russian counterfeits exist.

7.		100 Rubles, brown and dark brown. Oak tree on reverse (three signature varieties)	4.00
8.	1920	500 Rubles, light and dark green. Symbols of Agriculture, Industry and Shipping on reverse	
		a. Paper watermarked with light lines (two signature varieties)	37.50
		b. Paper watermarked with multiple waves	20.00

Excellent Russian counterfeits exist.

Latwijas Mainas Sihmes (Exchange Notes)

9.	(1920)	5 Kapeikas, red	.25
10.		10 Kapeikas, blue	.25
11.		25 Kapeikas, brown	.25
12.		50 Kapeikas, violet	.25
		Reverse inverted	5.00

Latvijas Bankas (Bank of Latvia)

13.	1920	10 Latu on 500 rubles. Red overprint on #8b	20.00
14.	1923	100 Latu, blue. Two seated women in national costumes on reverse (two signature varieties)	30.00
15.	1924	20 Latu, yellow, orange and grey. Peasant sowing seeds	RR

In circulation for very short time.

16.		50 Latu, green and brown. Daugava river and city of Riga	R
17.	1925	20 Latu, black on yellow and green. President J. Cakste	8.50
18.	1928	25 Latu, black on yellow. K. Valdemars in middle	5.00

188 × 104

19.	1929	500 Latu, blue and brown. Girl in national costume at right	10.00
20.	1934	50 Latu, blue. Prime Minister K. Ulmanis	3.00
21.	1938	25 Lati, green. Folk hero Lacplesis the Bear-killer at right	4.00

155 × 80

| 22. | 1939 | 100 Latu, red. Peasant family | 4.50 |

Latvijas Valsts Kases Zimes (State Treasury Notes)

Notes in Lat values

23.	1925	10 Latu, red brown. Oaks and grain field (five signature varieties)	11.50
24.	1926	5 Lati, brown. Symbols of Commerce and Shipping on reverse	37.50
25.	1933	10 Latu, blue green. Seated woman in national costume on reverse	5.00
26.	1934	10 Latu, blue green. Type of #25 (three signature varieties)	6.50
27.	1935	20 Latu, brown. Riga castle	2.00
28.	1936	20 Latu, brown. Type of #27	20.00
29.	1937	10 Latu, dark brown and multicolored. Fisherman with net	1.25
30.	1938	10 Latu, dark brown and multicolored. Type of #29	1.25
31.	1939	10 Latu, dark brown and multicolored. Type of #29	1.25
32.	1940	10 Latu, dark brown and multicolored. Type of #29	2.00
33.		20 Latu, blue. Academy of Agriculture in Jelgava	R

140 × 75

Latvijas Valsts Kases Mainas Zimes (State Treasury Exchange Notes)

| 34. | 1940 | 5 Lati, blue, grey and brown. Bridge over the Gauja River (two signature varieties) | 5.00 |

The following notes exist with the apparently unofficial overprint "Latvija 1941, 1. Julijs:"

> 5 Lati, 1940 (#34)
> 10 Latu, 1937 (#29)
> 20 Latu, 1940 (#33)
> 100 Latu, 1939 (#22)
> 500 Latu, 1929 (#19)

Latgales Partizanu Pulks (Latgalian Partisan Regiments)

Russian notes stamped:

a. "Latgales Partizanu Pulks 2 Rotas Komandeers"
b. "Latgales Partizanu Pulks 3 Rotas Komandeers"

M1.	20 Rubles (1917 issue), stamp b
M2.	250 Rubles (1917 issue), stamp a
M3.	10 Rubles (1918 issue), stamp b
M4.	25 Rubles (1918 issue), stamp b
M5.	50 Rubles (1918 issue), stamp b
M6.	100 Rubles (1918 issue), stamp a
M7.	100 Rubles (1918 issue), stamp b
M8.	500 Rubles (1918 issue), stamp b
M9.	15 Rubles (undated issue, 1919), stamp a
M10.	15 Rubles (undated issue, 1919), stamp b
M11.	60 Rubles (undated issue, 1919), stamp a
M12.	60 Rubles (undated issue, 1919), stamp b
M13.	250 Rubles (1919 issue), stamp a
M14.	250 Rubles (1919 issue), stamp b

In the past few years many counterfeit overprints have been noted. Genuine notes are R to RRR.

LIECHTENSTEIN

A Principality since 1719, Liechtenstein left the German Confederation and associated itself with Austria through a customs union and defense treaty (1852–1919). In 1924, a customs union was established with Switzerland which is still in effect.

1 Krone = 100 Heller (to 1924)

1.   (1920)   10 Heller, red and blue $ .25

71 × 45

2.   20 Heller, red and blue   .25
3.   50 Heller, red and blue   .25

LITHUANIA (Lietuva)

Along with Poland, Lithuania came under Russian control in 1795. In 1918 it was declared an independent republic but in 1940 the country was occupied by Russian troops, later by the Germans. At the end of World War II, Lithuania became a part of the Union of Soviet Socialist Republics.

1 Litas = 100 Centu

From 1919 to 1922 the notes of the Eastern German State Loan Office circulated in Lithuania. They were known as "Auksinas" and "Skatikas" after their inscriptions (see Germany R120–R134, also Memel).

Lietuvos Bankas (Bank of Lithuania)

80 × 53

1.	10. 9.1922	1 Centas, blue	$2.00
2.		5 Centai, green	2.00
3.		20 Centu, brown	4.00
4.		50 Centu, violet	6.50
5.		1 Litas, dark green	
		a. Paper watermarked with braids	7.50
		b. Paper watermarked with knots	9.00
6.		5 Litai, dark brown	15.00
7.	16.11.1922	1 Centas, blue and wine red	2.50
8.		2 Centu, dark green on grey violet	2.50
9.		5 Centai, blue on green	3.00
10.		10 Centu, brown on grey violet	4.00
11.		20 Centu, dark blue on grey	4.00
12.		50 Centu, violet and green	5.00
13.		1 Litas, brown on grey	6.50
14.		2 Litu, blue on grey	7.50
15.		5 Litai, blue, violet, brown and dark green. Peasant sowing seed in middle. Control number in black	10.00
16.		5 Litai, olive green, blue and black. Type of #15 but slight variations in the ornamentation. Control number in red	8.50
17.		5 Litai, brown and dark grey. Type of #16	12.50

18.		10 Litu, blue, yellow brown and dark green. Raftsman at right	17.50
19.		50 Litu, dark green and brown. Bust of Grand Duke Gediminas of Lithuania at right	50.00
20.		100 Litu, blue and violet. Bust of Grand Duke Vytautas the Great	R

198 × 92

21.	11.12.1924	500 Litu, brown	R
22.		1,000 Litu, grey and dark blue. Girl in Lithuanian national costume at left, seated youth at right	R
23.	24.11.1927	10 Litu, green. Peasant working in field at right	5.00
24.	31. 3.1928	50 Litu, dark blue. Head of Dr. J. Basanavicins at left	7.50
25.		100 Litu, dark violet, Seated woman at left, boy with Mercury staff at right	12.50
26.	24. 6.1929	5 Litai, brown. Head of Grand Duke Vytautas the Great	5.00
27.	5. 7.1930	20 Litu, brown. Grand Duke Vytautas the Great at left, Vytautas Church in middle	7.50
28.	1938	10 Litu, green and orange. Portrait of President A. Smetona at left	RRR

LUXEMBOURG (Letzeburg)

The 1815 Congress of Vienna joined the Grand Duchy of Luxembourg in personal union with the Netherlands. The Grand Duchy remained a member of the German Confederation until 1866. After dissolution of the union with the Netherlands, Luxembourg was ruled by the House of Nassau: Adolf 1890–1905; Wilhelm 1905–12; Marie Adelaide 1912–19; Charlotte 1919–64; Jean 1964– . Luxembourg joined in a customs union with Belgium in 1922.

1 Taler = 30 Groschen
1 Mark = 100 Pfennig
1 Franc = 100 Centimes

Banque Internationale a Luxembourg (International Bank in Luxembourg)

1.	1. 9.1856	10 Taler, yellow. Seated woman with three cupids on reverse	RRR
2.		25 Francs = 20 Mark, yellow. Type of #1	RRR
3.		100 Francs = 80 Mark, yellow. Type of #1	RRR
		An issue in Dutch gulden was authorized but no notes were issued.	
4.	1. 7.1900	20 Mark, blue, brown and multicolored. Mill and foundry worker at left	R
5.		50 Mark, green and red brown. Miner at left, peasant at right	R
6.	5. 8.1914	1 Mark, blue	$20.00
7.		2 Mark, brown	37.50
8.		5 Mark, blue	50.00
9.	10. 2.1923	100 Francs, yellow and blue. City of Luxembourg. Vianden Castle on reverse	37.50
10.	18.12.1930	100 Francs. Type of #9	25.00

#11
183 × 109

11.	1. 8.1936	100 Francs. Type of #9	20.00
12.	15. 5.1947	100 Francs, brown and blue. Grand Duchess Charlotte. Peasant woman at left, man at right	7.50
13.	21. 4.1956	100 Francs, dark green. Grand Duchess Charlotte. Peasant woman at left, man at right	6.50
14.	1. 5.1968	100 Francs, green blue and blue on multicolor. Grand Duke Jean at right	—

Die Grossherzoglich Luxemburgische Nationalbank (National Bank of the Grand Duchy of Luxembourg)

| 15. | 1. 7.1873 | 5 Taler | RRR |

139 × 94

16.		10 Taler	RRR
17.		20 Taler	RRR
18.	25. 3.1876	5 Mark	RRR
19.		10 Mark	RRR
20.		20 Mark	RRR

Bon de Caisse (State Treasury Notes)

21.	28.11.1914	1 Frank = 80 Pfennig, blue background	5.00
22.		2 Franken = 1 Mark 60 Pfennig, rose and green background	6.50
23.		5 Franken = 4 Mark, brown violet and green	9.00
24.		25 Franken = 20 Mark, violet and green	20.00
25.		125 Franken = 100 Mark	37.50
26.	28.11.1914– 11.12.1918 (issued 1919)	50 Centimes, lilac and violet background	2.00
27.		1 Franc, blue background	2.50
28.		2 Francs, rose and green background	4.00
29.		5 Francs, brown violet and green	6.50
30.		25 Francs, violet and green	17.50
31.		125 Francs	30.00
32.		500 Francs	RR
33.	(1919)	10 Francs. Woman with Mercury staff at left, woman with hammer and tongs at right (specimen note, not issued)	R

| 34. | (1923) | 10 Francs, blue. Peasant woman at left, worker at right. Grand Duchess Charlotte at left on reverse | 15.00 |

150 × 78

35.	28.11.1914– 11.12.1918 (issued 1926)	20 Francs, violet and green. Grand Duchess Charlotte with buildings at left and right on reverse	20.00
36.	(1927)	100 Francs. Grand Duchess Charlotte at left. Twelve coats-of-arms on reverse	25.00
37.	1.10.1929	20 Francs, blue. Grapes. Peasant plowing on reverse	3.00
38.	1.10.1932	50 Francs, green blue. Grand Duchess Charlotte at right. Palace in Luxembourg on reverse	4.50
39.	(1934)	100 Francs, green reverse. Grand Duchess Charlotte at left. Seated woman with globe and anvil on reverse	5.00
40.	1. 9.1939 (issued 1940)	1,000 Francs, dark brown and green. Arms in middle	R
41.	20. 4.1940	10 Frang. Man's head at left	RR
42.	1943	20 Frang. Grand Duchess Charlotte. Peasant with sickle and sheaf at left on reverse	2.50
43.	(1944)	5 Francs, olive green. Grand Duchess Charlotte in middle. Printed by American Bank Note Company	2.00
44.		10 Francs, violet. Type of #43	2.50
45.		50 Frang, dark green. Grand Duchess Charlotte. Vianden castle on reverse. Text overprinted with guilloche ornament	7.50

#47
184 × 108

46.		50 Frang, dark green. Type of #45 but no text at bottom of reverse and no guilloche	2.00
47.		100 Francs, blue. Reverse brown. Type of #39	4.00
48.	(1954)	10 Francs, green. Grand Duchess Charlotte at right. Vianden castle on reverse	1.25
49.	(1955)	20 Francs, blue. Grand Duchess Charlotte at right. View of Mosel river and village of Ehnen	1.50
50.	15. 6.1956	100 Francs, red brown. Grand Duchess Charlotte at right. Industrial plant on reverse	4.50
51.	6. 2.1961	50 Francs, dark brown. Grand Duchess Charlotte. Landscape on reverse	—
52.	18. 9.1963	100 Francs, red brown. Grand Duchess Charlotte. Foliage on reverse	—
53.	7. 3.1966	20 Francs, blue. Grand Duke Jean	—
54.	20. 3.1967	10 Francs, green. Grand Duke Jean	—
55.	15. 7.1970	100 Francs, red. Grand Duke Jean	—

MALTA

A group of three Mediterranean islands between Sicily and Africa. Under British control from 1800, Malta became an independent republic in 1964.

1 Pound = 20 Shillings
1 Shilling = 12 Pence

Banco Anglo-Maltese

1.	(circulated during the 1920's)	1 Pound	RRR
2.	(circulated during the 1920's)	5 Pounds	RRR

Notes of the Bank of Malta circulated until 1886.

Government of Malta

3.	12. 8.1914	10 Shillings	$17.50
4.	13. 8.1914	5 Shillings	15.00
5.	14. 8.1914	5 Pounds	R
6.		10 Pounds	RR
7.	20. 8.1914	1 Pound	40.00
8.	4. 9.1914	5 Shillings	12.50
9.	14. 9.1914	1 Pound	30.00
10.	20.11.1918	2 Shillings, green on light blue. King George V at right (not issued, see #11)	R

Malta did not have notes of its own from 1919 until 1939. Regular British notes were used in circulation.

120 × 70

11.	20.11.1918 (issued 1939/40)	1 Shilling on 2 shillings, green on light blue. Note #10 with red overprint of new value	12.50
12.	13. 9.1939 (date stamped)	2 Shillings 6 pence (2/6), lilac and blue. King George VI at right	3.75
13.		5 Shillings, green and red. King George VI at right	5.00

14.		10 Shillings, blue, lilac and olive. King George VI at right	7.50
15.		1 Pound. King George VI at right	11.25
16.	(1940)	1 Shilling, violet and lilac. King George VI in middle	2.00
17.		2 Shillings, brown and green. King George VI at right	2.50
18.		2 Shillings 6 Pence (2/6), lilac and blue. King George VI at right	3.75
19.		10 Shillings, blue, lilac and olive. King George VI at right	4.50
20.		1 Pound. King George VI at right	9.00
21.	1949	10 Shillings, green. King George VI at right	3.00

140 × 75

22.		1 Pound, brown. King George VI at right, cross at left	6.50
23.		10 Shillings, green. Queen Elizabeth II at right, cross at left	3.00
24.		1 Pound, brown. Queen Elizabeth II at right, cross at left	5.00
25.		10 Shillings, green, blue and multicolored. Queen Elizabeth II at right, cross in middle	—
26.		1 Pound, brown, lilac and multicolored. Queen Elizabeth II at right, cross in middle	—
27.		5 Pounds, blue and multicolored. Queen Elizabeth II at right, cross in middle	—

Central Bank of Malta

28.	1967	10 Shillings, red and multicolored. Type of #25	—
29.		1 Pound, green and multicolored. Type of #26	—
30.		5 Pounds, brown violet and multicolored. Type of # 27	—

MEMEL

In 1920 Memel separated from Germany and became an autonomous district under the administration of the League of Nations. The district was seized by Lithuania in 1923.

Handelskammer des Memelgebiets (Chamber of Commerce of the District of Memel)

Notes approved by the Interallied Commission

1.	22.2.1922	½ Mark, lilac. Lake on reverse	$.75
2.		1 Mark, brown. Narrow strip of land on reverse	1.00
3.		2 Mark, blue and olive brown. View of Memel in 1630 on reverse	
		a. Paper watermarked with single-line chain	1.25
		b. Paper watermarked with double-line chain	1.25
4.		5 Mark, blue and yellow. View of market place on reverse	
		a. Paper watermarked with single-line chain	1.50
		b. Paper watermarked with double-line chain	1.50
5.		10 Mark, yellow brown and blue. Lighthouse on reverse	
		a. Paper watermarked with single-line chain	1.75
		b. Paper watermarked with double-line chain	1.75
6.		20 Mark, lilac and violet. Peasant house on reverse	
		a. Paper watermarked with single-line chain	2.00
		b. Paper watermarked with double-line chain	2.00

165 × 111

7.		50 Mark, brown on green and violet. Buoy in harbor on reverse	
		a. Paper watermarked with single-line chain	2.50
		b. Paper watermarked with double-line chain	2.50
8.		75 Mark, brown on blue and rose. Old and new sawmills on reverse	3.00
9.		100 Mark, blue and light brown. View of Memel	4.00

MONACO

Annexed by the French in 1793, the ruling Grimaldi family was restored in 1814. Monaco entered into a customs union with France in 1869.

1 Franc = 100 Centimes

1.	16.3.(20.3.)1920	25 Centimes, brown	$1.25
2.		25 Centimes, blue violet	.75
3.		50 Centimes, blue grey	2.00

109 × 70

4.	1 Franc, brown. Thin paper	4.00
5.	1 Franc, blue grey and brown. Thicker paper	2.50

MONTENEGRO

This Balkan country became an independent principality in 1878 under Nicholas (1860–1918) who took the title of king in 1910. During World War I, Montenegro was occupied by Austrian troops and in 1918 it was merged with Serbia in the Kingdom of the Serbs, Croats and Slovenes (Yugoslavia).

1 Perper = 100 Para

(Treasury Notes) ГЛАВНА ДРЖАВНА БЛАГАЈНА

First Issue, dated 1912

1.	1.10.1912	1 Perper, blue	$1.00
2.		2 Perpera, lilac	1.25
3.		5 Perpera, green	1.00
4.		10 Perpera, brown	1.50
5.		50 Perpera, blue on brown	37.50
6.		100 Perpera	RR
7.	25. 7.1914	1 Perper, blue. Note #1 with red overprint of new date	1.25
8.		2 Perpera, lilac. Note #2 with red overprint of new date	1.75

Specimens of notes #1–8 pierced with large holes to cancel them are worth only 20% of the above prices.

Second Issue, dated 1914

Arms in middle on both sides. All notes are 155 × 107 mm. Prices are for notes without stamps.

9.	25. 7.1914	5 Perpera, blue	1.25
10.		10 Perpera, red	1.50

155 × 107

11.	20 Perpera, brown	2.50

12.		50 Perpera, olive	4.00
13.		100 Perpera, light brown	5.00
14.	11. 8.1914	100 Perpera, light brown (probably a trial note only)	RR

Third Issue, dated 1914. Arms in middle of all reverses. Prices are for notes without stamps.

15.	25.7.1914	1 Perper, blue (format 135 × 97 mm)	1.00
16.		2 Perpera, brown (format 135 × 97 mm)	1.25
17.		5 Perpera, red (format 135 × 97 mm)	1.50
18.		10 Perpera, blue. Arms above left (format 160 × 105 mm)	2.00
19.		20 Perpera, brown. Type of #18 (format 160 × 105 mm)	3.75
20.		50 Perpera, red. Two women with cornucopias and man plowing (format 186 × 110 mm)	4.50

186 × 110

21.		100 Perpera, blue. Type of #20 (format 186 × 110 mm)	5.00

Austrian Military Government 1916–18

Notes #9–13 and #15–21 overprinted "K.u.K. Militar-Generalgouvernement in Montenegro, Kreiskommando (and place name)." Stamped in black, red or violet.

M1.	Stamped "Cetinje"	5 Perpera, second issue	1.25
	(place name 11 mm)	10 Perpera, ,, ,,	1.50
M3.		20 Perpera, ,, ,,	2.00
M4.		50 Perpera, ,, ,,	1.50
M5.		100 Perpera, ,, ,,	3.00
M6.		1 Perper, third issue	.75
M7.		2 Perpera, ,, ,,	.75
M8.		5 Perpera, ,, ,,	.75
M9.		10 Perpera, ,, ,,	1.00
M10.		20 Perpera, ,, ,,	1.25
M11.		50 Perpera, ,, ,,	1.50
M12.		100 Perpera, ,, ,,	2.00
M13.	Stamped "Cetinje"	5 Perpera, second issue	1.00
	(place name 16 mm)		

M14.		10 Perpera, ,, ,,	1.25
M15.		20 Perpera, ,, ,,	1.50
M16.		50 Perpera, ,, ,,	1.25
M17.		100 Perpera, ,, ,,	2.50
M18.		1 Perper, third issue	.50
M19.		2 Perpera, ,, ,,	.50
M20.		5 Perpera, ,, ,,	.50
M21.		10 Perpera, ,, ,,	.75
M22.		20 Perpera, ,, ,,	1.00
M23.		50 Perpera, ,, ,,	1.25
M24.		100 Perpera, ,, ,,	1.75
M25.	Stamped "Ipek"	5 Perpera, second issue	1.50
M26.		10 Perpera, ,, ,,	2.00
M27.		20 Perpera, ,, ,,	2.50
M28.		50 Perpera, ,, ,,	3.00
M29.		100 Perpera, ,, ,,	6.50
M30.		1 Perper, third issue	1.00
M31.		2 Perpera, ,, ,,	1.00
M32.		5 Perpera, ,, ,,	1.00
M33.		10 Perpera, ,, ,,	1.25
M34.		20 Perpera, ,, ,,	1.75
M35.		50 Perpera, ,, ,,	2.00
M36.		100 Perpera, ,, ,,	2.50
M37.	Stamped "Kolasin"	5 Perpera, second issue	1.75
M38.		10 Perpera, ,, ,,	2.50
M39.		20 Perpera, ,, ,,	3.00
M40.		50 Perpera, ,, ,,	4.00
M41.		100 Perpera, ,, ,,	10.00
M42.		1 Perper, third issue	.75
M43.		2 Perpera, ,, ,,	.75
M44.		5 Perpera, ,, ,,	.75
M45.		10 Perpera, ,, ,,	1.00
M46.		20 Perpera, ,, ,,	1.25
M47.		50 Perpera, ,, ,,	1.50
M48.		100 Perpera, ,, ,,	2.00
M49.	Stamped "Nicsic"	5 Perpera, second issue	1.75
M50.	(place name 11mm)	10 Perpera, ,, ,,	2.50
M51.		20 Perpera, ,, ,,	3.00
M52.		50 Perpera, ,, ,,	4.00
M53.		100 Perpera, ,, ,,	10.00
M54.		1 Perper, third issue	1.00
M55.		2 Perpera, ,, ,,	1.25
M56.		5 Perpera, ,, ,,	1.25
M57.		10 Perpera, ,, ,,	1.50
M58.		20 Perpera, ,, ,,	1.75
M59.		50 Perpera, ,, ,,	2.50
M60.		100 Perpera, ,, ,,	2.50
M61.	Stamped "Nicsic"	5 Perpera, second issue	1.25
M62.	(place name 14 mm)	10 Perpera, ,, ,,	1.50
M63.		20 Perpera, ,, ,,	2.00

M64.		50 Perpera, ,, ,,		2.50
M65.		100 Perpera, ,, ,,		6.50
M66.		1 Perper, third issue		.75
M67.		2 Perpera, ,, ,,		1.00
M68.		5 Perpera, ,, ,,		1.00
M69.		10 Perpera, ,, ,,		1.25
M70.		20 Perpera, ,, ,,		1.25
M71.		50 Perpera, ,, ,,		1.50
M72.		100 Perpera, ,, ,,		2.00
M73.	Stamped "Pljevlje"	5 Perpera, second issue		1.50
M74.		10 Perpera, ,, ,,		2.00
M75.		20 Perpera, ,, ,,		2.50
M76.		50 Perpera, ,, ,,		3.00
M77.		100 Perpera, ,, ,,		9.00
M78.		1 Perper, third issue		.75
M79.		2 Perpera, ,, ,,		.75
M80.		5 Perpera, ,, ,,		.75
M81.		10 Perpera, ,, ,,		1.00
M82.		20 Perpera, ,, ,,		1.25
M83.		50 Perpera, ,, ,,		1.50
M84.		100 Perpera, ,, ,,		2.00
M85.	Stamped "Podgorica"	5 Perpera, second issue		1.75
M86.	(small letters, 13 mm)	10 Perpera, ,, ,,		2.25
M87.		20 Perpera, ,, ,,		3.00
M88.		50 Perpera, ,, ,,		4.00
M89.		100 Perpera, ,, ,,		10.00
M90.		1 Perper, third issue		1.00
M91.		2 Perpera, ,, ,,		1.25
M92.		5 Perpera, ,, ,,		1.50
M93.		10 Perpera, ,, ,,		1.50
M94.		20 Perpera, ,, ,,		2.00
M95.		50 Perpera, ,, ,,		2.50
M96.		100 Perpera, ,, ,,		4.00
M97.	Stamped "PODGORICA"	5 Perpera, second issue		2.00
M98.	(capital letters, 13 mm)	10 Perpera, ,, ,,		2.50
M99.		20 Perpera, ,, ,,		4.00
M100.		50 Perpera, ,, ,,		5.00
M101.		100 Perpera, ,, ,,		11.50
M102.		1 Perper, third issue		2.00
M103.		2 Perpera, ,, ,,		2.50
M104.		5 Perpera, ,, ,,		4.00
M105.		10 Perpera, ,, ,,		5.00
M106.		20 Perpera, ,, ,,		7.50
M107.		50 Perpera, ,, ,,		9.00
M108.		100 Perpera, ,, ,,		10.00
M109.	Stamped "PODGORICA"	5 Perpera, second issue		1.25
M110.	(capital letters, 17 mm)	10 Perpera, ,, ,,		1.50
M111.		20 Perpera, ,, ,,		2.00
M112.		50 Perpera, ,, ,,		1.50
M113.		100 Perpera, ,, ,,		3.00

M114.		1 Perper, third issue	.75
M115.		2 Perpera, ,, ,,	.75
M116.		5 Perpera, ,, ,,	.75
M117.		10 Perpera, ,, ,,	1.00
M118.		20 Perpera, ,, ,,	1.25
M119.		50 Perpera, ,, ,,	1.50
M120.		100 Perpera, ,, ,,	2.00
M121.	Stamped "Stari Bar"	5 Perpera, second issue	1.75
M122.	(imprint 11 mm wide)	10 Perpera, ,, ,,	2.25
M123.		20 Perpera, ,, ,,	3.00
M124.		50 Perpera, ,, ,,	4.00
M125.		100 Perpera, ,, ,,	10.00
M126.		1 Perper, third issue	2.50
M127.		2 Perpera, ,, ,,	4.00
M128.		5 Perpera, ,, ,,	5.00
M129.		10 Perpera, ,, ,,	6.50
M130.		20 Perpera, ,, ,,	7.50
M131.		50 Perpera, ,, ,,	9.00
M132.		100 Perpera, ,, ,,	10.00
M133.	Stamped "STARI BAR"	5 Perpera, second issue	1.75
M134.	(imprint 16 mm wide)	10 Perpera, ,, ,,	2.00
M135.		20 Perpera, ,, ,,	2.00
M136.		50 Perpera, ,, ,,	4.00
M137.		100 Perpera, ,, ,,	10.00
M138.		1 Perper, third issue	.75
M139.		2 Perpera, ,, ,,	.75
M140.		5 Perpera, ,, ,,	.75
M141.		10 Perpera, ,, ,,	1.00
M142.		20 Perpera, ,, ,,	1.25
M143.		50 Perpera, ,, ,,	1.50
M144.		100 Perpera, ,, ,,	2.00
M145.	Stamped "Belgrad"	1 Perper, third issue	R
M146.	Stamped "Steuer-u. Zollamt Kolasin"	10 Perpera, ,, ,,	R
M147.	Stamped "Cetinje"	1 Perper, first issue	R

> Specimens of overprinted notes have been observed with a narrow stamp of the place name on one side, a wide stamp of the place name on the other side.

Austrian Military Government 1916–18

Newly printed notes

M148.	1. 6.1917	10 Perpera = 5 Munzperper = 5 Kronen, blue and brown	2.00
M149.	5. 7.1917	1 Perper = 50 Munzpara = 50 Heller, blue green on orange	1.00
M150.		2 Perpera = 1 Munzperper = 1 Krone, violet on green	1.50

ANWEISUNG   059,539

FÜNF PERPER

in jenen Staats-kassenscheinen der Emission vom 25. Juli 1914 a. St. oder
vom 10. Mai 1915 a. St. oder vom 1. Dezember 1915 a. St., die in den
öffentlichen Kassen der

K. u. K. MILITÄRVERWALTUNG IN MONTENEGRO

erliegen. Nach dem in § 4 der Verordnung des Armeeoberkommandanten
vom 16. Juni 1916, Nr. 8 V. Bl. festgesetzten Wertverhältnisse beträgt der
Wert dieser Anweisung

ZWEI MÜNZPERPER FÜNFZIG PARA IN MÜNZEN

oder

ZWEI KRONEN FÜNFZIG HELLER

136 × 98

M151.		5	Perpera = 2 Munzperper 50 Para = 2 Kronen 50 Heller, lilac on green	1.75
M152.	20. 1.1917	20	Perpera = 10 Munzperper = 10 Kronen, red brown on green	3.00
M153.		50	Perpera = 25 Munzperper = 25 Kronen, lilac on green	5.00
M154.		100	Perpera = 50 Munzperper = 50 Kronen, blue on olive	10.00

During World War II Italian overprinted notes of Yugoslavia with "Verificato" were circulated in Montenegro.
(See Yugoslavia R10–R15.)

NETHERLANDS (Nederland)

The Kingdom of the Netherlands including Belgium, was established in 1815 under King William I. Belgium seceded in 1830. The Dutch monarchs have been William II, 1840–49; William III, 1849–90; Wilhelmina, 1890–1948 and Juliana, 1948– .

1 Gulden = 100 Cents

The dates shown in parenthesis are examples taken from notes actually observed.

Muntbiljets (State Notes)

1.	dates to 1914	10 Gulden (1.9.1888; 15.1.1902)	$30.00
2.		50 Gulden	R
3.		100 Gulden	RR

Zilverbons (Silver Certificates)

104 × 68

4.	7. 8.1914	1 Gulden, brown. Numeral "1" in middle	6.50
5.		2½ Gulden, blue on green. Numerals "2,50" in middle	10.00
6.		5 Gulden, green	12.50
7.	30. 3.1915	2½ Gulden, blue. Numerals "2,50" in middle and the four corners	10.00
8.	31. 3.1916	2½ Gulden, blue. Type of #7	10.00
9.	1. 5.1916	1 Gulden, brown. Numeral "1" in middle and the four corners	3.50
10.	1. 8.1917	2½ Gulden, blue. Type of #7	5.00
11.	1.11.1917	1 Gulden, brown. Type of #9	3.00
12.	1. 7.1918	2½ Gulden, blue on grey. Numerals at left middle and right top and bottom	10.00
13.	1.10.1918	1 Gulden, brown. Type of #9	2.50
14.		2½ Gulden, blue on grey. Type of #12	6.50
15.	1. 2.1920	1 Gulden, brown on light green. Woman's head in relief	2.50
16.	1.10.1920	2½ Gulden, blue on grey. Type of #12	5.00

17.　　1. 5.1922　　2½ Gulden, blue on grey. Type of #12　　　　5.00

Note dated 1.10.1922 is a counterfeit.

130 × 73

18.　　1.12.1922　　2½ Gulden, blue on grey. Type of #12　　　3.50
19.　　1.10.1923　　2½ Gulden, blue on grey. Type of #12　　　3.50
20.　　1.10.1927　　2½ Gulden, blue on grey. Type of #12　　　3.50

Nederlandsche Bank (Netherlands Bank)

Notes to 1945

21.　　Type of 1860–90　　25 Gulden, orange. Arms and lion above.
　　　　　　　　　　　　　　　　Blank reverse (27.9.1904; 2.10.1911;
　　　　　　　　　　　　　　　　13.2.1918; 13.9.1918; 15.6.1919)　　20.00
22.　　　　　　　　　　　　　　40 Gulden, green. As #21 (6.6.1910;
　　　　　　　　　　　　　　　　11.7.1921; 13.9.1921)　　　　　　　25.00

213 × 104

23.　　　　　　　　　　　　　　60 Gulden, lilac-brown. As #21 (11.8.1910;
　　　　　　　　　　　　　　　　1.3.1912;　　11.6.1918;　　29.11.1921;
　　　　　　　　　　　　　　　　1.9.1922)　　　　　　　　　　　　30.00
24.　　　　　　　　　　　　　100 Gulden, black. Blue reverse, helmeted
　　　　　　　　　　　　　　　　woman's　head　above　(1.3.1911;
　　　　　　　　　　　　　　　　2.1.1920; 13.10.1921)　　　　　　　37.50
25.　　　　　　　　　　　　　200 Gulden, black. Light brown reverse,
　　　　　　　　　　　　　　　　helmeted　woman's　head　above
　　　　　　　　　　　　　　　　(18.10.1910; 2.7.1921)　　　　　　　50.00

26.		300 Gulden, black. Green reverse, helmeted woman's head above (5.2.1909; 3.1.1921)	50.00
27.		1,000 Gulden, black on blue. Red reverse, helmeted woman's head above (3.10.1910; 22.5.1916)	R
28.	Type of 1904	10 Gulden. Blue reverse (29.7.1921)	20.00
29.	Type of 1904, modified 1922	10 Gulden	15.00
30.	Type of 1914	10 Gulden "Hulpbiljet," blue grey. Work and Welfare (7.10.1911; 23.10.1915; 16.5.1923)	20.00
31.		25 Gulden "Hulpbiljet"	25.00
32.		40 Gulden "Hulpbiljet"	30.00
33.		60 Gulden "Hulpbiljet"	37.50
34.		100 Gulden "Hulpbiljet"	50.00
35.		1,000 Gulden, black on blue. As #27 but reverse not printed (1.8.1914)	R
36.	Type of 1921	25 Gulden, red. William of Orange above, Mercury at left, sailor at right. Bank building on reverse. Handwritten signature	
		a. "Amsterdam" in date 17 mm wide, thick letters before control numbers (30.9.1921)	12.50
		b. "Amsterdam" in date 19 mm wide, double-lined letters before control numbers (15.8.1921)	15.00
37.	Type of 1921, dates from 15.7.1929	25 Gulden, red. As #36 but no picture on reverse and signature printed (19.7.1929; 18.2.1930)	7.50
38.	Type of 1921, dates from 5.7.1927	25 Gulden, blue. As #37, handwritten signature (19.1.1928)	10.00

173 × 99

39.		40 Gulden, green. Prince Maurits above	15.00
40.		60 Gulden. Prince Frederik-Hendrik above	20.00

41.	Type of 1921, dates from 23.1.1922	100	Gulden, blue. Seated woman at left	
			a. Letters and control numbers 4 mm wide. No serial letters in background on reverse (4.2.1922)	12.50
			b. Letters and control numbers 4 mm wide. Serial letters in background on reverse. Text reads "Hijdie biljetten . . ." (15.9.1924)	10.00
			c. As #41b but reverse text reads "Het namaken . . ." (12.3.1926)	8.50
			d. Letters and control numbers 3 mm wide, otherwise as #41c (11.2.1927; 4.12.1928)	7.50
42.	Type of 1921, dates from 1.12.1922	200	Gulden, red brown. Seated woman at left (8.4.1926)	25.00
43.	Type of 1921, dates from 2.12.1922	300	Gulden, green. Seated woman at left (9.4.1926)	30.00
44.	Type of 1921, dates from 23.6.1919	1,000	Gulden, sepia. Seated woman at left (24.6.1919)	37.50
45.	Type of 1921, dates from 1.10.1926	1,000	Gulden, dark green and lilac. Seated woman at left (two control number and signature varieties, 2.10.1926; 24.9.1938)	15.00
46.	Type of 1924, dates from 1.3.1924	10	Gulden, dark blue. Peasant girl of Zeeland in middle	
			a. Signature in black. Letters only in front of control numbers on reverse (29.3.1924; 12.9.1925; 11.4.1927; 16.1.1929; 17.1.1930)	3.50
			b. Signature in blue. Letters in front of control numbers and also on edges at lower left and upper right of reverse (11.9.1930)	6.50
47.	Type of 1926, dates from 2.1.1926	20	Gulden, olive. Sailor at rudder bar (7.4.1926)	5.00

143 × 101

48.	Type of 1929, dates from 18.4.1929	50	Gulden, grey blue. Head with helmet at right (Wisdom) (18.4.1929)	11.50

49.	Type of 1930, dates from 1.10.1930	100 Gulden, brown and olive. Woman's head at left and right (mirror images)	
		a. Date in lower middle of reverse (three signature varieties; 9.3.1931; 2.12.1940; 28.5.1941)	2.00
		b. Date at upper left and lower right of reverse (2.10.1942; 13.1.1944)	2.00
50.	Type of 1939, dates from 1.12.1930	500 Gulden, grey blue and multicolored. Stadholder William III in middle, ship in background (2.12.1930)	20.00
51.	Type of 1931, dates from 1.6.1931	25 Gulden, red. Bank President W.C. Mees at right (two signature varieties 25.2.1938; 9.2.1939; 19.3.1941)	1.50
52.	Type of 1933, dates from 1.6.1933	10 Gulden, dark blue. Head of old man (after Rembrandt) at right (18.11.1933; 11.6.1935; 12.5.1936; 25.11.1938; 22.6.1939)	1.25

153 × 81

53.	Type of 1939, dates from 20.7.1939	20 Gulden, violet. Queen Emma at right, warships of 1700's at left (16.12.1940; 19.3.1941)	1.00
54.	Type of 1939, dates from 19.3.1941	20 Gulden, violet. As #53 but date overprinted with "Amsterdam" above and "19.3.1941" below	RR
55.	Type of 1940, dates from 9.7.1940	10 Gulden, blue and green. Head of young girl (after P. Moreelsen) at right	
		a. Paper watermarked with head of old man (28.10.1940; 18.2.1941)	1.00
		b. Paper watermarked with bunch of grapes (16.7.1941; 4.8.1942)	1.00
56.	Dates from 1.6.1940	10 Gulden, brown and dark green. Queen Emma at right (20.6.1940; 2.1.1941)	1.25
57.	Dates from 20.5.1940	25 Gulden, olive brown. Young girl (after P. Moreelsen) at right. Edge unprinted at left (20.5.1940)	1.50

58.	Dates from 4.10.1943	25 Gulden, red brown. As #57 but frame bordered with "DNB" (5.10.1943; 6.4.1944)	1.00
59.	Type of 1941, dates from 2.1.1941	50 Gulden, dark brown and multicolored. Head of woman (after J. Steen), at left and right	
		a. "Amsterdam" in date is 17 mm wide (6.2.1941)	1.75
		b. "Amsterdam" in date is 16 mm wide (17.3.1941)	1.75
60.	Type of 1943, dates from 4.1.1943	10 Gulden, blue and multicolored. Man's head with hat (after Rembrandt) at right (29.1.1943; 9.11.1943; 3.2.1944)	.75

Zilverbons (Silver Certificates)

61.	1.10.1938	1 Gulden, brown. Type of #15	.25
62.		2½ Gulden, blue. Type of #12	.50
63.	16.10.1944	5 Gulden, green (two control number varieties)	1.25

Muntbiljets (State Notes)

64.	4. 2.1943	1 Gulden, red. Left-facing portrait of Queen Wilhelmina in middle. Printed by American Bank Note Company	.85
65.		2½ Gulden, green. Type of #64	1.25
66.		10 Gulden, blue. Type of #64	6.50
67.		25 Gulden, olive. Type of #64	25.00

151 × 73

68.		50 Gulden, brown. Type of #64	37.50
69.		100 Gulden, black. Type of #64	R
70.	18. 5.1945	1 Gulden, brown on light green. Right-facing portrait of Queen Wilhelmina in middle	1.50
71.		2½ Gulden, blue on lilac. Type of #70 (two control number varieties)	1.50
72.	8. 8.1949	1 Gulden, brown on light green. Queen Juliana at left	—
73.		2½ Gulden, blue. Queen Juliana at left	—

Nederlandsche Bank (Netherlands Bank)

Notes after 1945

74.	7. 5.1945	10 Gulden, blue and brown violet. Arms and lion in middle	15.00
75.		10 Gulden, blue. King William I at right. Coal mining scene on reverse	
		a. 1788 date at right of portrait (counterfeit)	R
		b. 1772 date at right of portrait	15.00
76.		20 Gulden, brown. King William III at right	20.00
77.		25 Gulden, brown. Young girl	25.00
78.		50 Gulden, brown. King William II as a youth	37.50
79.		100 Gulden, brown	R
80.		1,000 Gulden, blue. William the Silent at right	RRR

155 × 87

81.	19. 3.1947	25 Gulden, red and green. Young girl's head with flowers at right	15.00
82.	9. 7.1947	100 Gulden, brown. Woman's head at right	37.50
83.	4. 3.1949	10 Gulden, blue. Obverse as #75b. Landscape with windmill on reverse	6.50
84.	1. 7.1949	25 Gulden, orange. King Solomon at right	12.50
85.	2. 2.1953	100 Gulden, dark brown. Erasmus at right	—
86.	23. 3.1953	10 Gulden, blue, brown and green, Hugo de Groot at right	—
87.	10. 4.1955	25 Gulden, red and orange. Christian Huygens at right	—
88.	8.11.1955	20 Gulden, green and lilac. Farm house at right	15.00
89.	15. 7.1956	1,000 Gulden, brown and green. Rembrandt at right	—
90.	26. 4.1966	5 Gulden, green. Vondel at right	—
91.	25. 4.1968	10 Gulden, blue and violet. Frans Hals at right	—

Ministerie van Oorlog (Military money, Ministry of War)

Notes issued for use of Dutch troops in Germany

M1.	1 Gulden, brown	7.50
M2.	5 Gulden, green	15.00
M3.	25 Gulden, violet	30.00

A 10 gulden note was probably produced as well.

NORWAY (Norge)

The kingdom was united with Denmark from 1380 until 1814, when it was joined to Sweden following the Napoleonic Wars. This union was dissolved in 1905 and Norway became independent.

1 Krone = 100 Ore

Norges Bank (Bank of Norway)

Type I: Bust of bearded man at left, dates of issue handwritten

1.	1877–99	5 Kroner, blue	$8.50
2.		10 Kroner, yellow	12.50
3.		50 Kroner, green	37.50
4.		100 Kroner, rose	45.00
5.		500 Kroner, brown	R
6.		1,000 Kroner, orange brown	RR

Type II: Bust of man without beard (President Christie) at left, dates printed, "Hovedkasserer" below signature

7.	1901–25	5 Kroner, dark green	5.00
8.		10 Kroner, violet	7.50
9.		50 Kroner, blue green	15.00
10.		100 Kroner, violet	30.00

217 × 127

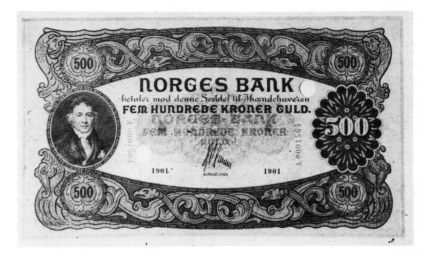

11.	500 Kroner, blue green	R
12.	1,000 Kroner, violet	RR

1 and 2 Kroner notes

13.	1917	1 Krone, green	2.00
14.	1918	2 Kroner, rose	3.00
15.	1922	2 Kroner, rose	7.50
16.	1940–50	1 Krone, brown on green	.75
17.		2 Kroner, rose	1.00

Also see #24 and 25.

Type II: As for notes #7–12 but "Hovedkasserer" printed wider

18.	1926–45	5 Kroner, dark green	.75
19.		10 Kroner, violet	.75
20.		50 Kroner, blue green	3.00

149 × 125

21.	100 Kroner, violet	5.00
22.	500 Kroner, blue green	7.50
23.	1,000 Kroner, violet	15.00

Type III: English printing, war issue

24.	1942	1 Krone, dark brown on green	3.50
25.		2 Kroner, rose	5.00
26.		5 Kroner, violet on green, red and brown	8.50
27.		10 Kroner, red on blue green and green	15.00

145 × 127

28.	50	Kroner, brown and multicolored	30.00
29.	100	Kroner, blue and multicolored	45.00
30.	500	Kroner, green and multicolored (not issued)	RRR
31.	1,000	Kroner, brown and multicolored (not issued)	RRR

Issues after 1945 (Also see #16 and #17)

125 × 70

32.	1945–54	5 Kroner, blue. Arms at left	2.50
33.	dates from 1955	5 Kroner, blue. Fridtjof Nansen at left	—
34.	1945–53	10 Kroner, yellow brown. Arms at left	7.50
35.	dates from 1954	10 Kroner, yellow brown. Statesman Christian Michelsen at left	—
36.	1945–50	50 Kroner, green. Arms at left	10.00
37.	1951–65	50 Kroner, green. Bjornstjerne Bjornson at left (format 142 × 128 mm)	7.50

38.	dates from 1966	50	Kroner, green. Type of #37 but different format (145 × 73 mm)	—
39.	1945–59	100	Kroner, red. Arms at left	20.00
40.	1950–62	100	Kroner, red. Henrik Wergeland at left (format 146 × 128 mm)	17.50
41.	dates from 1963	100	Kroner, red-violet. Type of #40 but different format (145 × 78 mm)	—
42.	1945–49	500	Kroner, dark green. Niels Henrik Abel at left	—
43.	1945–47	1,000	Kroner, light brown. Type of #23	R
44.	dates from 1948	1,000	Kroner, brown. Henrik Ibsen at left	—

Military High Command, 1940

Notes issued by Major General Steffens with approval of the branch office of the Bank of Norway in Voss.

M1.	14.4.1940	5	Kroner	37.50
M2.		10	Kroner	R
M3.		50	Kroner	RR
M4.		100	Kroner	RR

Bear Island

Privately issued notes of the Bjornoen coal company in the values of 10 and 50 ore, 1, 10 and 20 kroner circulated on this island in the Barents Sea along with regular Norwegian money. All of these notes are R–RRR

POLAND (Polska)

After the various partitions of Poland during the 18th and 19th centuries, the remaining territory came under Russian rule. In 1918, Poland re-emerged as an independent republic. Following the Russo-German treaty of 1939, the country was again partitioned but was restored in 1945. A communist regime has governed since 1947.

1 Mark = 100 Fenigow
1 Zloty = 100 Groszy (since 1923)

Military Government of Warsaw (Zarzad General Gubernatorstwa Warszawkiego)

Notes issued during German occupation in World War I

Polska Krajowa Kasa Pozyczkowa (Polish National Land Loan Office)

Text reads "Zarzad jeneral-gubernatorstwa . . ."

1.	9.12.(Grudnia) 1916	½ Mark. Blue and olive reverse	$.25
2.		1 Mark. Blue and red reverse	.25
3.		2 Mark. Orange and green reverse	.75
4.		20 Mark. Violet and light brown reverse	1.00

158 × 105

5.		50 Mark. Green and rose reverse	1.25
6.		100 Mark, blue and red	2.00

Text reads "Zarzad General-Gubernatorstwa"

7.	9.12.(Grudnia) 1916	½ Mark. Rev. Blue and olive. Type of #1	1.00
8.		1 Mark. Rev. Blue and red. Type of #2	.25
9.		2 Mark. Rev. Orange and green. Type of #3	.25

10.		5 Mark. Grey blue and yellow reverse. Text at left reads ". . . biletow Polskiej Krajowej . . ."	.50
11.		5 Mark. Grey blue and yellow reverse. As #10 but text reads ". . . Biletow Kasy Pozyczkowej . . ."	1.25
12.		10 Mark. Lilac brown and green reverse. Text at left reads ". . . biletow Polskiej Krajowej . . ."	1.25
13.		10 Mark. Lilac brown and green reverse. As #12 but text reads ". . . Biletow Kasy Pozyczkowej . . ."	8.50
14.		20 Mark. Violet and light brown reverse. Type of #4	2.50
15.		100 Mark, blue and red	1.50
16.		1,000 Mark, brown and red	4.00

Republic of Poland

Polska Krajowa Kasa Pozyczkowa (Polish National Land Loan Office)

17.	15. 1.(Stycznia) 1919	500 Mark, green and red. Polish eagle at left	4.00

185 × 110

18.	15. 2.(Lutego) 1919	100 Mark, green and grey violet. Kosciuszko at left	
		a. Brownish paper watermarked with honeycomb. Engraver's name at lower left and right	.50
		b. As #18a but without engraver's name	2.00
		c. Indistinct watermark of Polish eagle in white paper	2.50

19.	17. 5.(Maja) 1919	1 Mark, grey violet to violet (three control number varieties)	.25
20.		5 Mark, green. Rev. B. Glowacki at right	
		a. Engraver's name at lower left and right of reverse	.25
		b. As #20a but without engraver's name (two control number varieties)	.35
21.		20 Mark, brown. Kosciuszko in middle of reverse (two control number varieties)	.75
22.		1,000 Mark, green and brown. Head of Kosciuszko at left	
		a. Brownish paper watermarked with honeycomb. Engraver's name at lower left and right on reverse (two control number varieties)	1.00
		b. As #22a but without engraver's name	1.25
		c. Indistinct watermark of Polish eagle in white paper. Engraver's name at lower left and right on reverse	1.00
		d. As #22c but without engraver's name (two control number varieties)	.75
23.	23. 8.(Sierpna) 1919	1 Mark, red and brown. Woman's head at right (two control number varieties)	.25
		Error: Obverse without red plate	R
24.		5 Mark, green and brown. Man's head at right (two control number varieties)	.25
25.		10 Mark, blue and brown. Man's head at right (two control number varieties)	.25
26.		20 Mark, red and brown. Woman's head at right (two control number varieties)	.25
27.		100 Mark, blue and brown. Man's head at right (two control number varieties)	.25
28.		500 Mark, green and brown. Woman's head at right (two control number varieties)	.25

29.		1,000 Mark, violet and brown. Man's head at right (five control number varieties)	.25
30.	7. 2.(Lutego) 1920	½ Mark, green and brown. Man's head at right	.25
31.		5,000 Mark, blue and brown. Woman's head at left, man's head at right (two control number varieties)	.25
32.	11. 3.(Marca) 1922	10,000 Mark, grey green and yellow. Woman's head at left and right	.25
33.	10.10.(Pazdziernika) 1922	50,000 Mark, brown on olive	.25
34.	25. 4.(Kwietnia) 1923	250,000 Mark, grey brown (two control number varieties)	.40
35.	30. 8.(Sierpnia) 1923	100,000 Mark, Brown	.50
36.		500,000 Mark, grey (five control number varieties)	.75

189 × 94

37.		1,000,000 Mark, olive brown. City view at left (two control number varieties)	1.00
38.	20.11.(Listopada) 1923	5,000,000 Mark, brown and rose	2.00
39.		10,000,000 Mark, green and blue. City view at left (two towers)	3.00
40.		50,000,000 Mark. Blue background	30.00
41.		100,000,000 Mark. Red background	37.50

Ministerstwo Skarbu (Finance Ministry)

42.	28. 4.(Kwietnia) 1924	1 Groz. Red overprint on halved note #36	
		a. Left half	.75
		b. Right half	.75
43.		5 Groszy. Red overprint on halved note #39	
		a. Left half	1.25
		b. Right half	1.25

44.		10 Groszy, blue. Buildings with columns	.75
45.		20 Groszy, brown. Copernicus Memorial	.75
46.		50 Groszy, red. Equestrian statue (J. Poniatowski)	1.00
47.	1. 5.(Maja) 1925	2 Zloty, "Bilet Zdawkowy," grey violet on grey green	4.00
		Error: Reverse inverted	R

128 × 83

48.		5 Zloty, "Bilet Zdawkowy," green and brown	8.50
49.	25.10.(Pazdziernika) 1926	5 Zloty, "Bilet Panstwowy," dark olive. Woman's head in middle	7.50
50.	1.10.(Pazdziernika) 1938	2 Zloty, "Bilet Panstwowy," grey and yellow brown. Man's head with crown at right	2.00

Bank Polski (Bank of Poland)

51.	28. 2.(Lutego) 1919 (issued 1924)	1 Zloty, violet. Kosciuszko at left	1.25
52.		2 Zloty, light blue. Kosciuszko at left	5.00
53.		5 Zloty, brown. Prince Poniatowski at right	4.00
54.		10 Zloty, violet and brown. Kosciuszko at left	5.00
55.		20 Zloty, multicolored. Kosciuszko at left	6.50
56.		50 Zloty, brown lilac and violet. Kosciuszko at left	20.00
57.		100 Zloty, blue and brown. Kosciuzko at left	12.50
58.		500 Zloty, violet and green. Kosciuszko at left	15.00

182 × 110

59.		1,000	Zloty, brown. Kosciuszko at left (not issued)	RR
			Pattern	25.00
60.		5,000	Zloty, green. Kosciuszko at left (pattern note)	37.50
61.	15. 7.(Lipka) 1924	5	Zloty, brown. Type of #53	3.00
62.		10	Zloty, violet. Type of #54	
			a. White paper	4.50
			b. Grey paper	4.50
63.		20	Zloty, multicolored. Type of #55	
			a. White paper	6.50
			b. Grey paper	6.50
64.	28. 8.(Sierpnia) 1925	50	Zloty, green, brown and blue. ·Peasant girl at left, Mercury at right	15.00
65.	1. 3.(Marca) 1926	20	Zloty, blue and olive. Type of #64	10.00
66.	20. 7.(Lipca) 1926	10	Zloty, olive brown and blue. Female allegorical figures at left and right	5.00
67.	2. 1.(Stycznia) 1928	10	Zloty. Youth's head at right (not issued)	R
68.		20	Zloty (not issued)	RR
69.	20. 7.(Lipca) 1929	10	Zloty, olive brown and blue. Type of #66	1.25
70.	1. 9.(Wrzesnia) 1929	20	Zloty, blue and olive. Type of #65	30.00
71.		50	Zloty, green, brown and olive. Type of #64	1.25
72.	2. 1.(Stycznia) 1930	5	Zloty, grey blue. Woman's head at right	1.00
73.	20. 6.(Czerwca) 1931	20	Zloty, blue and brown. Emilie Plater at right	1.00
74.	2. 6.(Czerwca) 1932	100	Zloty, brown. Prince J. Poniatowski	.75

75.	9. 9.(Listopada) 1934	100 Zloty, brown. Type of #74	.75
76.	26. 2.(Lutego) 1936	2 Zloty, grey olive. Girl in Dabrowki costume	1.00
77.	11. 9.(Listopada) 1936	20 Zloty, blue. Emilie Plater at right	.75
78.		50 Zloty. Man's head at right (not issued)	R
		Reverse only printed	15.00
79.	15. 8.(Sierpnia) 1939	1 Zloty, lilac (not issued)	R
80.		2 Zloty, green (not issued)	R
81.		5 Zloty, blue. Girl in costume cap at right (not issued)	R
82.		10 Zloty, red orange. Young woman with scarf (not issued)	R
83.		20 Zloty, blue. Old woman with scarf at right (not issued)	R

162 × 80

84.		50 Zloty, green. Man in costume at right (not issued)	R
85.		100 Zloty, brown. Man with moustache at right (not issued)	R
86.		500 Zloty, violet. Sailor at right (not issued)	R
87.	20. 8.(Sierpnia) 1939	20 Zloty, blue. Young woman in costume at right (not issued)	R
88.		50 Zloty, green. Young peasant woman at right (not issued)	R

Generalgouvernement (German Military Government)

Older notes overprinted during World War II "Generalgouvernement fur die besetzten polnischen Gebiete"

89.	2. 6.1932 (1939)	100 Zloty. Note #74 with red brown overprint	11.50
90.	9. 9.1934	100 Zloty. Note #75 with red brown overprint	10.00

Overprints have been frequently counterfeited.

Bank Emisyjny w Polsce (Emission Bank of Poland)

Notes issued during the German occupation

91.	1. 3.(Marca) 1940	1 Zloty, grey blue	.75
92.		2 Zloty, brown. Woman's head with scarf	.75
93.		5 Zloty, green blue. Girl's head at right	5.00

170 × 85

| 94. | | 10 Zloty, brown. Female allegorical figures at left and right | .75 |
| 95. | | 20 Zloty, grey blue. Emilie Plater at right | .75 |

179 × 100

| 96. | | 50 Zloty, green. Head of young man at right | 3.50 |

97.		100 Zloty, brown. Aged Warsaw aristocrat at left	1.00
98.		500 Zloty, grey blue and olive. Man's head (Gorale) at right	1.50
99.	1. 8.(Sierpnia) 1941	1 Zloty, grey blue. Type of #91 (two control number varieties)	.25
100.		2 Zloty, brown. Type of #92	.35
101.		5 Zloty, green blue. Type of #93	.50
102.		50 Zloty, dark green. Type of #96	.75
103.		100 Zloty, brown and blue	.75

Various notes of the series #91–103 are known stamped with the overprint of the Warsaw resistance fighters of 1944 "A. K. Regula, Pierwszy zold powstanczy, Sierpien, 1944," also "Okreg Warzawski-Dowodztwo zgrup IV" or "Braterstwo Broni Anglii Ameryki Polski Niech Zyje."

Narodowy Bank Polski (National Bank of Poland)

104.	1944	50 Groszy, red	1.00
105.		1 Zloty, dark green	.50
106.		2 Zloty, brown. Text below reads "Obowiazkowym"	.50
107.		2 Zloty, brown. Text below reads "Obowiazkowe"	1.25
108.		5 Zloty, lilac brown on green. Text as #106	1.00
109.		5 Zloty, lilac brown on green. Text as #107	1.00
110.		10 Zloty, blue on green. Text as #106	1.25
111.		10 Zloty, blue on green. Text as #107	1.00
112.		20 Zloty, green on lilac. Text as #106	1.50
113.		20 Zloty, green on lilac. Text as #107 (two control number varieties)	1.25
114.		50 Zloty, blue on lilac. Text as #106	2.00
115.		50 Zloty, blue on lilac. Text as #107	1.75
116.		100 Zloty, red on blue. Text as #106	3.00
117.		100 Zloty, red on blue. Text as #107	2.50

118.		500 Zloty, green black on light brown. Text as #106	6.50
119.		500 Zloty, green black on light brown. Text as #107	8.50
120.	1945	1,000 Zloty, brown	15.00

175 × 93

121.	15. 1.(Stycznia) 1946	500 Zloty, dark blue and green. Man with ship at left, fisherman at right	7.50
122.		1,000 Zloty, brown. Miner at left, worker at right (four control number varieties)	6.50
123.	15. 5.(Maja) 1946	1 Zloty, lilac	.40
124.		2 Zloty, green	.50
125.		5 Zloty, grey blue	.75
126.		10 Zloty, brown on green	1.25
127.		20 Zloty, green on lilac	1.50
128.		50 Zloty, brown and violet. Ship at left and right	3.00
129.		100 Zloty, red. Peasant girl at left, peasant at right	4.50
130.	15. 7.(Lipca) 1947	20 Zloty, green	5.00
131.		100 Zloty, red. Peasant girl in middle	6.50
132.		500 Zloty, blue. Woman with rudder and anchor in middle	7.50
133.		1,000 Zloty, brown on olive. Worker in middle	10.00
134.	1. 7.(Lipca) 1948	2 Zloty, dark green	.75
135.		5 Zloty, red brown	1.00
136.		10 Zloty, brown. Man's head at right	1.50
137.		20 Zloty, blue. Woman's head in scarf at right	—

138.		50 Zloty, green. Sailor's head	—
139.		100 Zloty, red. Man's head at right	—
140.		500 Zloty, dark brown. Miner at right	—
141.	29.10.(Pazdziernika) 1965	1,000 Zloty, multicolored. Copernicus at right	—

PORTUGAL

This small seafaring nation was an independent kingdom from 1140 until 1910. The last kings were Charles I (1889–1908) and Manuel II (1908–10). A revolution in 1910 led to the founding of a republic.

1 Milreis = 1,000 Reis
1 Escudo = 100 Centavos

Banco de Portugal (Bank of Portugal)

Notes in milreis values. The various types of notes are differentiated by their plate numbers ("Ch" for "Chapa" = plate) and various dates.

1.	dates to 1900	500 Reis Prata (silver). "Ch 1"	$10.00
2.	dates to 1905	500 Reis Prata. "Ch 2"	7.50
3.	dates to 1929	500 Reis Prata. "Ch 3." Woman's head on reverse	5.00

120 × 74

4.		500 Reis Prata. "Ch 3." Note #3 with overprint "Republica"	4.00
5.	dates to 1896	1 Milreis Prata. "Ch 1"	12.50
6.	dates to 1902	1 Milreis Prata. "Ch 2"	12.50
7.	dates to 1929	1 Milreis Prata. "Ch 3"	10.00
8.	dates to 1893	2½ Milreis Prata. "Ch 1"	20.00
9.	dates to 1904	2½ Milreis Prata. "Ch 2"	20.00
10.	dates to 1907	2½ Milreis Prata. "Ch 3"	17.50
11.	dates to 1928	2½ Milreis Prata. "Ch 4," Alf. de Albuquerque	12.50
12.	dates to 1890	5 Milreis Prata. "Ch 1"	25.00
13.	dates to 1891	5 Milreis Prata. "Ch 2"	25.00
14.	dates to 1895	5 Milreis Prata. "Ch 3"	25.00
15.	dates to 1901	5 Milreis Prata. "Ch 4"	20.00
16.	dates to 1903	5 Milreis Prata. "Ch 5"	20.00
17.	dates to 1911	5 Milreis Prata. "Ch 6"	17.50
18.	dates to 1916	5 Milreis Prata. "Ch 7"	17.50
19.		10 Milreis Ouro (gold). "Ch 1"	37.50
20.	dates to 1897	10 Milreis Ouro. "Ch 2"	37.50
21.	dates to 1917	10 Milreis Ouro. "Ch 3"	30.00

22.	dates to 1929	10 Milreis Ouro. "Ch 4"	30.00
23.	dates to 1900	20 Milreis Ouro. "Ch 7"	37.50
24.	dates to 1911	20 Milreis Ouro. "Ch 8"	32.50
25.	dates to 1913	20 Milreis Ouro. "Ch 8" (altered plate)	30.00
26.	dates to 1916	20 Milreis Ouro. "Ch 9"	30.00
27.	dates to 1901	50 Milreis Ouro. "Ch 2"	50.00
28.	dates to 1929	50 Milreis Ouro ."Ch 3," Bartholomew Diaz	45.00
29.	dates to 1929	50 Milreis Ouro. "Ch 4." Rev. Lusitania	37.50
30.	dates to 1916	100 Milreis Ouro. "Ch 1"	R
31.	dates to 1926	100 Milreis Ouro. "Ch 2" and "Arrival 8.3.1500"	50.00

Casa da Moeda (State Notes of the Mint)

32.	6. 8.1891	50 Reis, green on lilac	4.00
33.		50 Reis, blue	1.50
34.		100 Reis, grey brown. Type of #32	5.00
35.		100 Reis, brown. Type of #33	2.00
36.		100 Reis, brown. Drapery, man sitting on anvil at left, cupid at right	2.50
		Trial printings in various colors	5.00
37.	6. 8.1891 (crossed out)	5 Centavos Bronze, blue green (probably only a trial printing)	12.50
38.		5 Centavos Bronze, blue (probably only a trial printing)	12.50
39.	15. 8.1917	10 Centavos Bronze, dark brown. Type of #36	2.00
		Trial printings in various colors	3.00
40.		10 Centavos Bronze, dark blue half oval. Columns at left and right. Thin grey paper or thick yellow paper	1.25
		Trial printings in various colors	3.00
41.		10 Centavos Bronze, blue on green. Seated woman at left and right	
		a. Paper watermarked with oval	4.00
		b. Paper watermarked with "Casa da Moeda"	1.00
		c. Unwatermarked paper	1.00
42.		10 Centavos Bronze, brown. Seated figure at left, smokestacks, ships and bridge. Paper white, grey, yellow brown or brown	2.00
43.	5. 4.1918	5 Centavos Bronze, green on grey violet. Thin grey paper or thick yellow paper	1.00
44.		5 Centavos Bronze, red on yellow. Cupid at left, bust at right. Paper white or grey	1.00
45.		5 Centavos Bronze, red on light green	2.00
46.		5 Centavos Bronze, red without background color	2.00

47.		5 Centavos Bronze, dark brown on yellow brown. Paper white and yellow	1.00
48.		5 Centavos Bronze, dark brown without background color	1.50
49.	4. 8.1922	20 Centavos Copper Nickel, dark brown on blue	1.00
50.	15. 8.1917–11. 4.1925	10 Centavos, brown. Woman with torch. Printed by Waterlow	.75

101 × 64

51.	4. 8.1922–11. 4.1925	20 Centavos, brown. Woman's head at left. Printed by Waterlow	1.25

Banco de Portugal (Bank of Portugal)

Notes in escudo values. The various types of notes are differentiated by their plate numbers ("Ch" for "Chapa" = plate). The notes carry various dates and signatures. The dates shown in parentheses are examples taken from notes actually observed.

52.	valid to 5. 2.1930	50 Centavos Prata, violet. "Ch 1," woman with ship in hand at left (5.7.1918; 25.6.1920)	2.00
53.	valid to 30. 1.1929	1 Escudo Prata, red and violet. "Ch 1," seated woman with book and lamp at left (7.9.1917; 29.11.1918; 25.6.1920)	2.50
54.	valid to 24. 6.1929	2 Escudos 50 Centavos Prata, green. "Ch 1," D. Nuno Alvarez Pereira (10.7.1920; 3.2.1922; 17.11.1922)	4.00
55.	valid to 31.12.1933	2 Escudos 50 Centavos Prata, blue. "Ch 2," M. da Silveira in middle (18.11.1925; 18.11.1926)	5.00
56.	valid to 7. 4.1931	5 Escudos Ouro. "Ch 1," Alexander Herculano	15.00
57.	valid to 7. 4.1931	5 Escudos Ouro, violet, brown and green. "Ch 2," Joao das Regras at left (10.7.1920; 14.6.1922; 13.1.1925)	8.75
58.		5 Escudos Ouro. "Ch 3"	15.00

138 × 80

59.	valid to 31.12.1933	5 Escudos Ouro, grey and yellow brown. "Ch 4," D. Alvaro Vaz d'Almada	12.50
60.	valid to 24. 6.1929	10 Escudos Ouro. "Ch 1," Alf. de Albuquerque	20.00

162 × 105

61.	valid to 31.12.1933	10 Escudos Ouro, brown and yellow green. "Ch 2," Marques de Sa da Bandeira (9.8.1920)	20.00
62.	valid to 31.12.1933	10 Escudos Ouro, black on red. "Ch 3," Eca de Queiros (13.1.1925)	12.50
63.	valid to 24. 6.1929	20 Escudos Ouro. "Ch 1"	30.00
64.	valid to 24. 6.1929	20 Escudos Ouro. "Ch 2," J. de Castro	25.00
65.	valid to 7. 4.1931	20 Escudos Ouro. "Ch 3," Jose Estevao Coeho de Magalhaes	25.00
66.	valid to 31. 8.1934	20 Escudos Ouro, red. "Ch 4," Marques de Pombal (13.1.1925)	20.00
67.		20 Escudos Ouro, red brown. "Ch 5," M. de Albuquerque at left (17.9.1929; 13.5.1938)	12.50
68.	still valid	20 Escudos Ouro, green and violet. "Ch 6," D. Antonio Luiz de Menezas at right (26.6.1951; 27.1.1959)	—

69.		20 Escudos Ouro, dark green. "Ch 6A," D. Antonio Luiz de Menezas, altered design (26.7.1960)	—
70.		20 Escudos Ouro, olive and violet. "Ch 7," St. Anthony at right (26.5.1964)	—
71.	valid to 7. 4.1931	50 Escudos Ouro. "Ch 1," Manuel Passos	37.50
72.		50 Escudos Ouro. "Ch 2," Angel of Peace	37.50
73.	valid to 31. 8.1934	50 Escudos Ouro, blue on red and green. "Ch 3," Chr. da Gama (13.1.1925)	30.00
74.		50 Escudos Ouro, violet. "Ch 4," B. Carneiro in middle (17.9.1929)	30.00
75.		50 Escudos Ouro, violet. "Ch 5," Duke of Saldanha at left (18.11.1932; 24.4.1936)	25.00
76.	valid to 31.12.1963	50 Escudos Ouro, brown lilac. "Ch 6." Dark green reverse, Ramalho Ortigao at right (3.3.1938)	20.00
77.	valid to 31.12.1963	50 Escudos Ouro, brown lilac. "Ch 6A." Brown lilac and green reverse, Ramalho Ortigao, altered design (25.11.1941; 28.6.1949)	7.50
78.	still valid	50 Escudos Ouro, blue. "Ch 7," Fontes Pereira de Mello at right (28.4.1953; 24.6.1955)	6.50
79.		50 Escudos Ouro, blue. "Ch 7A," Fontes Pereira de Mello at right, altered design (24.6.1940)	—
80.		50 Escudos Ouro, brown lilac and rose. "Ch 8," Queen Isabella (28.2.1964)	—
81.	valid to 7. 4.1931	100 Escudos Ouro. "Ch 1," Pedro Alvarez Cabral	50.00

208 × 134

82.	valid to 31.12.1930	100 Escudos Ouro, brown. "Ch 2," Diogo do Couto at left (31.8.1920)	50.00

83.		100	Escudos Ouro. "Ch 3"	50.00
84.		100	Escudos Ouro, blue on green and red. "Ch 4," Gomes Freire at left (4.4.1928)	37.50
85.	valid to 1. 1.1959	100	Escudos Ouro, blue green and brown. "Ch 5," Joao Pinto Ribeiro (21.2.1935)	25.00
86.	still valid	100	Escudos Ouro, dark green and lilac. "Ch 6," Pedro Nunes at right (28.10.1947; 24.10.1950; 25.6.1957)	—
87.		100	Escudos Ouro, lilac, green and brown. "Ch 6A," Pedro Nunes at right, altered design (19.12.1961)	—
88.		100	Escudos Ouro, blue. "Ch 7," Camilo Castelo Branco at right (30.11.1965)	—
89.	valid to 17. 9.1929	500	Escudos Ouro. "Ch 1," Joao de Deus	R
90.	valid to 7.12.1925	500	Escudos Ouro. "Ch 2," Vasco da Gama	R
91.		500	Escudos Ouro. "Ch 3," Vasco da Gama	R
92.		500	Escudos Ouro, red violet. "Ch 4," Duke de Palmela at right (4.4.1928)	50.00
93.		500	Escudos Ouro, brown violet. "Ch 5," Jose da Silva Carvalho at left (18.11.1932; 31.8.1934)	50.00
94.	valid to 1. 1.1959	500	Escudos Ouro, red violet. "Ch 6," Don Henrique at right	37.50
95.	still valid	500	Escudos Ouro, brown violet and green. "Ch 7," Damiao de Goes at right (29.9.1942)	—
96.		500	Escudos Ouro, red brown and grey. "Ch 8," D. Joao IV at right (28.11.1944; 11.3.1952)	—
97.	valid to 31. 8.1967	500	Escudos Ouro, olive brown. "Ch 9," D. Francisco d'Almeida at right (27.5.1958)	R
98.	still valid	500	Escudos Ouro, brown and multi-colored. "Ch 10," D. Joao at right (25.1.1966)	—
99.	valid to 20. 2.1926	1,000	Escudos Ouro. "Ch A," Duke de Terceira	RRR
100.	valid to 14.10.1927	1,000	Escudos Ouro. "Ch 1," Luiz de Camoes	RRR
101.	valid to 14. 8.1931	1,000	Escudos Ouro. "Ch 2," A. F. Castilho	RR
102.	valid to 14. 8.1931	1,000	Escudos Ouro, blue. "Ch 3," Oliveira Martins (25.11.1927)	RR
103.		1,000	Escudos Ouro, green. "Ch 4," Marques de Sa da Bandeira at right (17.9.1929)	RR
104.		1,000	Escudos Ouro, dark green. "Ch 5," Conde de Castelo-Melhor at left (18.11.1932)	RR
105.	valid to 1. 1.1959	1,000	Escudos Ouro, green on red brown. "Ch 6," Mestre de Avis in middle (17.6.1938)	RR

164 × 103

106.	still valid	1,000 Escudos Ouro, dark green and blue. "Ch 7," D. Alfonso Henrique at right (29.9.1942) —
107.		1,000 Escudos Ouro, violet. "Ch 8," D. Felipa de Lencastre at right (31.1.1956) —
108.		1,000 Escudos Ouro, blue green and lilac. "Ch 8A," D. Felipa de Lencastre at right, altered design (30.5.1961) —
109.	valid to 31. 8.1967	1,000 Escudos Ouro, green. blue and red brown. "Ch 9," D. Diniz at right (2.4.1965) RR
110.	still valid	1,000 Escudos Ouro, blue. "Ch 10," Maria II at right (19.5.1967) —

RUMANIA

A communist-dominated republic since 1947, Rumania came into being in 1859 when the principalities of Wallachia and Moldavia were united. The country became a kingdom in 1881 under Carol I (1881–1914).

1 Leu = 100 Bani

Bilets Hypothecar (State Notes of the Principality)

1.	12. 6.1877	5 Lei, blue. Two women with children	$37.50
2.		10 Lei, blue. Two women with children	45.00
3.		20 Lei, blue. Two Roman men and women at left	50.00
4.		50 Lei, blue. Two Roman men and women at left	50.00
5.		100 Lei, blue. Woman with children in middle	R
6.		500 Lei, blue. Five women and two children	R

Ministerul Finantelor (Finance Ministry)

7.	1917	10 Bani, green. King Ferdinand I in middle	.75
8.		25 Bani, brown. Type of #7	1.25
9.		50 Bani, blue and light brown. Type of #7	1.00

Notes of the Austro-Hungarian Bank with overprint "Romania Timbru Special" stamped on the German or Hungarian side of the note

10.	(1919)	10 Kronen. Austria #9 with overprint	5.00
11.		10 Kronen. Austria #19 with overprint	.75
12.		20 Kronen. Austria #10 with overprint	RR
13.		20 Kronen. Austria #13 with overprint	2.00
14.		20 Kronen. Austria #14 with overprint	1.00
15.		50 Kronen. Austria #6 with overprint	RR
16.		50 Kronen. Austria #15 with overprint	1.25
17.		100 Kronen. Austria #11 with overprint	RR
18.		100 Kronen. Austria #12 with overprint	1.00
19.		1,000 Kronen. Austria #8 with overprint	2.50
20.		10,000 Kronen. Austria #25 with overprint	10.00

These notes are also known with additional overprints in the Yugoslavian or Hungarian language.

Banca Nacionala a Romaniei (National Bank of Rumania)

The numerous date varieties of the various note types make chronological classification difficult. The notes are, therefore, arranged by denomination with the known dates of issue indicated. The valuations shown are for the commonest varieties.

21.	1 Leu, violet blue on light rose (12.3.1915)	.50
22.	1 Leu, blue on light rose. As #21 but larger date on reverse (17.7.1920)	.75
23.	1 Leu, brown on rose. As #22 but date on obverse. Two signature varieties (28.10.1937; 21.12.1938)	1.25
24.	2 Lei, violet blue on light rose. Two signature varieties (12.3.1915)	.50
25.	2 Lei, violet blue on light rose. As #24 but larger date on reverse (17.7.1920)	.75
26.	2 Lei, brown on rose. As #25. Two signature varieties (21.12.1938)	1.25
27.	5 Lei, Type I, violet. Peasant woman with distaff at left. Numeral of value in violet on reverse. Paper watermarked with heads of Trajan and Minerva. Six signature varieties (31.7.1914; 4.8.1916; 26.1.1917; 21.8.1917; 25.3.1920; 22.11.1928; 19.9.1929)	.75
28.	5 Lei, Type I, lilac brown. As #27 but numeral of value on reverse in yellow. Paper watermarked with light and dark hemisphere. Format 133 × 79 mm or 139 × 87 mm (16.2.1917)	1.25

20 Lei notes

29.	20 Lei, Type I, blue. Two boys in middle, one with Mercury staff. Seven signature varieties (19.1.1881; 28.2.1881 3.6.1881; 30.9.1881; 18.11.1881; 7.4.1882; 21.6.1882; 25.8.1882; 10.11.1882; 30.3.1883; 10.11.1883; 3.9.1884; 19.6.1885; 6.11.1885; 25.6.1886; 20.5.1887; 9.7.1888; 19.4.1889; 31.8.1889; 12.10.1889; 4.5.1890; 2.8.1890; 10.11.1890; 11.7.1891; 26.6.1892; 18.3.1893; 31.8.1895)	20.00
30.	20 Lei, Type II, blue. Woman with six children in middle. Three signature varieties (14.3.1896; 5.12.1896; 25.9.1897; 15.5.1898; 25.11.1898; 20.1.1900; 7.9.1900; 12.4.1901; 20.9.1901; 5.12.1901; 29.8.1902; 6.3.1903; 8.1.1904; 27.5.1904; 30.6.1905; 3.11.1905; 18.5.1906; 28.9.1906; 1.2.1907; 7.6.1907; 6.9.1907; 23.1.1908; 1.5.1908; 28.8.1908)	7.50

#31
161 × 95

31.   20 Lei, Type III, blue violet. Girl with fruit at left, boy with rudder at right. Twelve signature varieties (26.2.1909; 29.10.1909; 12.11.1909; 14.1.1911; 31.3.1911; 2.6.1911; 13.10.1911; 15.3.1912; 14.7.1912; 15.11.1912; 1.2.1913; 6.3.1914; 27.3.1914; 30.6.1914; 15.1.1915; 12.5.1916; 26.1.1917; 6.7.1917; 7.3.1919; 31.7.1919; 25.3.1920; 21.1.1921; 3.11.1921; 26.5.1922; 1.2.1923; 23.8.1923; 5.2.1924; 12.6.1924; 2.10.1924; 14.5.1925; 10.6.1926; 16.12.1927; 7.6.1928; 18.10.1928; 31.1.1929)   1.50

32.   20 Lei, Type III, blue violet. As #31 but only two signatures (19.9.1929)   2.50

100 Lei notes

33.   100 Lei, Type I, blue. Two cupids at upper left and right, eagle in middle. Nine signature varieties (28.2.1881; 3.6.1881; 16.7.1881; 18.11.1881; 7.4.1882; 25.8.1882; 18.5.1883; 7.9.1883; 5.9.1884; 19.6.1885; 12.11.1886; 14.4.1888; 19.4.1889; 15.9.1889; 25.10.1889; 2.8.1890; 30.8.1890; 11.4.1891; 22.8.1891; 5.11.1892; 13.5.1893; 17.2.1894; 14.8.1896; 8.5.1897; 15.5.1898; 29.4.1899; 20.1.1900; 3.1.1902; 29.8.1902; 6.3.1903; 30.9.1904; 18.8.1905; 23.3.1906; 12.4.1907; 12.10.1907; 11.11.1907)   12.50

34.   100 Lei, Type II, violet blue. Seated woman in costume at left. Nine signature varieties. Paper watermarked with heads of Trajan and Minerva (14.10.1910; 20.5.1910; 2.6.1911; 15.3.1912; 13.11.1912; 7.9.1913; 23.1.1914; 6.3.1914; 27.3.1914; 1.10.1915; 12.5.1916; 22.12.1916; 22.6.1917; 8.10.1919; 25.3.1920; 14.6.1920; 9.2.1921; 24.11.1921; 26.5.1922; 1.2.1923; 23.8.1923; 1.11.1923; 8.5.1924; 14.5.1925; 4.2.1926; 12.1.1927; 10.3.1927; 28.6.1928; 17.1.1929; 31.1.1929)   5.00

35.   100 Lei, Type II, lilac. As #34 but paper watermarked with light and dark hemisphere (16.2.1917)   6.50

36.   100 Lei, Type II, violet. As #34 but only two signatures. Paper watermarked with heads of Trajan and Minerva (19.9.1929)   6.50

37.   100 Lei, Type II, olive brown. As #36. Three signature varieties (13.5.1930; 16.10.1930; 5.12.1931; 31.3.1931; 22.10.1931; 3.12.1931; 13.5.1932)   4.00

38.   100 Lei, Type II, dark brown. As #36, paper watermarked with heads of Trajan and Minerva (19.2.1940)   5.00

39.   100 Lei, Type II, dark brown. As #38 but paper watermarked with "BNR" (19.2.1940; 1.11.1940)   4.00

500 Lei notes

40.   500 Lei, Type I, violet blue. Woman with boy at left, seated peasant woman at right. Six signature varieties (11.2.1916; 7.4.1916; 18.8.1916; 26.1.1917; 29.3.1918; 30.8.1918; 26.4.1919; 31.7.1919; 12.2.1920)   2.50

41.	500 Lei, Type II, multicolored. Peasant woman with distaff at left, woman with infant at right. Three signatures (12.6.1924)	5.00

42. 500 Lei, Type II, multicolored. As #41 but only two signatures. Six signature varieties (1.10.1925; 4.2.1926; 15.12.1927; 13.5.1930; 16.10.1930; 16.2.1931; 31.3.1931; 22.10.1931; 3.12.1931; 13.5.1932; 27.10.1932; 21.4.1933; 21.9.1933; 14.12.1933; 15.3.1934; 27.1.1938)   3.00

43. 500 Lei, Type III, green. King Carol II in half profile at left (31.7.1934)   4.00

44. 500 Lei, Type IV, grey. King Carol II in profile at left (30.4.1936; 26.5.1939; 1.11.1940)   2.50

45. 500 Lei, Type V, brown. Two peasant women at left (1.11.1940; 2.4.1941; 22.7.1941; 20.4.1942; 26.1.1943)   1.00

1,000 Lei notes

46. 1,000 Lei, Type I, lilac. Woman with sickle at left, woman with rudder at right. Ten signature varieties (28.2.1881; 2.11.1883; 30.5.1884; 15.5.1885; 9.2.1889; 23.8.1890; 24.6.1893; 31.3.1894; 1.6.1895; 19.9.1902; 23.3.1906; 20.5.1910; 2.6.1911; 27.8.1911; 15.12.1911; 15.3.1912; 14.6.1912; 23.7.1915; 24.9.1915; 24.3.1916; 12.5.1916; 15.10.1916; 10.7.1917; 15.11.1917; 10.7.1919; 22.4.1920; 19.5.1920; 26.5.1922; 23.8.1923; 6.3.1924; 20.11.1924; 3.9.1925; 4.2.1926; 7.6.1928; 18.10.1928; 31.1.1929; 19.9.1929; 16.10.1930; 31.3.1931; 22.10.1931)   20.00

47. 1,000 Lei, Type I, multicolored (15.6.1933)   25.00

219 × 129

48. 1,000 Lei, Type II, multicolored. Bust of King Carol II at left (15.3.1934)   11.50

49. 1,000 Lei, Type III, brown and green. Two peasant women and two children at left and right. Paper watermarked with head of King Carol II with wreath (25.6.1936)   3.00

50. 1,000 Lei, Type III, brown and green. As #49 but obverse overprinted with two peasant women (25.6.1936)   2.50

51. 1,000 Lei, Type III, brown and green. As #49 but no wreath in watermark (21.12.1938; 28.4.1939; 1.11.1940)   2.50

52. 1,000 Lei, Type III, brown and green. As #51 but obverse over-printed with two peasant women (21.12.1938; 28.4.1939; 1.11.1940)   2.50

53. 1,000 Lei, Type III, blue and rose. As #49 but paper watermarked with head of Trajan. Three signature varieties (10.9.1941; 23.3.1943; 2.5.1944; 10.10.1944; 20.3.1945)   1.25

2,000 and 5,000 Lei notes

54. 2,000 Lei, brown. violet and yellow. Peasant woman with distaff at left, woman with infant at right. Two signature varieties. Paper watermarked head of Trajan (18.11.1941; 10.10.1944)   1.00

55. 2,000 Lei, brown, violet and yellow. As #54 but paper water-marked with "BNR" in shield. Two signature varieties (23.3.1943; 1.9.1943; 2.5.1944)   .75

56. 5,000 Lei, Type I, dark blue. Danube landscape at left, King Carol II at right (31.3.1931 overprinted 6.9.1940 at right)   15.00

57. 5,000 Lei, Type II, light blue. Two men's heads (Trajan and Decebal). Two signature varieties. Paper watermarked with head of Trajan (28.9.1943; 2.5.1944; 22.8.1944)   1.00

58. 5,000 Lei, Type II, light blue. As #57 but paper watermarked with "BNR". Two signature varieties (10.10.1944; 15.12.1944; 20.3.1945; 21.8.1945; 20.12.1945)   .75

10,000 to 5,000,000 Lei notes

59. 10,000 Lei, brown and red. Two peasant women with two children at left and right. Two signature varieties (18.5.1945; 20.12.1945; 28.5.1946)   1.25

60. 100,000 Lei, green and grey. Woman with boys at left, peasant woman at right (1.4.1945; 7.8.1945; 28.5.1946; 21.10.1946; 20.12.1946; 8.5.1947)   1.00

61. 100,000 Lei, lilac and multicolored. Two men's heads (Trajan and Decebal) in middle (25.1.1947)   2.50

62. 1,000,000 Lei, green and grey brown. Type of #61 (16.4.1947)   5.00

#63
207 × 106

63. 5,000,000 Lei, olive green and brown. She-wolf with Romulus and
      Remus in middle (25.6.1947)
        a. White paper   11.50
        b. Lined paper   20.00

1947 Currency Reform: *20,000 old Lei = 1 new Leu*

Ministerul Finantelor (Finance Ministry)

64.	1945	20 Lei, brown. King Michael in middle	.50
65.		100 Lei, blue. King Michael in middle	.50
66.	(1947)	20 Lei, brown and green. Two men's heads at left (Trajan and Decebal). Two signature varieties. Paper watermarked with "M.F."	1.25
67.	(1948)	20 Lei, brown and green. As #66 but watermarked with "N.N.R." Text reads "Directorul General . . ."	1.25
68.		20 Lei, brown and green. As #67 but "Directorul Bugetului"	1.25
69.	15. 6.1950	20 Lei, dark green. Girl's head at right	1.00
70.	1952	1 Leu, brown	.40
71.		3 Lei, lilac brown and green	.50
72.		5 Lei, blue and brown. Girl's head at left	.75

Banca Nacionala a Romaniei (National Bank of Rumania)

Notes issued after the currency reform of 1947

73.	25. 6.1947	100 Lei, brown. Three men with tools at right	1.00
74.		500 Lei, brown. Woman's head in middle	5.00
75.		1,000 Lei, blue. Tudor Vladimirescu	10.00
76.	27. 8.1947	100 Lei, brown. Type of #73	1.00
77.	30. 9.1947	1,000 Lei, blue. Type of #75	10.00
78.	5.12.1947	100 Lei, brown. Type of #73	1.00
79.		1,000 Lei, blue. Type of #75	10.00
80.	18. 6.1948	1,000 Lei, blue and multicolored. Tudor Vladimirescu in middle	3.00

Second currency reform 1952: *20 old Lei = 1 new Leu*

Banca Republicii Populare Romane, Banca de Stat (Bank of the Peoples Republic of Rumania)

#81
156 × 73

81.	15.10.1949	500 Lei, brown. Three men's heads	2.50
82.	20. 9.1950	1,000 Lei, blue. N. Balcescu at left	4.00
83.	1952	10 Lei, brown. Worker's head at left	1.00
84.		25 Lei, blue violet. Tudor Vladimirescu at left	1.50
85.		100 Lei, blue. N. Balcescu at left	3.00

Banca Nacionala a Republicii Socialiste Romania (National Bank of the Socialist Republic of Rumania)

86.	1966	1 Leu, brown	—
87.		3 Lei, blue grey	—
88.		5 Lei, lilac brown	—
89.		10 Lei, lilac	—
90.		25 Lei, multicolored. Tudor Vladimirescu at left	—
91.		50 Lei, dark green. Alexander Cuza at left	—
92.		100 Lei, dark blue. N. Balcescu at left	—

Banca Generala Romana (General Bank of Rumania)

Notes issued during the German occupation in World War II

M1.	(1917)	25 Bani, olive brown	.40
M2.		50 Bani, blue	.50
M3.		1 Leu, green	.75
M4.		2 Lei, lilac rose	1.00
M5.		5 Lei, violet	2.00
M6.		20 Lei, brown	5.00
M7.		100 Lei, olive green	10.00
M8.		1,000 Lei, lilac brown	37.50

> Notes M1–M8 also exist with many different overprints of military units and Rumanian administrative authorities.

Comandamentul Armatei Rossii

Notes issued during the Russian occupation at end of World War II

M9.	1944	1 Leu	37.50
M10.		5 Lei	37.50
M11.		10 Lei, brown	20.00
M12.		20 Lei, blue	30.00
M13.		100 Lei, brown olive	25.00
M14.		500 Lei	50.00
M15.		1,000 Lei	R

RUSSIA—U.S.S.R.

The last Russian Czar, Nicholas II (1894–1917), was forced to abdicate after the February 1917 revolution. The Provisional Government of Alexander Kerensky followed but it in turn was overthrown by the October Revolution in 1917. During the civil war that followed, many organizations and national states were formed but the complete victory of the Red Army led to the formation of the Russian Socialist Federated Soviet Republic (R.S.F.S.R.). The name was later changed to the Union of Soviet Socialist Republics (U.S.S.R.).

1 Ruble = 100 Kopecks
1 Tscherwonez = 10 Gold Rubles

Empire

ГОСУДАРСТВЕННЫЙ КРЕДИТНЫЙ БИЛЕТЪ   (State Paper Money)
1898–1917

These notes carry signatures of the various State Bank Directors as follows:

E. Pleske, 1898–1904	A. Konschin, 1910–12
S. Timaschew, 1905–10	I. Schipow, 1912–17

			Pleske	Timaschew	Konschin	Schipow
1.	1898	1 Ruble, blue on brown	$0.50	$0.75	$1.00	$0.25
2.		3 Rubles, blue on brown	2.50	2.00	—	—
3.		5 Rubles, blue on multicolor	4.00	4.00	—	—
4.		10 Rubles, red on multicolor	5.00	7.50	—	—
5.		100 Rubles, green background	10.00	8.50	10.00	—

272 × 126

6.	500 Rubles		12.50	12.50	10.00	—

7.	1899	25 Rubles, violet	12.50	6.50	—	—
8.		50 Rubles, green background	30.00	25.00	2.50	1.25
9.	1905	3 Rubles, green and multi-color	—	1.00	.50	.25
10.	1909	5 Rubles, blue and multi-color Note with serial number, see #35.	—	—	.25	.25
11.		10 Rubles, green and red	—	2.00	.25	.25
12.		25 Rubles, red and blue	—	—	.75	.25
13.	1910	100 Rubles, light brown background	—	—	1.25	.25
14.	1912	500 Rubles, green and multi-color	—	—	1.50	.25
15.	1898 (issued 1915)	1 Ruble, blue on brown. As #1 but serial number instead of control number	—	—	—	.25

Some of the Schipow notes were re-printed by the Provisional Government and again by the Soviet government. The re-prints have brighter colors than those printed under the empire.

Postage Stamp Currency

Postage stamps of the Romanov Tercentenary issue were printed on thin cardboard for use as small change. The reverses are imprinted with text and an eagle.

16.	(1915–17)	1 Kopeck, brown. Stamp side overprinted "1"	.50
17.		1 Kopeck, brown. As #16 without overprint	7.50
18.		2 Kopecks, green. Stamp side overprinted "2"	.50
19.		2 Kopecks, green. As #18 without overprint	7.50
20.		3 Kopecks, red	.75
21.		10 Kopecks, blue	.25
22.		15 Kopecks, brown	.25
23.		20 Kopecks, green	.25

For postage stamp money without eagle on reverse, see #32–34.

КАЗНАЧЕЙСКІЙ РАЗМѢННЫЙ ЗНАКЪ (Small Denomination Notes)

24.	(1915–17)	1 Kopeck, light brown	.50
25.		2 Kopecks, grey brown	.50
26.		3 Kopecks, green	.50
27.		5 Kopecks, blue	.50
28.		10 Kopecks, blue and rose	5.00

#29
80 × 44

29.		15 Kopecks, red brown and yellow	5.00
30.		20 Kopecks, green and lilac	5.00
31.		50 Kopecks, blue and yellow	.25

Provisional Government of Russia

Postage Stamp Currency

32.	(1917)	1 Kopeck, brown. As #16–17 but without eagle on reverse	.75
33.		2 Kopecks, green. As #18–19 but without eagle on reverse	.75
34.		3 Kopecks, red. As #20 but without eagle on reverse	.75

ГОСУДАРСТВЕННЫЙ КРЕДИТНЫЙ БИЛЕТЪ (State Credit Notes)

35.	1909 (1917)	5 Rubles, blue and multicolor. As #10 but three digit serial numbers instead of control numbers	.25
		Error: Upper serial letters "AY" lower letters "YA"	R
36.	(1917)	250 Rubles, lilac. Swastika in background on reverse	.50
37.		1,000 Rubles, green. Swastika in background	1.00

Many signature varieties exist of notes #35–37.

КАЗНАЧЕЙСКІЙ ЗНАКЪ (So-called "Kerensky Rubles")

60 × 49

| 38. | (1917) | 20 Rubles, brown | .25 |
| 39. | | 40 Rubles, red on green | .25 |

ГОСУДАРСТВЕННЫЙ КРЕДИТНЫЙ БИЛЕТЪ

Notes printed in America for the Provisional Government (never issued)

40.	(1917)	50 Kopecks, orange (brownish with age)	.25
41.	1918	25 Rubles, dark blue on blue. Seated woman (varieties with and without signatures)	1.00
42.		100 Rubles, background brown and red brown. Seated woman (varieties with and without signatures)	1.00

Note #40 was released by Adm. Kolchak. Notes #41 and 42 were issued in the Far Eastern District with an overprint. Notes in denominations of 50, 250, 500 and 1,000 rubles dated 1919 were also ordered from the U.S. These are known only as trial printings or specimens (RR) and were never issued.

АКЦІОНЕРН КОММЕРЧ БАНКОВЪ   (Union of Russian Stock Commerce Banks)

43.	(1917)	25 Rubles, green	50.00
44.		50 Rubles, brown	R
45.		100 Rubles	R
46.	1917	100 Rubles	RR
47.		500 Rubles	RR

Russian Socialist Federated Soviet Republic

БИЛЕТЪ ГОСУДАРСТВЕННАГО КАЗНАЧЕЙСТВА (State Treasury Notes)

48.	1915	(issued 1918)	25 Rubles, green on lilac	.75
49.	1908	,, ,,	50 Rubles, brown on green	3.00

155 × 138

50.	1912	,, ,,	50 Rubles, brown on green	2.50
51.	1913	,, ,,	50 Rubles, brown on green	2.00
52.	1914	,, ,,	50 Rubles, brown on green	.75
53.	1915	,, ,,	50 Rubles, brown on green	.75
54.	1908	,, ,,	100 Rubles, dark blue on rose	4.00
55.	1912	,, ,,	100 Rubles, dark blue on rose	3.00
56.	1913	,, ,,	100 Rubles, dark blue on rose	2.00
57.	1914	,, ,,	100 Rubles, dark blue on rose	1.00
58.	1915	,, ,,	100 Rubles, dark blue on rose	.75
59.	1915	,, ,,	500 Rubles, dark blue on blue	1.25
60.	1916	,, ,,	500 Rubles, dark blue on blue	1.50

5 % КРАТКОСРОЧНОЕ ОБЯЗАТЕЛЬСТВО ГОСУДАР.
КАЗНАЧЕЙСТВА (5% Short-term State Treasury Notes)

61.	1916	(issued 1918)	1,000 Rubles (12 month), lilac brown	2.00
62.	1917	,, ,,	1,000 Rubles (9 month), lilac brown	2.00
63.	1917	,, ,,	1,000 Rubles (12 month), lilac brown	1.00

64.	1916–17	,,	,,	5,000 Rubles (12 month), orange	2.00
65.	1916	,,	,,	10,000 Rubles (12 month), red	4.00
66.	1916	,,	,,	10,000 Rubles (9 month), red	5.00
67.	1917	,,	,,	10,000 Rubles (12 month), red	4.00
68.	1916	,,	,,	25,000 Rubles (12 month)	7.50
69.	1917	,,	,,	25,000 Rubles (9 month)	9.00
70.	1917	,,	,,	25,000 Rubles (12 month)	6.50
71.	1916–17	,,	,,	50,000 Rubles (12 month)	9.00
72.	1917	,,	,,	50,000 Rubles (9 month)	10.00
73.	1916–17	,,	,,	100,000 Rubles (12 month)	15.00
74.	1916–17	,,	,,	500,000 Rubles (12 month)	25.00
75.	1917	,,	,,	500,000 Rubles (9 month)	30.00
76.	1916–17	,,	,,	1,000,000 Rubles (12 month)	37.50

5 % ОБЛИГАЦІЯ ЗАЙМЪ СВОБОДЫ (5% Obligations of Freedom Loan)

These notes are known with and without an overprint of their value.

			without	with
77.	1917 (issued 1918)	20 Rubles, yellow	.75	.50
78.		40 Rubles	.75	.50
79.		50 Rubles, green	.65	.40
80.		100 Rubles, brown	.65	.40

Many kinds of interest coupons from certificates of the various Russian loans also circulated as money.

РАСЧЕТНЫЙ ЗНАК (Accounting Notes)

81.	(1919)	1 Ruble, brown. Multicolor reverse	.25
82.		2 Rubles, dark brown. Multicolor reverse	.25
83.		3 Rubles, green. Multicolor reverse. Paper watermarked with lozenges	.25
84.	(1921)	3 Rubles, both sides green	
		a. Paper watermarked with spades	.50
		b. Paper watermarked with stars	.40
85.		5 Rubles, both sides dark blue	
		a. Paper watermarked with lozenges	.25
		b. Paper watermarked with spades	1.00
		c. Paper watermarked with stars	1.00
		d. Unwatermarked paper	.75

ГОСУДАРСТВЕННЫЙ КРЕДИТНЫЙ БИЛЕТЪ (State Credit Notes)

86.	1918	1 Ruble, brown	.25
87.		3 Rubles, green	.25
88.		5 Rubles, blue	.25
89.		10 Rubles, red	.25
90.		25 Rubles, red-brown	.25
91.		50 Rubles, dark brown	.25
92.		100 Rubles, brown	.25

147 × 100

93.	250 Rubles, green	.25
94.	500 Rubles, dark green	.25
95.	1,000 Rubles, brown	.35
	Error: Inverted reverse	7.50
96.	5,000 Rubles, blue. Swastika in background	.75
97.	10,000 Rubles, brown. Swastika in background	1.00

Many signature varieties exist of notes #86–97.

РАСЧЕТНЫЙ ЗНАК (Accounting Notes)

Because of the multi-language text, these notes are sometimes called "Babylonians."

98.	(1919)	15 Rubles, brown	.25
99.		30 Rubles, green	.25
		Error: inverted reverse	5.00
100.		60 Rubles, grey	.25
101.	1919 (issued 1920)	100 Rubles, brown on light brown	.25
102.		250 Rubles, violet	
		a. Paper watermarked with "250"	.25
		b. Paper watermarked with stars	.50
103.		500 Rubles, olive	
		a. Paper watermarked with "500"	.25
		b. Paper watermarked with stars	.50
104.		1,000 Rubles, green	
		a. Paper watermarked with "1000"	.25
		b. Paper watermarked with small stars	.40
		c. Paper watermarked with large stars	.40
		d. Paper watermarked with lozenges	.40

165 × 115

105.		5,000 Rubles, blue	
		a. Paper watermarked with broad waves	.25
		b. Paper watermarked with narrow waves	.50
		c. Paper watermarked with stars	1.00
106.		10,000 Rubles, red	
		a. Paper watermarked with broad waves	.50
		b. Paper watermarked with narrow waves	1.00
		c. Paper watermarked with stars	1.00

РАСЧЕТНЫЙ ЗНАК (Accounting Notes)

107.	(1921)	50 Rubles, brown	
		a. Paper watermarked with lozenges	.50
		b. Paper watermarked with large stars	.25
		c. Paper watermarked with small stars	.75
108.		100 Rubles, yellow	.50
109.		100 Rubles, orange	.40
110.		250 Rubles, green	
		a. Paper watermarked with "250"	.40
		b. Paper watermarked with stars	.75
111.		500 Rubles, blue	
		a. Paper watermarked with "500"	.40
		b. Paper watermarked with stars	.75
		c. Paper watermarked with lozenges	.75
112.		1,000 Rubles, red	
		a. Paper watermarked with "1000"	.40
		b. Paper watermarked with small stars	.75
		c. Paper watermarked with large stars	1.25
		d. Paper watermarked with lozenges	.75
113.		5,000 Rubles, blue	.50
		Error: "PROLETAPIER"	1.00
114.		10,000 Rubles, red brown	.50
115.		25,000 Rubles, lilac	
		a. Paper watermarked with large stars	.50
		b. Paper watermarked with small stars	1.00

116.		50,000 Rubles, green	
		a. Paper watermarked with large stars	.50
		b. Paper watermarked with small stars	1.50
		c. Paper watermarked with crosses	4.00
117.		100,000 Rubles, red	.50
118.		50,000 Rubles, War loan type	4.00
119.		100,000 Rubles, War loan type	5.00

Currency Reform 1921: *10,000 old Rubles = 1 new Ruble*

КРАТКОСРОЧНОЕ ОБЯЗАТЕЛЬСТВО (Short-term Obligations)

120.	1921	1,000,000 Rubles, black on yellowish paper	2.50
121.		5,000,000 Rubles, black on bluish paper	4.00
122.		10,000,000 Rubles	5.00
123.	1922	5,000 Rubles	5.00
124.		10,000 Rubles, black on grey-blue paper	6.50
125.		25,000 Rubles (known only as a pattern)	15.00

ГОСУДАРСТВЕННЫЙ ДЕНЕЖНЫЙ ЗНАК (State Promissory Notes)

126.	1922	50 Kopecks (trial printing only)	RRR
127.		1 Ruble, light brown	.25
128.		3 Rubles, green	.40
129.		5 Rubles, blue	.40

155 × 80

130.		10 Rubles, red brown	.50
131.		25 Rubles, brown lilac	.50
132.		50 Rubles, blue	.50
133.		100 Rubles, red	.75
134.		250 Rubles, dark green	1.00
135.		500 Rubles, dark blue	1.25
136.		1,000 Rubles, brown	1.50
137.		5,000 Rubles, violet	2.00
138.		10,000 Rubles, red	2.50

Many signature varieties exist of notes #127–138.

БАНКОВЫЙ БИЛЕТ (State Bank)

139.	1922	1 Tscherwonez. Multicolored guilloche (ornament) at left	6.50
140.		2 Tscherwonez (known only as a pattern)	25.00
141.		3 Tscherwonez	10.00

142.		5 Tscherwonez	12.50
143.		10 Tscherwonez	20.00
144.		25 Tscherwonez	25.00
145.		50 Tscherwonez (known only as a pattern)	25.00

ГОСУДАРСТВЕННЫЙ ДЕНЕЖНЫЙ ЗНАК (State Promissory Notes)

Notes #146–151 are the promissory note type; notes #152–156 are coin notes without the promissary designation.

146.	1922	1 Ruble, brown and yellow	.50
147.		3 Rubles, green	.50
148.		5 Rubles, blue	.75
149.		10 Rubles, red	.75
150.		25 Rubles, violet	1.00
151.		50 Rubles, green	1.00
152.	1923	10 Kopecks	RRR
153.		15 Kopecks	RRR
154.		20 Kopecks	RRR
155.		50 Kopecks, blue	1.00

Second Currency Reform 1923: *1,000,000 old Rubles = 1 new Ruble*

ГОСУДАРСТВЕННЫЙ ДЕНЕЖНЫЙ ЗНАК (State Promissory Notes)

Reverse text reads ОДИН РУБЛЬ . . . in seven lines

156.	1923	1 Ruble, brown	.25
157.		5 Rubles, green	.25
158.		10 Rubles, violet	.25
159.		25 Rubles, blue	.25
160.		50 Rubles, olive	.40

161

141 × 95

| 161. | | 100 Rubles, violet and multicolored | .40 |
| 162. | | 250 Rubles, dark blue | .50 |

Many signature varieties exist of notes #156–162.

Reverse text reads ДЕНЕЖНЫЕ ЗНАКИ . . . in eight lines

163.	1923	1 Ruble, brown	.25
164.		5 Rubles, green	.25
165.		10 Rubles, violet	
		a. Paper watermarked with lozenges	.25
		b. Paper watermarked with stars	.50
166.		25 Rubles, olive brown	
		a. Paper watermarked with lozenges	.25
		b. Paper watermarked with stars	.50
167.		50 Rubles, brown	
		a. Paper watermarked with lozenges	.40
		b. Paper watermarked with stars	1.00
168.		100 Rubles, violet and multicolored	
		a. Paper watermarked with lozenges	.40
		b. Paper watermarked with stars	.50
169.		500 Rubles, dark brown	1.00
170.		1,000 Rubles, red	1.50
171.		5,000 Rubles, green	2.00

Many signature varieties exist of notes #163–171.

Third Currency Reform 1924: *5,000 Rubles = 1 Gold Ruble*

ПЛАТЕЖНОЕ ОБЯЗАТЕЛЬСТВО НКФ РСФСР (Payment Commitments)

Known only as patterns

172.	1923 (1924)	100 Gold Rubles	25.00
173.		250 Gold Rubles	25.00
174.		500 Gold Rubles	25.00
175.		1,000 Gold Rubles	25.00

ТРАНСПОРТНЫЙ СЕРТИФИКАТ КПС (Transport Certificates)

176.	1923 1.3.1924	3 Gold Rubles	37.50
177.		5 Gold Rubles. Series 1–5	12.50
178.	1.5.1924	5 Gold Rubles. Series 6–10	10.00
179.		5 Gold Rubles. Series 11–15. As #178 but text differences	8.50
180.		5 Gold Rubles. Series 16–24. As #179 but further text differences	7.50

Union of Soviet Socialist Republics
ГОСУДАРСТВЕННЫЙ ДЕНЕЖНЫЙ ЗНАК (State Promissory Notes)

155 × 77

181.	1923 (issued 1924)	10,000 Rubles, lilac on green. View of Kremlin	1.25
182.		15,000 Rubles, brown. Man's head	1.50
183.		25,000 Rubles, dark blue and green on violet. Soldier	1.50

Many signature varieties exist of notes #181-183.

ПЛАТЕЖНОЕ ОБЯЗАТЕЛЬСТВО НКФ СССР (Payment Commitments)

184.	1924	100 Gold Rubles (known only as patterns)	12.50
185.		500 Gold Rubles (known only as patterns)	12.50

ГОСУДАРСТВЕННЫЙ КАЗНАЧЕЙСКИЙ БИЛЕТ (State Treasury Notes)

186.	1924	1 Gold Ruble, blue on light brown. Vertical format, with and without	2.00
187.		3 Gold Rubles, green. Two reclining men	2.50

182 × 88

188.		5 Gold Rubles, blue. Tractor plowing	3.00
189.	1925	3 Rubles, dark green	1.00
190.		5 Rubles, dark blue. Head of worker at left	1.25

Small Denomination Notes (vertical format)

191.	1924	1 Kopeck, light brown	.40
192.		2 Kopecks, brown	.40
193.		3 Kopecks, green	.40

194.		5 Kopecks, blue	.40
195.		20 Kopecks, brown on rose (known only as a pattern)	10.00
196.		50 Kopecks, blue on brown	1.25

БИЛЕТ ГОСУДАРСТВЕННОГО БАНКА СССР (State Bank Notes)

197.	1924	3 Tscherwonez, dark blue. Peasant sowing seeds at left	7.50
198.	1926	1 Tscherwonez, dark blue	4.00
199.	1928	2 Tscherwonez, green	
		a. Signature in green	7.50
		b. Signature in black	5.00
200.		5 Tscherwonez, dark blue	10.00

156 × 88

201.	1932	3 Tscherwonez, green	7.50
202.	1937	1 Tscherwonez, grey. Lenin at right	.50
203.		3 Tscherwonez, red. Lenin at right	.40
204.		5 Tscherwonez, green. Lenin at right	.50
205.		10 Tscherwonez, dark blue. Lenin at right	1.00

ГОСУДАРСТВЕННЫЙ КАЗНАЧЕЙСКИЙ БИЛЕТ (State Treasury Notes)

206.	1928	1 Gold Ruble, blue on light brown. With and without СЕРИЯ	1.25
207.	1934	1 Gold Ruble, blue. With signature	1.50
208.		1 Gold Ruble, blue. Without signature	.50
209.		3 Gold Rubles, green. With signature	1.50
210.		3 Gold Rubles, green. Without signature	.50
211.		5 Gold Rubles, grey blue on light blue. With signature	2.00
212.		5 Gold Rubles, grey blue on light blue. Without signature	.75
213.	1938	1 Ruble, brown. Miner at right	.40
214.		3 Rubles, dark green. Soldiers	.40
215.		5 Rubles, dark blue. Aviator	.50
216.	1947	1 Ruble, blue on brown. Arms surrounded by 16 inscribed ribbons	.50
217.		1 Ruble, blue on brown. As #216 but 15 ribbons (later issue)	.40
218.		3 Rubles, green. Type of #216	.75
219.		3 Rubles, green. Type of #217	.50

220.		5 Rubles, blue. Type of #216	1.00
221.		5 Rubles, blue. Type of #217	.75
222.	1961	1 Ruble, brown	—
223.		3 Rubles, green. View of Kremlin	—
224.		5 Rubles, blue	—

БИЛЕТ ГОСУДАРСТВЕННОГО БАНКА СССР (State Bank Notes)

225.	1947	10 Rubles, blue and multicolored. Arms surrounded by 16 inscribed ribbons. Lenin on reverse	3.00
226.		10 Rubles, blue and multicolored. As #225 but 15 ribbons	1.50
227.		25 Rubles, green. Type of #225. Lenin on reverse	4.00
228.		25 Rubles, green. Type of #226. Lenin on reverse	2.00
229.		50 Rubles, blue on green and multicolored. Type of #225. Lenin on reverse	5.00
230.		50 Rubles, blue on green and multicolored. Type of #226. Lenin on reverse	2.50

230
×
115

231.		100 Rubles, multicolored. Type of #216 with Lenin at left. View of Kremlin on reverse	7.50
232.		100 Rubles, multicolored. Type of #217 with Lenin at left. View of Kremlin on reverse	4.00
233.	1961	10 Rubles, red brown. Lenin	—
234.		25 Rubles, violet. Lenin	—
235.		50 Rubles, green. Lenin	—
236.		100 Rubles, olive. Lenin	—

Archangel Government
АРХАНГЕЛЁСКАЯ ГУБЕРН

R1.	(1918)	3 Rubles, green	1.00
		Error: Obverse without black plate	7.50
R2.		3 Rubles, green. As R1 but reverse with red overprint	1.25
R3.		5 Rubles, grey blue	2.00
R4.		10 Rubles, red brown	1.00
		Error: Obverse without black plate	7.50
R5.		10 Rubles, red brown. As R4 but reverse with black overprint	1.25

165 × 104

| R6. | | 25 Rubles, grey blue | 1.25 |
| R7. | | 25 Rubles, grey blue. As R6 but reverse with red overprint | 1.50 |

Armenian Republic
РЕСПУБЛИКИ АРМЕНИИ

Notes dated August (АВГУСТЬ) 1919 on obverse, 15 November (НОЯБРЯ) 1919 on reverse. Large format (175 × 104 mm)

R8.	1919	100 Rubles, green. Value numerals in black	4.00
R9.		250 Rubles, orange. Type of R8	4.00
R10.		500 Rubles, blue. Type of R8	3.00
R11.		1,000 Rubles, lilac. Type of R8	4.00
R12.		25 Rubles, dark grey. Value numerals in middle and four corners	10.00
		Error: Printed in brown	R
R13.		50 Rubles, green. Type of R12	12.50
R14.		50 Rubles, green. Value numerals ornamented	1.50
R15.		100 Rubles, light green. Type of R14	1.25
		Error: Printed in yellow	5.00
R16.		250 Rubles, light brown. Type of R14	1.75
R17.		500 Rubles, blue. Type of R14	1.75
R18.		1,000 Rubles, lilac. Type of R14	2.50

Notes dated 15 November (НОЯБРЯ)1919 on reverse. Small format (110×65 mm)

R19.	1919	5	Rubles, blue, without Armenian text	.50
R20.		10	Rubles, rose	.75
			Error: Background inverted	2.50
R21.	1919	5	Rubles, grey blue. With Armenian text	.50
	(issued 1920)		Error: Text reads ГОСКУДАРСТВЕНАГО	1.00
			Error: Reverse overprinted on obverse	1.50
R22.		10	Rubles, rose brown	.50
			Error: Text reads ГОСКУДАРСТВЕНАГО	1.00
			Error: Background inverted	.75
			Error: Text reads ДЕЕСЯТЬ	1.25
R23.		25	Rubles, brown	.75
			Error: Text reads ГОСКУДАРСТВЕНАГО	1.25
			Error: Text reads ДВАДЧАШЬ	2.00

109 × 68

R24.		50	Rubles, turquoise	.75
			Error: Background inverted	1.00
			Error: Reverse text inverted	1.00
			Error: Text reads ГОСКУДАРСТВЕНАГО	1.00
R25.		100	Rubles, yellow green	.75
			Error: Reverse text inverted	1.25
			Error: Text reads ГОСКУДАРСТВЕНАГО	1.50
			Error: Text reads МИНС — ТЕРСТВОМЪ	2.00

Notes dated 15 January (ЯНВАРЯ)1920 on reverse. Large format (175 × 104 mm)

R26.		250	Rubles, rose. Background of waves on reverse	3.00
R27.		500	Rubles, light blue	5.00
R28.		1,000	Rubles, lilac	4.00
R29.		50	Rubles, green. Background of groups of waves on reverse	3.00
R30.		500	Rubles, light blue	2.00
R31.		25	Rubles, grey brown. Signature stamped on reverse	1.50
			Error: Obverse background inverted	4.00
			Error: Reverse text inverted	4.00
R32.		50	Rubles, green blue	2.00
R33.		100	Rubles, light green	1.00
R34.		250	Rubles, rose	1.00
			Error: Text reads ПЯТЬДЕСТЯЪ	2.50
			Error: Reverse text inverted	1.50

R35.		500 Rubles, light blue to grey blue	1.00
		Error: Background inverted	1.75
R36.		1,000 Rubles	
		a. Light violet	1.00
		b. Orange brown	1.00
		c. Rose	1.00
		Error: Reverse text inverted	2.00
		Error: Background inverted	1.50

176 × 106

R37.		5,000 Rubles	
		a. Grey	.75
		b. Violet	1.25
		Error: Background inverted	1.50
R38.		10,000 Rubles, green. Signature stamped on reverse	.50
		Error: Numerals of value inverted	2.00
		Error: Reverse text inverted	1.50
		Error: Edge text at left reads from top to bottom	1.50
		Also see R45.	
R39.		25 Rubles, brown. Reverse signature facsimile printed	.50
		Error: Reverse text inverted	1.50
		Error: Background inverted	1.25
R40.		250 Rubles, yellow brown. Numerals of value in black	.75
R41.		250 Rubles, yellow brown. Numerals of value in light blue	4.00

Printed by Waterlow and Sons Ltd., London

R42.	1919	50 Rubles, brown. Dragons at left and right	.75
R43.		100 Rubles, green. Landscape with mountains	1.00
R44.		250 Rubles, violet on green. Rev. Woman spinning	1.00

Armenia, Soviet Socialist Republic
СОВЕТСКАЯ СОЦИАЛИСТИЧ РЕСПУБЛИКА АРМЕНИИ

| R45. | August (НОЯБРЯ) 1919 | 10,000 Rubles, light green. As R38 but reverse signature facsimile printed | 1.00 |

R46.	1921	5,000 Rubles, blue	.75
R47.		10,000 Rubles	
		a. Rose, watermarked paper	1.00
		b. Rose to brown, unwatermarked paper	1.00
		c. Lilac, unwatermarked paper	1.50
		d. Trial printing in green	R
R48.	1922	25,000 Rubles, blue. Setting sun	
		a. Watermarked paper	1.00
		b. Unwatermarked paper	1.00
R49.		100,000 Rubles, grey green on yellow	1.25
R50.		500,000 Rubles	2.50
R51.		1,000,000 Rubles, red	2.00
R52.		5,000,000 Rubles, black on grey olive, ОБЯЗАТЕЛЬСТВО	
		a. Watermarked paper	1.25
		b. Unwatermarked paper	1.50
R53.		5,000,000 Rubles, blue-green on light green, ДЕНЕЖНЫЙ ЗНАКЪ	2.50

Azerbaijan, Independent Republic
АЗЕРБАЙДЖАНСКАЯ РЕСПУБЛИКА

Many variations of color, paper and serial numbers are known

R54.	1919	25 Rubles, lilac and brown	.75
R55.		50 Rubles, blue green and brown	.75
R56.		100 Rubles, brown. Text reads АЗЕРБАЙДЖАНСКОЕ ПРАВИТЕЛЬСТВО	1.25
R57.		100 Rubles, brown. Text reads АЗЕРБАЙДЖАНСКАЯ РЕСПУБЛИКА	.75

151 × 95

R58.		250 Rubles, lilac and brown	1.00
		Trial printing in green, brown, rose	R
R59.	1920	500 Rubles, lilac and brown. Series I–LV (the later series fall, by rights, in the time of the Soviet Republic of Azerbaijan)	1.25
R60.		1 Ruble (unfinished trial printing)	4.00

Azerbaijan, Soviet Republic
АЗЕРБАЙДЖАНСКАЯ СОЦ. СОВ. РЕСПУБЛИКА

R61.	(1920)	5 Rubles. Worker and farmer. Factory on reverse		
		a. Yellow	1.00
		b. Orange	1.50
R62.		100 Rubles, olive and violet. Train engine	1.00
R63.	1920	1,000 Rubles, olive and multicolored (format 167 × 107 mm)	1.50
		Trial printing in grey and light blue	10.00
R64.		1,000 Rubles, green (format 107 × 66 mm)	1.25

147 × 93

R65.	1921	5,000 Rubles, multicolored. Worker at left, seated farmer at right	.50
R66.		10,000 Rubles, rose and green. Worker and farmer standing	.50
R67.		25,000 Rubles, brown and grey	
		a. Unwatermarked paper	.75
		b. Watermarked paper	1.00
R68.		50,000 Rubles, grey green	1.00
R69.	1922	100,000 Rubles	
		a. Violet, unwatermarked paper	.50
		b. Blue, unwatermarked paper	1.00
		c. Watermarked paper	1.25
R70.		250,000 Rubles, blue and brown	1.00
R71.		1,000,000 Rubles, red	1.25
R72.	1923	5,000,000 Rubles, green and light green	1.25

Don Cossack Government
ВСЕВЕЛИКОЕ ВОЙСКО ДОНСКОЕ

Values are for completely filled-out notes. Blank notes are worth very little. All notes are red brown and olive. Reverses indicate acceptance by the state bank branches as follows:

Nowotscherkassk (НОВОЧЕРКАССК)
Taganrog (ТАГАНРОГ)
Rostow (РОСТОВ)

R73.	1 January 1919	500 Rubles, Nowotscherkassk	3.00
R74.	(ЯНВАРЯ)	1,000 Rubles, Nowotscherkassk	4.00
R75.		5,000 Rubles, Nowotscherkassk	5.00
R76.		10,000 Rubles, Nowotscherkassk	12.50
R77.		25,000 Rubles, Nowotscherkassk	25.00
R78.		50,000 Rubles, Nowotscherkassk	37.50
R79.	1 April 1919	500 Rubles	
	(АПРѢЛЯ)	a. Nowotscherkassk	2.50
		b. Taganrog	8.50
R80.		1,000 Rubles	
		a. Nowotscherkassk	3.75
		b. Taganrog	12.50
		c. Rostow	RRR
R81.		5,000 Rubles	
		a. Nowotscherkassk	7.50
		b. Taganrog	37.50
		c. Rostow	RRR
R82.		10,000 Rubles	
		a. Nowotscherkassk	50.00
		b. Taganrog	50.00
R83.		25,000 Rubles	
		a. Nowotscherkassk	20.00
		b. Rostow	RRR
R84.		50,000 Rubles, Nowotscherkassk	R
R85.	1 July 1919	500 Rubles	
	(ІЮЛЯ)	a. Nowotscherkassk	2.00
		b. Taganrog	3.00
R86.		1,000 Rubles	
		a. Nowotscherkassk	3.00
		b. Taganrog	3.75
R87.		5,000 Rubles	
		a. Nowotscherkassk	5.00
		b. Taganrog	5.00

307 × 117

R88.		10,000 Rubles	
		a. Nowotscherkassk	8.75
		b. Taganrog	12.50

R89.		25,000 Rubles	
		a. Nowotscherkassk	20.00
		b. Taganrog	R
R90.		50,000 Rubles	
		a. Nowotscherkassk	50.00
		b. Taganrog	RR
R91.	1 October 1919	500 Rubles	
	(ОКТЯБРЯ)	a. Nowotscherkassk	2.50
		b. Taganrog	2.00
R92.		1,000 Rubles	
		a. Nowotscherkassk	3.75
		b. Taganrog	3.00
R93.		5,000 Rubles	
		a. Nowotscherkassk	7.50
		b. Taganrog	5.00
R94.		10,000 Rubles	
		a. Nowotscherkassk	11.25
		b. Taganrog	10.00
R95.		25.000 Rubles, Taganrog	20.00
R96.		50,000 Rubles, Taganrog	45.00

Volunteer Western Army, Mitau, Col. Avaloff-Bermondt
ЗАПАДНАЯ ДОБРОВОЛЬЧЕСКАЯ АРМІЯ,
ПОЛК АВАЛОВЪ—БЕРМОНДТЪ

Treasury Notes, obverses in Russian, reverses in German

R97.	10.10.1919	1 Mark, black on light brown	
		a. With stamped imprint	.50
		b. Without stamped imprint	.40
R98.		5 Mark, black on violet-blue	
		a. With stamped imprint	.65
		b. Without stamped imprint	.50

131 × 94

R99.		10 Mark, black on greenish background	
		a. With stamped imprint	5.00
		b. Without stamped imprint	1.25

Unfinished sheets of this note (printed on one side only)
were used to print Latvian postage stamps in 1920.

R100.		10 Mark, black. Without background on obverse	
		a. With stamped imprint	.75
		b. Without stamped imprint	.75
R101.		50 Mark. Grey green on brown reverse	
		a. With stamped imprint	1.75
		b. Without stamped imprint	1.00

Georgia, Independent Republic
ГРУЗИНСКАЯ РЕСПУБЛИКА

ОБЯЗАТЕЛЬСТВО КАЗНАЧЕЙСТВА (Obligation Notes)

R102.	15.1.1919	25 Rubles	2.50
R103.		100 Rubles	2.00
R104.		500 Rubles	3.00
R105.		1,000 Rubles	4.00
R106.		5,000 Rubles	6.50

State Notes

R107.	(1919)	50 Kopecks, blue and light brown	.50
R108.	1919	1 Ruble, rose background. Knight with lance	.25
R109.		3 Rubles, green background. Type of R108	.40
R110.		5 Rubles, dark green and orange. Type of R108	.50
R111.		10 Rubles, brown and red brown. Type of R108	.75
R112.		50 Rubles, violet and green. Type of R108	1.00
R113.		100 Rubles, green and lilac. Type of R108	1.00

163 × 102

R114.		500 Rubles, dark green and red brown. Seated woman with shield and lance	
		a. Paper watermarked with braided design	1.50
		b. Unwatermarked paper, thick and thin varieties	.75
R115.	1920	1,000 Rubles, brown and blue. Knight with lance	
		a. Paper watermarked with braided design	2.50
		b. Unwatermarked paper	.75

R116.   1921   5,000 Rubles, lilac to brown. Building with flags.
                      Single circles around corner figures of value
                      on both sides
                      a. Paper watermarked with monogram   1.00
                      b. Unwatermarked paper   .50
                      c. Lined reverse   1.50

Georgia, Soviet Socialist Republic
ГРУЗИНСКАЯ СОЦ. СОВЕТСКАЯ РЕСПУБЛИКА

R117.   1921   5,000 Rubles, lilac to brown. As R116 but double
                      circles around corner figures of value
                      a. Thick paper   .75
                      b. Thin paper, black printing   1.50
                      c. Thin paper, blue printing   .50
                      Error: Background inverted   2.50

174 × 105

R118.   1922   10,000 Rubles. Buildings with flags
                      a. Green background   .75
                      b. Light blue background   1.25
                      Error: Background inverted   2.50

Obligation Notes, ОБЯЗАТЕЛЬСТВО НАРОДН БАНКА

R119.   31.5.1922   100,000 Rubles   1.25
R120.   500,000 Rubles   2.00
R121.   1,000,000 Rubles   2.50
R122.   5,000,000 Rubles   4.00

Crimea District Government
КРЫМСКОЕ КРАЕВОЕ ПРАВИТЕЛЬСТВО

ОБЯЗАТЕЛЬСТВО КРАЕВОГО КАЗНАЧЕЙСТВА (Obligation Notes)

R123.   1.9.1918   500 Rubles   6.50
R124.   1,000 Rubles   12.50
R125.   5,000 Rubles   45.00
Stamp Notes
R126.   (1918)   50 Kopecks, brown. Double-headed eagle   1.50

ДЕНЕЖНЫЙ ЗНАКЪ (Promissory Notes)

R127.	1918	5 Rubles, blue and brown. Map of the Crimea on the reverse	
		a. Control numbers 3 mm wide	.75
		b. Control numbers 3½–6 mm (Soviet issue, 1920)	.65
R128.		10 Rubles, red and brown. Map of the Crimea on the reverse	
		a. Control numbers 3 mm wide	1.00
		b. Control numbers 3½–6mm (Soviet issue, 1920)	.75
R129.		25 Rubles, green and lilac. Map of the Crimea on the reverse	
		a. Control numbers 3 mm wide	1.25
		b. Control numbers 3½–6mm (Soviet issue, 1920)	.75

Kuban, District Government
КУБАНСКОЕ КРАЕВОЕ ПРАВИТЕЛЬСТВО

These notes were not in circulation.

R130.	15.3.1918	5 Rubles	RRR
R131.	25.3.1918	3 Rubles	RRR
R132.		5 Rubles	RRR
R133.		10 Rubles	RRR
R134.		20 Rubles	RRR
R135.		100 Rubles	RRR
R136.	1.3.1920	250 Rubles, green	
		a. Reverse reads АПРѢЛЯ"	1.00
		b. Reverse reads АДРѢЛЯ"	.75

Kuban, (Soviet) Republic
КУБАНСКАЯ РЕСПУБЛИКА

Loan Notes

Russian notes #77–80 with a four-cornered counter stamp

R137.	(1918)	20 Rubles	2.50
R138.		40 Rubles	3.00
R139.		50 Rubles	2.00
R140.		100 Rubles	2.00

ЕКАТЕРИНОДАРСКОГО ОТДЕЛЕНИЯ ГОСУДАРТВЕННОГО БАНКА

R141.	1918	10 Rubles, blue on brown	
		a. Guaranteed amount 25,000 rubles	2.00
		b. Guaranteed amount 50,000 rubles	2.00
		c. Guaranteed amount 100,000 rubles	2.00

R142.	(1918)	50 Rubles. Colored guilloche (ornament) at left. Promissory note paper	
		a. With perforation	1.25
		b. Without perforation	2.00

235
×
129

R143.		100 Rubles. Type of R142	1.25

Northern Army, Special Corp under General Rodzianko
ОТДѢЛЬНЫЙ КОРПЧСЪ СѢВЕРНОЙ АРМІИ, ГЕН. РОДЗЯНКО

R144.	(1919)	50 Kopecks, light green. Both sides printed	RR
R145.		50 Kopecks, light green	
		a. Obverse only of R144	2.00
		b. Reverse only of R144	2.00
R146.		50 Kopecks, dark green	
		a. Obverse only of R144	6.50
		b. Reverse only of R144	6.50
R147.	1919	1 Ruble, brown on yellow	1.00
R148.		3 Rubles, green	1.25

101 × 68

R149.		5 Rubles, blue	5.00
R150.		10 Rubles, red	1.00

Northern District (Tschaikowskij)
СѢВЕРНОЙ ОБЛАСТИ

5 % КРАТКОСРОЧНОЕ ОБЯЗАТЕЛЬСТВО ВЕРХОВНАГО
УПРАВЛЕНІЯ СѢВЕРНОЙ ОБЛАСТИ (5% Obligation Notes)

R151.	15.8.1918	100 Rubles, yellow	4.50

R152.		500 Rubles, blue	6.50
R153.		1,000 Rubles, red	8.50
R154.		5,000 Rubles	25.00
R155.		10,000 Rubles	37.50

5 % КРАТКОСРОЧНОЕ ОБЯЗАТЕЛЬСТВО ВЕРХОВНАГО ПРАВИТЕЛЬСТВА СѢВЕРНОЙ ОБЛАСТИ (5% Obligation Notes)

Notes exist both with and without *и* after ФИНАНСОВЪ

R156.	15.8.1918	50 Rubles, green	1.25
R157.		100 Rubles	
		a. With *и*	1.25
		b. Without *и*	5.00
R158.		500 Rubles, blue	
		a. Control numbers green or black. With *и*	1.50
		b. Without *и*	2.50
R159.		1,000 Rubles, red	
		a. With *и*	2.00
		b. Without *и*	4.00

Small Denomination Notes

Similar to the Czarist notes #28, 30 and 31 but text reads СѢВЕРНАЯ РОССІЯ

R160.	(1919)	10 Kopecks, green and rose	.75

90 × 52

R161.		20 Kopecks, brown and green	.75
R162.		50 Kopecks, blue and yellow. Eagle with crown	.75
R163.		50 Kopecks. Eagle without crown	2.50

Notes similar to Czarist issues #10–13 but text reads СѢВЕРНАЯ РОССІЯ
Eagle with crown, stamp on reverse reads ЧЛЕНѢ ГОРОДСКОЙ ЗМИССІОННОЙ КАССЫ

R164.	1918	5 Rubles, blue green (also known without reverse stamp)	2.50
R165.		10 Rubles, red and green	2.50
R166.		25 Rubles, rose and green	7.50
R167.		100 Rubles, brown, red and green	R

Notes similar to R164–R167 but reverse stamp reads ЧЛЕНѢ ГОСУДАРСТВ ЗМИССІОННОЙ КАССЫ

R168.	1918	5 Rubles, blue green	3.50
R169.		10 Rubles, red and green	3.50

R170.	25 Rubles, rose and green	
	a. Eagle overprinted	7.50
	b. Eagle without overprint	8.50
R171.	100 Rubles, brown, red and green	25.00
R172.	500 Rubles	R

Notes similar to issues #1 and #9–14 but text reads СѢВЕРНАЯ РОССІЯ
Eagle without crown

R173.	1919	1 Ruble	2.50
R174.		3 Rubles	3.00
R175.		5 Rubles, green and brown	4.00
R176.		10 Rubles	6.50

178 × 106

R177.	25 Rubles, rose and green	7.50
R178.	100 Rubles	30.00
R179.	500 Rubles	50.00

Notes of the Czarist and the Provisional Government with perforation "CO"
Many counterfeits exist.

R180.	50 Kopecks. Note #31 with perforation	1.50
R181.	1 Ruble. Note #1 with perforation	2.50
R182.	1 Ruble. Note #15 with perforation	1.00
R183.	3 Rubles. Note #9 with perforation	1.25
R184.	5 Rubles. Note #3 with perforation	5.00
R185.	5 Rubles. Note #10 with perforation	2.50
R186.	5 Rubles. Note #35 with perforation	.75
R187.	10 Rubles. Note #4 with perforation	10.00
R188.	10 Rubles. Note #11 with perforation	1.25
R189.	20 Rubles. Note #38 with perforation	2.00
R190.	20 Rubles. Note #77 with perforation	5.00
R191.	25 Rubles. Note #12 with perforation	2.50
R192.	25 Rubles. Note #48 with perforation	4.00
R193.	40 Rubles. Note #39 with perforation	2.00
R194.	40 Rubles. Note #78 with perforation	5.00
R195.	50 Rubles. Note #8 with perforation	6.00

R196.	50 Rubles. Note #49 (but dated 1909) with perforation	12.50
R197.	50 Rubles. Note #52 with perforation	3.50
R198.	50 Rubles. Note #53 with perforation	4.50
R199.	50 Rubles. Note #79 with perforation	4.50
R200.	100 Rubles. Note #5 with perforation	12.50
R201.	100 Rubles. Note #13 with perforation	5.00
R202.	100 Rubles. Note #56 with perforation	12.50
R203.	100 Rubles. Note #57 with perforation	5.00
R204.	100 Rubles. Note #58 with perforation	5.00
R205.	100 Rubles. Note #80 with perforation	4.50
R206.	250 Rubles. Note #36 with perforation	2.50
R207.	500 Rubles. Note #6 with perforation	17.50
R208.	500 Rubles. Note #14 with perforation	7.50
R209.	500 Rubles. Note #59 with perforation	6.00
R210.	500 Rubles. Note #60 with perforation	6.00
R211.	1,000 Rubles. Note #61–63 with perforation	7.50
R212.	1,000 Rubles. Note #37 with perforation	2.50
R213.	5,000 Rubles. Note #64 with perforation	10.00
R214.	10,000 Rubles. Note #65–67 with perforation	12.50
R215.	100,000 Rubles. Note #73 with perforation	20.00

North Caucasian Soviet Socialist Republic
СЕВЕРО—КАВКАЗСКАЯ СОВ. СОЦ. РЕСПУБЛИКА

ВРЕМЕН. ЦЕНТР. УПРАВЛ. ОТД. НАРОД. БАНКА
Notes printed on promissory note paper

R216.	1918	25 Rubles, blue green	1.00
R217.		50 Rubles, yellow brown	1.00
R218.		100 Rubles, green	1.00
R219.		10 Rubles, red and yellow brown. Sickle and grain	
		a. Obverse text reads ОБЩЕГОСУДАР . . . ОГО	1.25
		b. Obverse text reads ОБЩЕГООУДАР . . . АГО	1.00

131 × 82

R220.	25 Rubles, violet, yellow and green. Sickle and grain	
	a. Obverse text reads ОБЩЕГОСУДАР . . . ОГО	1.00
	b. Obverse text reads ОБЩЕГООУДАР . . . АГО	1.00

КРАЕВОГО ИСПОЛНИТ. КОМИТЕТА СОВЕТОВ СЕВ. КАВКАЗА
ДЕНЕЖНЫЙ ЗНАК

R221.	5 Rubles, blue and rose	1.00

R222.	50 Rubles, green	1.25
R223.	100 Rubles, brown	2.00
R224.	250 Rubles	2.00
R225.	500 Rubles, multicolored	2.00

North Caucasian Emirate
СЕВЕРО—КАВКАЗСКИЙ ЭМИРАТ

Notes of Terek and North Caucasia with the stamp of the Iman or Vizier Kjamil-Khan

R226.	(1919)	50 Rubles. Note R303b with round stamp of the Vizier	RR
R227.		50 Rubles. Note R303a with round stamp of the Vizier	5.00
R228.		100 Rubles. Note R304 with oval imprint of the ring of the Iman	RR
R229.		100 Rubles. Note R304 with oval imprint of the ring of the Iman and the round stamp of the Vizier. Signature and date	15.00
R230.		100 Rubles. Note R304 with only the round stamp of the Vizier. Signature and date handwritten	RR
R231.		100 Rubles. Note R304 with only the round stamp of the Vizier but without signature and handwritten date	7.50
R232.		100 Rubles. Note R223 with round stamp of the Vizier, signature and handwritten date	RRR
R233.		100 Rubles. Note R223 with round stamp of the Vizier but without signature and handwritten date	RRR
R234.		500 Rubles. Note R225 with round stamp of the Vizier, signature and handwritten date	RRR

КРЕДТНЫЙ БИЛЕТЪ

Scale with rifle and sabre on all notes

62 × 65

R235.	1919	5 Rubles, blue green. Mountain with flags	
		a. Printed top to top	2.50
		b. Reverse inverted	5.00
R236.		25 Rubles	
		a. Printed top to top	4.00
		b. Reverse inverted	6.50
R237.		50 Rubles	
		a. Printed top to top	4.00
		b. Reverse inverted	6.50
R238.		100 Rubles, green and light brown. Mountain and flag	
		a. No text below the Arabic numeral of value in background on reverse	2.00
		b. As R238a but with Arabic text	2.50
		c. As R238b but reverse inverted	4.00

R239.	250 Rubles, green. Large arms	5.00
R240.	250 Rubles, light blue. Small arms	2.50

R241.	500 Rubles, light blue and light brown. Mountains and sea with setting sun	
	a. Printed top to top	2.50
	b. Reverse inverted	4.00
R242.	1,000 Rubles. Reverse blank (not issued)	RRR

Northwest Front (under General N. N. Judenitch) Field Notes
СЕВЕРО—ЗАПАДНЫЙ ФРОНТЪ
ДЕНЕЖНЫЙ ЗНАКЪ

The reverses of all notes show a double eagle without crown and the memorial to Peter the Great in the middle.

R243.	1919	25 Kopecks, yellow green	.50
R244.		50 Kopecks, grey	.50
R245.		1 Ruble, light and dark green	.50
R246.		3 Rubles, rose and green	
		a. Control number without letters (1st issue)	.75
		b. A in control number (2nd issue)	1.00
R247.		5 Rubles, blue	
		a. Type of R246a	.75
		b. Type of R246b	1.00
R248.		10 Rubles, blue green and brown	
		a. Type of R246a (1st issue)	.65
		b. Type of R246b (2nd issue)	1.00
		c. Control number (3rd issue)	1.00

160 × 73

R249.	25 Rubles, violet background	
	a. Type of R246a	1.25
	b. Type of R246b	1.50
	c. Type of R248c	1.75
R250	100 Rubles, brown and green	1.50
R251.	500 Rubles, green and brown	2.00
R252.	1,000 Rubles, red and violet	2.00

South Russia, Armed commandos of Generals Deniken and Wrangel
ГЛАВНОЕ КОМАНДОВАНIЕ ВООРУЖЕННЫМИ СИЛАМИ

Stamp Notes

R253.	(1918)	20 Kopecks, green. Ticket printed with text, eagle and St. George at right	2.00

Small Denomination Notes

R254.   (1918)   50 Kopecks, light brown   1.00

ДЕНЕЖНЫЙ ЗНАКЪ (Exchange Notes)

R255.   1918   1 Ruble, brown
               a. White, thin paper   .40
               b. Yellow, thick paper   .40
R256.   3 Rubles, green
               a. White, thin paper without watermark   .40
               b. Grey, thin paper without watermark   .40
               c. Yellow, thick paper without watermark   .40
               d. Paper with watermark   1.25
R257.   5 Rubles, blue
               a. Unwatermarked paper   .40
               b. Paper watermarked with monogram   .40
R258.   10 Rubles, red brown and greenish
               a. Unwatermarked paper   .65
               b. Paper watermarked with monogram   .40
R259.   25 Rubles, lilac brown and green. Woman with sword
               at left
               a. Unwatermarked paper   .40
               b. Paper watermarked with monogram   .40
R260.   100 Rubles, dark brown and grey blue. Helmeted man's
               head and seated woman   .65
R261.   250 Rubles, red brown and green. Seated women at left
               and right
               a. White, unwatermarked paper   .50
               b. Yellowish, unwatermarked paper   .50
               c. Paper watermarked with monogram   .40
R262.   500 Rubles, dark green and brown. Rev. Seated woman
               at left
               a. White, unwatermarked paper   .65
               b. Yellowish, unwatermarked paper   .65
               c. Paper watermarked with monogram   .65
R263.   1919 50 Rubles, brown, grey and blue. Rev. Woman with
               flag   .40
R264.   100 Rubles, yellow green and multicolored. Warrior in
               armor with standard at right of reverse, memorial
               with two warriors
               a. Unwatermarked paper   .65
               b. Paper watermarked with monogram   .50
R265.   1,000 Rubles, grey green and red brown to blue violet.
               Woman seated with shield and sword in middle of
               reverse
               a. Unwatermarked paper   .65
               b. Paper watermarked with monogram   .50
               c. Paper watermarked with mosaic design   .50

R266.   5,000 Rubles, lilac and green. Warrior in armor with shield,
               flag and snake at left on reverse
               a. White, unwatermarked paper   .65
               b. Grey, unwatermarked paper   .75
               c. Paper watermarked with monogram   .50
               d. Paper watermarked with mosaic design   .50

БИЛЕТЪ ГОСУДАРСТВЕННАГО КАЗНАЧЕЙСТВА (State Treasury Notes)

R267. 1919   3 Rubles, green
               a. Unwatermarked paper   5.00
               b. Paper watermarked with mosaic design   .50
R268.   10 Rubles, red brown. Memorial with two warriors on
               reverse
               a. Unwatermarked paper   .50
               b. Paper watermarked with wavy lines   .50
R269.   50 Rubles, background olive brown. Woman with two
               children
               a. Paper watermarked with lines   .40
               b. Paper watermarked with spades   .40
R270.   200 Rubles, lilac and grey violet. Equestrian statue and
               soldiers on reverse   .75
R271.   1,000 Rubles, multicolored. Bell at left, St. George and
               dragon at right
               a. Unwatermarked paper (two control number
               varieties)   .50
               b. Paper watermarked with mosaic design   .50
R272.   10,000 Rubles, green and brown. Seated woman with lance
               at left, seated woman with sword at right   .25
R273. 1920   5 Rubles, blue green
               a. Printed on both sides   RRR
               b. Printed on obverse only   1.50
R274.   25,000 Rubles, grey blue and brown (unfinished printing) 1.00

6 % КРАТК. ОБЯЗАТЕЛЬСТВО ГОСУД. КАЗНАЧЕЙСТВА
(6% Obligation Notes)

R275. 1.1.1920   100,000 Rubles, brown on red brown
               a. Maturity date (СРОК) 1. IV.   R
               b. Maturity date (СРОК) 15. VIII.   R
               c. Maturity date (СРОК) 15. XI.   5.00

БИЛЕТЪ ГОСУДАРСТВЕННАГО КАЗНАЧЕЙСТВА (State Treasury Notes)

Issued by General Wrangel. All reverses show memorial with cross.

R276. 1920   100 Rubles, red brown
               a. Paper watermarked with stars   .50
               b. Paper watermarked with waves   .75
               c. Paper watermarked with mosaic design   .50

154 × 76

R277.		250 Rubles, lilac brown	
		a. Brown paper watermarked with spades	.45
		b. White paper watermarked with mosaic design	.25
R278.		500 Rubles, blue	.25

ГОСУДАРСТВО РОССІЙСКОЕ КАЗНАЧЕЙСКІЙ ЗНАКЪ

English printing, not issued.

R279.		1 Ruble	RRR
R280.		3 Rubles	RRR
R281.		5 Rubles	RRR
R282.		50 Rubles, blue on yellow. Helmeted woman's head at left	.75
R283.	1919	100 Rubles, brown on green. Helmeted woman's head at left on reverse. Serial letters in the plate or printed with control numbers	1.00
R284.		500 Rubles, green and orange. Type of R283	.75

ХЕРСОНСКІИ ГУБ. УПОЛНОМОЧ. УПРАВЛ. ПРОДОВОЛЬСТВІЕМЪ
ОДЕССА (Food authorization notes for the Cherson district)

R285.	10.10.1919	25 Rubles	1.25
R286.		50 Rubles	1.25
R287.		100 Rubles	1.25
R288.		250 Rubles	1.25
R289.		500 Rubles	2.00

Terek-Daghestan District
ТЕРСКО=ДАГЕСТАНСКАЯ ОБЛАСТ

Pasted-on control stamps of savings banks. Reverses are printed with:
   a. Narrow "Н" in date, no period after 1918 (issued by Iman Gozinskij)
   b. Broad "Н" in date, period after 1918 (issued by Soviet Peoples Commissar)

			a.	b.
R290.	25.1 (ЯНВАРЯ) .1918	25 Kopecks	7.50	3.75
R291.		50 Kopecks	8.50	3.75
R292.		1 Rubie	4.50	2.00
R293.		3 Rubles	5.00	4.00
		Error "БИЛЕТЕМИ"	—	7.50
R294.		5 Rubles	7.50	2.00

R295.		10 Rubles	2.50	2.00
R296.		25 Rubles	1.50	1.25
R297.		100 Rubles	3.00	1.25

Terek Republic
ТЕРСКАЯ РЕСПУБЛИКА

R298.	1918	1 Ruble, brown background	.75
R299.		3 Rubles, green background	.75
R300.		5 Rubles, blue on grey	.65
		Error: Reverse inverted	1.25
R301.		10 Rubles, red background	.75

152 × 96

R302.		25 Rubles, dark green	1.75
R303.		50 Rubles, yellow and orange background	
		a. Brown printing	.50
		b. Black printing	.65
R304.		100 Rubles	
		a. Brown on red brown printing	1.00
		b. Brown on light brown printing, at bottom left	1.25

Stamp Currency

Tickets with double-headed eagle in middle, text on reverse

R305.		10 Kopecks, blue	1.25
R306.		15 Kopecks, brown	1.25
R307.		20 Kopecks, green	1.25

Transcaucasian Commissariat
ЗАКАВКАЗСКІЙ КОМИССАРІАТЪ

All notes are known with and without a network of varnish as a background pattern.

R308.	1918	1 Ruble, blue on light blue	.25
R309.		3 Rubles, green background	.25
R310.		5 Rubles, blue on grey	.40

119 × 78

R311.	10 Rubles, red brown on olive	.50
R312.	50 Rubles, blue grey background	.75
R313.	100 Rubles, brown and blue green	.85
R314.	250 Rubles, grey olive on pale lilac	1.00

Federation of Socialist Soviet Republics of Transcaucasia
ФЕДЕРАЦИЯ СОВ. СОЦ. РЕСПУБЛИК ЗАКАВКАЗЬЯ
ДЕНЕЖНЫЙ ЗНАК

All notes show a building with flags on their obverse. Ornamentation on the reverse runs in one direction.

R315.	1923	1,000 Rubles, yellow brown background	.75
R316.		5,000 Rubles, lilac brown background	1.00
R317.		10,000 Rubles, grey or red background	.50
R318.		25,000 Rubles, brown background	.65
R319.		50,000 Rubles, green background	
		a. Paper watermarked with stars	4.00
		b. Unwatermarked paper	.65
R320.		100,000 Rubles, red brown background	
		a. Paper watermarked with stars	4.00
		b. Unwatermarked paper	.75

166 × 98

| R321. | 250,000 Rubles, green background | .75 |
| | Error: Reverse inverted | 2.50 |

R322.		500,000 Rubles, light blue blackground	
		a. Paper watermarked with stars	2.00
		b. Unwatermarked paper	.75
R323.		1,000,000 Rubles, violet background	
		a. Paper watermarked with stars	1.50
		b. Unwatermarked paper	.75
R324.		5,000,000 Rubles, green and lilac background	1.00
R325.		10,000,000 Rubles, blue, green, yellow and red background	1.25

ДЕНЕЖНЫЙ ЗНАК

Reverse ornamentation runs in various directions.

R326.	1923	5,000 Rubles, lilac brown background	.50
R327.		10,000 Rubles, grey background	.75
R328.		50,000 Rubles, green background	1.00
R329.		100,000 Rubles, red brown background	1.00
R330.		250,000 Rubles, green background	.75
R331.		500,000 Rubles, light blue background	1.00
R332.		1,000,000 Rubles, violet background	1.00
R333.		5,000,000 Rubles, green and lilac background	1.00
R334.		10,000,000 Rubles, blue, green, yellow and red background	1.25

Transcaucasian Socialist Federation of Soviet Republics

R335.	1924	25,000,000 Rubles, grey background. Building with flag in middle	
		a. Watermarked paper	1.50
		b. Unwatermarked paper	1.25
		Error: Reverse inverted	5.00
R336.		50,000,000 Rubles, grey-violet background. Type of R335 (format 167 × 100 mm)	2.00
R337.		50,000,000 Rubles, horizontal format. Printed on reverse side only (unfinished)	4.00
R338.		75,000,000 Rubles, brown background. Oil derrick on reverse	
		a. Watermarked paper	2.50
		b. Unwatermarked paper	2.00
R339.		100,000,000 Rubles, green background. Type of R335	2.00
R340.		250,000,000 Rubles, brown. Oil derrick on reverse	3.00
R341.		1,000,000,000 Rubles, lilac. Seated woman with fruit and grains on reverse	
		a. Text in green	4.00
		b. Text in black	5.00
R342.		10,000,000,000 Rubles	7.50

Ukrainian Peoples Republic
УКРАИНСЬКА НАРОДНЯ РЕСПУБЛИКА

1 Karbowanez (КАРБОВАНЕЦ) = *1 Ruble* = *2 Griwen* (ГРИВЕНЬ)
= *200 Schahiw* (ШАГІВ)

Central Control

R343. 1917   100 Karbowanez, brown, orange and yellow
       a. Printed top to top   RR
       b. Reverse inverted   2.00

ЗНАК ДЕРЖАВНОІ СКАРБНИЦІ (Treasury Notes)

R344. (1918)   25 Karbowanez, green. Man with spade at left, woman with sheafs at right. Without serial letters (issued in Kiev)
       a. Text reads КРЕДІТОВИМ   2.50
       b. Text reads КРЕДИТОВИМ   12.50
R345.   25 Karbowanez, green. As R344 but serial letters AO (issued in Odessa)   1.25
R346.   50 Karbowanez, green. Type of R344 (issued in Kiev)
       a. Text reads КРЕДИТОВИМ   4.00
       b. Text reads КРЕДИТОВИМИ   1.00

131 × 74

R347.   50 Karbowanez, green. As R346 but serial letters AKI or AKII (issued in Kiev)   .50
       Error: Reverse printed only in red (AKII)   6.50
R348.   50 Karbowanez, green. As R346 but with serial letters AO (issued in Odessa)
       a. Serial numbers to 209   .25
       b. Serial numbers from 210 (issued by General Deniken and labeled as false by the Ukrainian Government)   .25

Postage Stamp Currency

Postage stamps (Michel catalogue #1–5 of Ukraine) printed on cardboard. Reverses have arms and text.

R349. (1918)   10 Schahiw, yellow brown. Arms   .25

R350.	20 Schahiw, dark brown. Peasant	.25
R351.	30 Schahiw. Ceres head	
	a. Ultramarine	.25
	b. Grey violet	.75
R352.	40 Schahiw, green. Arms	.25
R353.	50 Schahiw, red	.25

3,6 % БІЛЕТ ДЕРЖАВНОЇ СКАРБНИЦІ   (3.6% Loan Notes and Interest Coupons)

R354.	1918	50 Griwen, green and brown	1.00
R355.		100 Griwen, brown on green and red	.75
R356.		200 Griwen, blue	.75
R357.		1,000 Griwen, brown on yellow brown	.75
R358.		90 Schahiw, green	.25
R359.		1 Griwnja 80 Schahiw, red brown	.25
R360.		3 Griwnja 60 Schahiw, blue	.25
R361.		18 Griwen, yellow-brown	.25

5 % КР. ОБЯЗАТ. ГОСУД. КАЗНАЧ (5% Obligation Notes)

With various stamps of the State Bank branches.

R362.	(1918)	1,000 Rubles, red brown on grey	2.50
R363.		5,000 Rubles	4.00
R364.		10,000 Rubles	7.50
R365.		25,000 Rubles	15.00
R366.		50,000 Rubles	20.00

ДЕРЖАВНИЙ КРЕДИТОВИЙ БІЛЕТ

R367.	1918	2 Griwen, green	
		a. Yellowish background, serial letter A	.40
		b. Brown background, serial letter B	.75
R368.		10 Griwen, red brown	.40

R 369
174 × 114

R369.	100 Griwen, violet. Peasant woman at left, worker at right	
	a. Blue background, serial letter A	.65
	b. Grey violet background, serial letter (not issued)	RR
R370.	500 Griwen, green and orange. Woman's head in middle	.65
R371.	1,000 Griwen, blue on orange and yellow	1.00
R372.	2,000 Griwen, red on blue	1.00

ЗНАК ДЕРЖАВНОЇ СКАРБНИЦІ

Beginning with R374, the notes are issues of the Directorate under Sjemen Petljura.

R373.	1,000 Karbowanez, brown. Reverse brown, two allegorical female figures	
	a. Paper watermarked with wavy lines	.50
	b. Zigzag lines of varnish printed on paper (appear as watermark)	1.00
R374.	1,000 Karbowanez, brown. As R373 but reverse violet brown	
	a. Paper watermarked with wavy lines	1.50
	b. Paper watermarked with stars	1.25
R375.	100 Karbowanez, brown and grey green	
	a. Paper watermarked with stars (two control number varieties)	.75
	b. Paper watermarked with spades (two control number varieties)	1.00
R376.	250 Karbowanez, brown and olive (two control number varieties)	1.00
R377. (1919)	10 Karbowanez, brown on grey paper watermarked with spades (two control number varieties)	.50
	Also see R383.	
R378.	25 Karbowanez, violet brown. With and without control numbers	1.00

РОЗМІННИЙ ЗНАК ДЕРЖАВНОЇ СКАРБНИЦІ

R379. (1920)	5 Griwen, grey	.50
	Error: ГИВЕНЬ	R

ДЕРЖАВНИЙ КРЕДИТОВИЙ БІЛЕТ

Printing trials, Austrian printer

R380.	1920	50 Griwen, blue grey	RR
R381.		50 Griwen, brown	RR
R382.		1,000 Griwen, grey and orange	RRR

Ukrainian Soviet Republic

СОВЕТСКАЯ УКРАИНСКАЯ РЕСЛУБЛИКА

ЗНАК ДЕРЖАВНОІ СКАРБНИЦІ

R383.	(1920)	10 Karbowanez, red brown. As R377 but white paper and no control numbers	.50
R384.		50 Karbowanez. Trial printings	
		a. Green	25.00
		b. Light blue	25.00
		c. Violet	25.00
		d. Brown	25.00

РАСЧЕТНАЯ БОНА ВУЦИК

All notes printed in green blue on obverses, lilac figures of value on reverses. Control numbers are handwritten. R385–R389 also have control numbers printed.

R385.	1923	5 Kopecks	1.25
R386.		10 Kopecks	1.25

75 × 55

R387.	25 Kopecks	1.50
R388.	50 Kopecks	2.00
R389.	1 Ruble	2.25
R390.	3 Rubles	2.50
R391.	5 Rubles	4.00
R392.	10 Rubles	4.00
R393.	25 Rubles	7.50
R394.	50 Rubles	12.50

German Occupation during World War II

Zentralnotenbank Ukraine (Central Ukrainian Bank)

R395.	10.3.1942	1 Karbowanez, olive	.50
R396.		2 Karbowanez (not issued)	RRR
R397.		5 Karbowanez, brown violet. Head of child at right	.75
R398.		10 Karbowanez, red brown. Head of peasant woman at right	.65
R399.		20 Karbowanez, grey brown. Head of industrial worker at right	.75

R400.　　　　　　50 Karbowanez, green. Head of miner at right　　　1.00

176 × 92

R401.　　　　　100 Karbowanez, blue. Head of sailor at right　　　1.50
R402.　　　　　200 Karbowanez, olive. Peasant woman at right　　　2.00
R403.　　　　　500 Karbowanez, violet. Chemical worker at right　　　2.25

Notes also exist of the Bank of Kiev (1941 1 ruble, 1 and 5 tscherwonez) but they were not circulated.

Ukrainian Revolutionary Army–Ukrainski Powstanscha Armyia (У П А)

R404.　(1946)　　　5 Karbowanez, brown violet and multicolored. Soldier at machine gun and soldier with hand grenade　　　　　　　　　　　　　　　　　　　RRR

SAAR (Sarre)

The rich Saar district was occupied by France after World War I. Governed by the League of Nations, the area was returned to Germany after a plebiscite vote in 1935. Following World War II, the Saar was again declared an autonomous district to be returned to Germany in 1957.

Mines Domaniales de la Sarre, Etat Francaise (Mining interests of the Saar, French State)

1.	dates to 1.1.1930	50 Centimes, blue grey. Woman's head at left	$1.00
2.	1919 to 1.1.1930	1 Franc, red brown. Woman's head at right	1.50

Issue of 1947 (without any identification of issuing authority)

3.	1947	1 Mark, blue and brown. Bearded head of man	2.50
4.		2 Mark, lilac and brown. Type of #3	15.00
5.		5 Mark, rose and violet. Type of #3	4.00
6.		10 Mark, multicolored. Woman's head	11.50
		Error: Reverse without text	

130 × 84

7.	50 Mark, multicolored. Type of #6	30.00
8.	100 Mark, multicolored. Type of #6	R

SERBIA

At the beginning of the 19th century Serbia became an autonomous principality under the Turks, breaking away completely in 1878. In 1882 the country became a kingdom under Milan II who ruled until 1889. After the Balkan War of 1912–13 and World War I, Serbia became part of the Kingdom of Yugoslavia.

1 Dinar (ДИНАР) = *100 Para* (ПАРА)

Dinar in gold = ДИНАР У ЗЛАТУ
Dinar in silver = ДИНАР У СРЕВРУ

Government Notes

1.	1. 7.1876	1 Dinar	$45.00
2.		5 Dinar	50.00
3.		10 Dinar	50.00
4.		50 Dinar	R
5.		100 Dinar	R
6.	1.11.1885	10 Dinar	R

Privilegovana Narodna Banka Kraljevine Srbije (Privileged National Bank of the Kingdom of Serbia) ПРИВИЛЕГОВАНА НАРОДНА БАНКА КРАЉЕВИНЕ СРБИЈЕ

7.	2. 7.1884	100 Dinar Zlatu (gold), green on brown. Woman with tablet at left and at right	RR

157 × 95

8.	1. 5.1886	50 Dinar Zlatu, green on light brown. Woman in costume at left, woman with sword at right	R

9.	14. 1.1887	10 Dinar Srebru, (silver), blue. Woman with sword at left, allegorical figures at right	32.50
10.	2. 1.1893	10 Dinar Srebru, blue on brown. Woman with musical instrument	6.50
11.	5. 1.1905	20 Dinar Zlatu, blue on brown. Woman at left, man with sword at right	37.50
12.		100 Dinar Srebru, blue on brown. Woman with sword at right	8.50
13.	1. 8.1914	50 Dinar Srebru	40.00
14.	(1916–17)	5 Dinar Srebru, blue. Man's helmeted head	2.00

Also see Yugoslavia #36–47.

Postage Stamp Currency, 1915

Due to the war, only two values, the 5 and 10 para, of an already prepared set of postage stamps were released for use on mail. The other five values, all showing King Peter II and his Military Staff on the battlefield, were circulated as emergency currency. The stamps were all perforated but some imperforate specimens from unfinished sheets are known.

15.	(1915)	5 Para, light green	.25
16.		10 Para, vermilion	.50
17.		15 Para, grey black	1.75
		Error: Dark blue	25.00
18.		20 Para, brown	.75
19.		25 Para, dark blue	5.00
20.		30 Para, light olive	2.50
21.		50 Para, red brown	10.00

The 15 para stamps pasted onto cardboard with text and value overprinted were local issues of emergency currency (*Osijek, Prima Frankova tiskara*).

Austrian Military Government, 1917–18

Notes #10 and 12 with stamp "K.u.K. Militar-Gouvernement in Serbien, Kreis-kommando (area)" were issued during the Austrian occupation.

M1.	(1917–18)	10 Dinar (dated 2.1.1893), stamped "Belgrad"	15.00
M2.		100 Dinar (dated 5.1.1905), stamped "Belgrad"	30.00
M3.		10 Dinar, stamped "Belgrad-Land"	20.00
M4.		100 Dinar, stamped "Belgrad-Land"	37.50
M5.		10 Dinar, stamped "Čačak"	22.50
M6.		100 Dinar, stamped "Čačak"	40.00
M7.		10 Dinar, stamped "Gornji Milanovac"	R
M8.		100 Dinar, stamped "Gornji Milanovac"	R
M9.		10 Dinar, stamped "Kragujevac"	15.00
M10.		100 Dinar, stamped "Kragujevac"	40.00

M11.	10 Dinar, stamped "Kruševac"	22.50
M12.	100 Dinar, stamped "Kruševac"	40.00
M13.	10 Dinar, stamped "Sabac"	25.00
M14.	100 Dinar, stamped "Sabac"	45.00
M15.	10 Dinar, stamped "Semendria"	30.00
M16.	100 Dinar, stamped "Semendria"	50.00

138 × 84

M17.	10 Dinar, stamped "Smederevo"	22.50
M18.	100 Dinar, stamped "Smederevo"	40.00
M19.	10 Dinar, stamped "Užice"	30.00
M20.	100 Dinar, stamped "Užice"	50.00
M21.	10 Dinar, stamped "Valjevo"	37.50
M22.	100 Dinar, stamped "Valjevo"	50.00

Notes of 20 and 50 dinar (#11 and 13) were probably also overprinted.

SLOVAKIA

The eastern part of Czechoslovakia, Slovakia was declared an independent state led by Dr. Joseph Tiso under German protection. The area was returned to Czechoslovakia after World War II.

1 Krone = 100 Heller

As with the paper money of Czechoslovakia, Slovakian notes marked "Specimen" were supplied to collectors. The values indicated in the first column are for regular notes, those in the second column for specimens.

Government Notes

1.	(June 1939)	100 Kronen, green. Czech note #24 (dated 10.1.1931) with red overprint "Slovensky Stat"	$37.50	$2.50
2.	(April 1939)	500 Kronen, red. Czech note #22 (dated 2.5.1929) with blue overprint "Slovensky Stat"	R	5.00
3.	(April 1939)	1,000 Kronen, green and blue. Czech note #26 (dated 25.5.1934) with lilac overprint "Slovensky Stat"	RR	10.00
4.	15. 9.1939	10 Kronen, blue and brown. A. Hlinka at right	7.50	1.50
5.		20 Kronen, brown. A. Hlinka at right	12.50	2.00
6.	11. 9.1942	20 Kronen, brown and blue. Poet J. Holly at right	1.50	.50
7.	20. 7.1943	10 Kronen, blue and violet. Poet L. Stur at right	3.00	.50
8.	(1950)	5 Kronen, lilac and brown. Girl's head at right	1.50	.50

Slovenska Narodna Banka (Slovakian National Bank)

9.	7.10.1940	100 Kronen, blue. Prince Pribina at right	3.50	1.00
10.		100 Kronen, blue. As #9 but "II Emisia" at left edge of reverse	5.00	1.00
11.	15.10.1940	50 Kronen, violet and lilac. Two girls in Slovakian costume at left	2.00	.50

191 × 90

12.	25.11.1940	1,000 Kronen, brown. King Swatopluk and his three sons at right	10.00	1.50
13.	12. 7.1941	500 Kronen, green. Young man in costume at right	7.50	1.50
14.	18.12.1944	5,000 Kronen, brown and green. Prince Knieza Mojmir on reverse	20.00	2.50

For notes #9, #10, #12 and #13 with stamps affixed, see Czechoslovakia #51–54.

SPAIN (España)

As a result of the Carlist Wars, the weakened monarchy was deposed and a provisional government installed from 1868 to 1870. The monarchy was re-established under King Amadeo but he was forced to abdicate in 1873 and the First Republic came into being. It lasted only until 1875 when Alfonso XII was put on the throne. He was followed by Maria Christina who ruled as regent for her son Alfonso XIII from 1885 until 1902 when he came of age to rule in his own right. Alfonso ruled well but social unrest sent him into voluntary exile in 1931 and the Republic of Spain was created. Although Spain remained neutral during both world wars the country was devastated by a civil war that raged from 1936 to 1939.

1 Peseta = 100 Centimos

Issues of the First Republic and the Kingdom up to 1931

Banco de España (Bank of Spain)

1.	1. 7.1874	25	Pesetas	R
2.		50	Pesetas	R
3.		100	Pesetas	R
4.		500	Pesetas	RR
5.		1,000	Pesetas	RRR
6.	1. 7.1875	25	Pesetas	R
7.		50	Pesetas	R
8.		100	Pesetas	R
9.		500	Pesetas	RR
10.		1,000	Pesetas	RRR
11.	1. 7.1876	100	Pesetas	RR
12.		500	Pesetas	RR
13.		1,000	Pesetas	RRR
14.	1. 1.1878	50	Pesetas	R
15.		100	Pesetas	R
16.		125	Pesetas	RRR
17.		250	Pesetas	RRR
18.		500	Pesetas	RRR
19.		1,000	Pesetas	RRR

#20
174 × 90

20.	1. 4.1880	50 Pesetas	R
21.		100 Pesetas	R
22.		500 Pesetas	R
23.		1,000 Pesetas	RR
24.	1. 1.1884	25 Pesetas	R
25.		50 Pesetas	R
26.		100 Pesetas	R
27.		500 Pesetas	RR
28.		1,000 Pesetas	RR
29.	1. 7.1884	25 Pesetas	RR
30.		50 Pesetas	R
31.		100 Pesetas	R
32.		500 Pesetas	RR
33.		1,000 Pesetas	RR
34.	1.10.1886	25 Pesetas	$50.00
35.		50 Pesetas	R
36.		100 Pesetas	50.00
37.		500 Pesetas	R
38.		1,000 Pesetas	RR
39.	1. 6.1889	25 Pesetas	45.00
40.		50 Pesetas	50.00
41.		100 Pesetas	37.50
42.	24. 7.1893	25 Pesetas	37.50
43.		50 Pesetas	50.00
44.		100 Pesetas	45.00
45.	1. 5.1895	1,000 Pesetas, black on light yellow	RR
46.	2. 1.1898	25 Pesetas	45.00
47.		50 Pesetas, dark blue on light yellow. Jovellanos at left	30.00
48.	24. 6.1898	100 Pesetas, blue on light yellow. Type of #47	30.00
49.	17. 5.1899	25 Pesetas, blue on green. Quevedo at left	25.00
50.	25.11.1899	50 Pesetas, black on green. Type of #49	30.00
51.	1. 5.1900	100 Pesetas, blue on green. Type of #49	37.50
52.	30.11.1902	50 Pesetas, black on yellow. Velasquez at left	32.50
53.	1. 7.1903	100 Pesetas, grey	R
54.	1.10.1903	500 Pesetas	RR
55.	1. 1.1904	25 Pesetas	R
56.	19. 3.1905	50 Pesetas, black on rose. Echegaray at left	30.00

#59

130 × 90

57.	30. 6.1906	100	Pesetas, multicolored. Seated woman at left and right	3.00
58.	24. 9.1906	25	Pesetas, multicolored. Seated woman at left	3.50
59.	24. 9.1906	50	Pesetas, multicolored. Woman with Mercury staff and globe in middle	3.50
60.	28. 1.1907	500	Pesetas, black on green and violet	50.00
61.	10. 5.1907	1,000	Pesetas, blue	R
62.	15. 7.1907	25	Pesetas, background in green and red. Reclining woman in middle	3.50
63.		50	Pesetas, multicolored. Standing woman at left and right	5.00
64.		100	Pesetas, multicolored. Seated woman at left	3.50
65.		500	Pesetas, multicolored. Standing woman at left, three angels at right	37.50
66.		1,000	Pesetas, multicolored. Seated woman in middle	50.00
67.	1.12.1908	25	Pesetas	RR
68.		100	Pesetas	RR
69.	1. 7.1925	100	Pesetas, blue and green. Philip II at left	.50
70.		1,000	Pesetas, brown and violet. Charles I at right	3.50
71.	12.10.1926	25	Pesetas, blue and lilac. St. Xavier at left	3.00
72.	17. 5.1927	50	Pesetas, violet. Alfonso XIII at left, without stamp	7.50

For note with embossed stamp, see #80.

149 × 110

73.	24. 7.1927	500	Pesetas, blue and brown. Isabella the Catholic at right	8.50
74.	15. 8.1928	25	Pesetas, blue and brown. Calderon de la Barca at right	.75
75.		50	Pesetas, lilac. Velasquez at right	.75
76.		100	Pesetas, violet. Cervantes at left	.75
77.		500	Pesetas, green and lilac. Cardinal Cisneros at left	3.00
78.		1,000	Pesetas, blue and yellow green. San Fernando at right	3.50

Banco de España (Bank of Spain)

Issues of the Second Republic, 1931–36

79.	(1931)	100 Pesetas. Note #69 (dated 1.7.1925) with embossed stamp "Gobierno Provisional de la Republica"	12.50
80.	(1931)	50 Pesetas. Note #72 (dated 17.5.1927) with colored stamp "Republica Espanol"	3.50
81.	25. 4.1931	25 Pesetas, green and multicolored. Vincente Lopez at right	.75
82.		50 Pesetas, blue, lilac and multicolored. E. Rosales at left	.75
83.		100 Pesetas, violet. G. F. de Cordoba at left	1.00
84.		500 Pesetas, brown and blue. Juan S. de Elcano at left	3.00
85.	1935	5 Pesetas, green. Woman's head at left	.50
86.		10 Pesetas, red-brown. Woman's head at right	.75
87.	7. 1.1935	500 Pesetas, blue and brown. Hernando Cortez at left	40.00
88.	22. 7.1935	50 Pesetas, lilac. Santiago Ramon Ygajal at right	.50
89.	31. 8.1936	25 Pesetas, blue, brown and violet	R
90.		50 Pesetas	RR
91.		100 Pesetas	RR
92.		500 Pesetas	RRR

Ministerio de Hacienda (Ministry of Finance)

93.	1937	50 Centimos, blue. Woman's head in middle	.50
94.		1 Peseta, brown and green. Nike of Samothrace at left	.75
95.		2 Pesetas, blue, brown and green. Woman's head in middle	.50

Postage Stamp Currency (1938)

Brown pasteboard printed on the obverse with the Spanish arms and "Plus Ultra." The reverse has a printed stamp or postage stamp attached. Initially issued only by the Finance Ministry but later also by banks as small denomination money.

96.	Printed stamps "Especial Movil" of 5, 10, 15, 30 centimos denominations from	1.25
	Postage stamps of 5, 10, 15, 20, 25, 30, 40, 50, 60 centimos values from	1.25

Banco de España (National Bank of Spain)

Issues since 1936

97.	21.11.1936	5 Pesetas, brown and blue green. Arms at right	20.00
98.		10 Pesetas, blue and orange. Arms at right	17.50
99.		25 Pesetas, blue and olive. Printed by Giesecke and Devrient	3.00

100.		50 Pesetas, brown. Type of #99		5.00
101.		100 Pesetas, green. Type of #99		7.50
102.		500 Pesetas, dark blue. Type of #99		20.00

181 × 105

103.		1,000 Pesetas, green. Type of #99	30.00
104.	18. 7.1937	5 Pesetas, brown. Woman with Mercury staff at right	10.00
105.	12.10.1937	1 Peseta, lilac and blue. Arms at left	2.00
106.		2 Pesetas, green. Buildings at left	4.50
107.	28. 2.1938	1 Peseta, brown and green. Arms at left	3.00
108.	30. 4.1938	1 Peseta, brown and green. Type of #107	2.00
109.		2 Pesetas, dark green. Type of #106	2.50
110.	20. 5.1938	25 Pesetas, green and rose. Eagle in background	3.00
111.		50 Pesetas, red brown and green. Eagle in background	5.00
112.		100 Pesetas, lilac brown and orange. Eagle in background	7.50
113.		500 Pesetas, yellow green and lilac. Eagle in background	20.00
114.		1,000 Pesetas, blue and red. Eagle in background	30.00
115.	10. 8.1938	5 Pesetas, green and red brown. Printed by Giesecke and Devrient	2.00
116.	9. 1.1940	25 Pesetas, grey blue. Philip II at left	2.50
117.		50 Pesetas, green. Menendez Pelayo at left	3.50
118.		100 Pesetas, lilac brown. Columbus in middle	7.50
119.		500 Pesetas, dark green. John of Austria at right	20.00
120.		1,000 Pesetas, grey and brown. B. Murillo in middle	27.50
121.	1. 6.1940	1 Peseta, blue and orange. Cortez on horseback at right	2.00
122.	4. 9.1940	1 Peseta, multicolored. Sailing ship (Santa Maria) in middle	1.00
123.		5 Pesetas, orange and blue. Segovia castle at right	1.50
124.	21.10.1940	500 Pesetas, multicolored. Death scene of Count Orgaz at right	20.00
125.		1,000 Pesetas, lilac and violet. Charles I at left	27.50

126.	13. 2.1943	5 Pesetas, multicolored. Isabella the Catholic	2.00
127.	21. 5.1943	1 Peseta, dark brown and multicolored. Ferdinand the Catholic at left	.75
128.	15. 6.1945	1 Peseta, brown. Isabella the Catholic at left	.75
129.		5 Pesetas, green. Isabella and Columbus at left	1.00

122 × 78

130.	19. 2.1946	25 Pesetas, violet. Florez Estrada at left	2.00
131.		100 Pesetas, lilac brown. Goya at right	4.50
132.		500 Pesetas, blue. Francisco de Vitoria at right	15.00
133.		1,000 Pesetas, green and brown. J. L. Viveo at right	25.00
134.	12. 4.1947	5 Pesetas, brown lilac. Seneca on reverse	2.50
135.	5. 3.1948	5 Pesetas, green. Sebastian Elcano at right	.75
136.	2. 5.1948	100 Pesetas, brown. Francisco Bayea at left	3.75
137.	19. 6.1948	1 Peseta, brown. Dame v. Elche at right	.40
138.	4.11.1949	1,000 Pesetas, black and green. Ramon Santillan at right	25.00
139.	16. 8.1951	5 Pesetas, green. J. Balmes at left	.50
140.	15.11.1951	500 Pesetas, dark blue. Mariano Belliure at left	12.50
141.	19.11.1951	1 Peseta, brown. Don Quixote	.25
142.	31.12.1951	50 Pesetas, lilac. Santiago Rusinol at right	—
143.		1,000 Pesetas, green. J. Sorolla in middle	25.00
144.	7. 4.1953	100 Pesetas, brown. Julio Romero de Torres in middle	—
145.	22. 7.1953	1 Peseta, brown. Santa Cruz	—
146.	22. 7.1954	5 Pesetas, green. Alfonso El Sabio at right	—
147.		25 Pesetas, violet. Isaac Albeniz at left	—
148.		500 Pesetas, blue. Ignacio Zuloaga in middle	—
149.	29.11.1957	1,000 Pesetas, green. "Reyes Catolicos," the Catholic Monarchs in middle	—
150.	19.11.1965	100 Pesetas, brown. C. A. Becquer	—

Bank of Spain, Bilbao

First issue, reverse not printed, name of issuing bank stamped at lower right. The following banks issued notes:

a. Banco de Bilbao
b. Banco Central de Bilbao
c. Banco del Comercio de Bilbao
d. Banco Guipuzcoano
e. Banco Hispano Americano
f. Banco Urquijo Vascongado
g. Banco de Viscaya
h. Caja de Ahorros Vizcaina
i. Caja de Ahorros y Monte de Piedad Municipal de Bilbao

R1.	30.8.1936	5 Pesetas, red on olive. With stamps "a"–"i"	each	2.00
R2.	Various dates (stamped)	25 Pesetas, violet on olive. With stamps "a"–"i"	each	2.50
R3.		50 Pesetas, green on olive. With stamps "a"–"i"	each	2.50
R4.		100 Pesetas, blue on olive. With stamps "a"–"i"	each	3.00

Bank of Spain, Bilbao

Second issue, picture reverse, name of issuing bank imprinted at lower right. The following banks issued notes:

a. Banco de Bilbao
b. Banco del Comercio
c. Banco Guipuzcoano
d. Banco Hispano Americano
e. Banco Urquijo Vascongado
f. Banco de Vizcaya
g. Caja de Ahorros Vizcaina
h. Caja de Ahorros, y Monte de Piedad Municipal de Bilbao

Values indicated are for the commonest varieties. Seldom seen are:

5 Pesetas: c, e
10 Pesetas: g
25 Pesetas: d, e
50 Pesetas: g

R5.	1.1.1937	5 Pesetas, green. Shepherd with flock and tree on reverse. With bank names a, c, e, f, g, h	each	.75
R6.		10 Pesetas, brown. Building entrance on reverse. With bank names a, f, g, h	each	1.00

R7.		25 Pesetas, brown. Blacksmith on reverse. With bank names b, d, e, g	each	1.25
R8.		50 Pesetas, blue. Worker on reverse. With bank names a, f, g, h	each	1.50
R9.		100 Pesetas, green. Peasant plowing with two oxen on reverse. With bank names a, f, h	each	3.00

158 × 103

R10.		500 Pesetas. With bank name b (not issued)		37.50
R11.		1,000 Pesetas, lilac. Stamped a. Factory on reverse. With bank name a (not issued)		37.50

Bank of Spain, Gijon

R12.	5.11.1936	5 Pesetas, rose with brown diagonal lines		1.25
R13.		10 Pesetas, rose with green diagonal lines		1.50
R14.		25 Pesetas, rose with blue diagonal lines		2.00
R15.		50 Pesetas, rose with light green diagonal lines		2.50
R16.		100 Pesetas, rose with red brown diagonal lines		3.50
R17.	Sept. 1937	100 Pesetas, blue on light brown. Two peasants at work on reverse		3.50

Bank of Spain, Santander

Name of issuing bank stamped at lower right. The following banks issued notes:

    a. Banco de Bilbao-Santander
    b. Banco Espanol de Credito
    c. Banco Hispano Americano
    d. Banco Mercantil
    e. Banco de Santander
    f. Monte de Piedad

R18.	1.11.1936	5 Pesetas, grey. With stamps "a"–"f"	each	2.50
R19.		10 Pesetas, grey. With stamps "a"–"f"	each	3.50
R20.		25 Pesetas, grey. With stamps "a"–"f"	each	5.00
R21.		50 Pesetas, grey. With stamps "a"–"f"	each	6.50
R22.		100 Pesetas, grey. With stamps "a"–"f"	each	12.50

Generalitat de Catalunya (Catalonia)

R23. 25. 9.1936   2.50 Pesetas, grey green. Worker and factory on reverse (two control number varieties)   1.00

R24.   5 Pesetas, brown. Weapons in middle, worker at left and peasant at right on reverse   1.25

R25.   10 Pesetas, green. Fishing boat on reverse   1.50

Notes R23–R25 are seldom seen in good condition.

Primitive-looking notes with a printed heading "Generalitat de Catalunya" in denominations of 10, 25, 50, 100, 500 and 1,000 pesetas, dated by machine are known. They are counterfeits presumably made for collectors.

Consejo de Asturias y León (Asturias and Leon)

R26. (1936)   25 Centimos, grey violet and blue. Harbor work on reverse   .40

R27.   40 Centimos, brown violet and green. Reverse as R26   .50

R28.   50 Centimos, blue and violet. Blacksmith on reverse   .90

103 × 56

R29.   1 Peseta, red brown and yellow. Seated woman with lion at left   .50

R30.   2 Pesetas, grey violet and red. Type of R29   .50

SWEDEN (Sverige)

The last separation of the Scandinavian states took place under King Oscar II when the personal union of Norway and Sweden was set aside. Under King Gustav V (1907–50) Sweden remained neutral during both world wars. Gustav VI Adolf became king in 1950.

1 Krona = 100 Ore

Sveriges Riksbank (Swedish Riksbank)

"Seated Svea" type, various dates of issue. All printing is black or dark brown on multicolored guilloche. Many signature varieties.

1.	1890–97	5 Kronor	$15.00
2.	1898–1905	5 Kronor. As #1 but with a letter at lower left and right on reverse	12.50

120 × 70

3.	1906–17	5 Kronor. As #2 but different background color	7.50
4.	1918–52	5 Kronor. As #3 but numerals of value in red	3.00
5.	1892–97	10 Kronor	20.00
6.	1898–1905	10 Kronor. As #5 but with a letter at lower left and right on reverse	17.50
7.	1906–17	10 Kronor. As #6 but different background color	12.50
8.	1918–40	10 Kronor. As #7 but numerals of value in red	5.00
9.	1896–97	50 Kronor	30.00
10.	1898–1903	50 Kronor. As #9 but with a letter at lower left and right on reverse	22.50
11.	1903–06	50 Kronor. As #10 but both signatures printed	20.00
12.	1907–17	50 Kronor. As #11 but different background color	17.50
13.	1918–54	50 Kronor. As #12 but numerals of value in red	12.50
14.	1955–57	50 Kronor. As #13 but with two letters at lower left and right on reverse	15.00
15.	1958–62	50 Kronor. As #14 but second signature at left	12.50
16.	1898–1903	100 Kronor	50.00

#8

120 × 70

17.	1903–06	100 Kronor. As #16 but both signatures printed	45.00
18.	1907–17	100 Kronor. As #17 but different background color	37.50
19.	1918–54	100 Kronor. As #18 but numerals of value in red	22.50
20.	1955–58	100 Kronor. As #19 but with two letters at lower left and right on reverse	25.00
21.	1959–63	100 Kronor. As #20 but second signature at left	25.00
22.	1894–97	1,000 Kronor, bluish paper with red threads	RRR
23.	1898–1906	1,000 Kronor. As #22 but with a letter at lower left and right on reverse	RRR
24.	1907–08	1,000 Kronor. As #23 but different background color	RRR
25.	1909–17	1,000 Kronor. As #24 but different color paper (reddish with blue threads)	RR
26.	1918–31	1,000 Kronor. As #25 but numerals of value in red	RR
27.	1932–50	1,000 Kronor. As #26 but both signatures printed	RR

134 × 76

28.	1874–75	1 Krona, green (format 134 × 76 mm)	7.50
29.	1914–21	1 Krona, green (format 120 × 70 mm)	
		a. 1914–16	4.00
		b. 1917–19	2.50
		c. 1920–21	2.00
		Error: 1 Krona 1920 wrong text "lagen om rikets mynt av den"	R

"Seated Svea" type, additional issues

30.	1948	5 Kronor, dark green. Jubilee issue for 90th birthday of King Gustav V (originally sold for double face value)	6.50

31.	1954–61	5 Kronor, dark brown. Portrait of King Gustav VI Adolf. Paper watermarked with king's portrait	3.00
32.	1962–63	5 Kronor, dark brown. As #31 but paper watermarked with portrait of Esaias Tegnér. Paper with metallic threads	4.00
33.	dates from 1965	5 Kronor, violet and multicolored. Gustav Vasa at right	—

119 × 69

34.	1940–52	10 Kronor, grey blue. Gustav Vasa at left. Date and control numbers in red	5.00
35.	1953–62	10 Kronor, grey blue. As #34 but date and control numbers in blue	4.00
36.	dates from 1962	10 Kronor, dark green. King Gustav VI Adolf	—
37.	(1968)	10 Kronor, blue and multicolored. "Sveriges Riksbank 1668–1968"	—
38.	dates from 1965	50 Kronor, blue. King Gustav III at right	—
39.	dates from 1962	100 Kronor, brown and blue. King Gustav II Adolf at right	—
40.	dates from 1952	1,000 Kronor, brown. Standing Svea	—
41.	1939	10,000 Kronor, black and blue. Arms	RRR
42.	dates from 1958	10,000 Kronor, green and multicolored. Svea with shield	—

Enskilda Banken (Private Banks)

After 1903, all private bank notes were recalled from circulation and the Swedish Riksbank given the exclusive right to issue paper money. The private bank notes still in circulation in 1900 were in denominations of 5, 10, 50, 100 and 500 kronor and are from the following banks (date in parenthesis is expiration of bank's authority to issue notes):

Bohus Lans Enskilda Bank (1901)
Boras Enskilda Bank (1902)
Christianstads Enskilda Bank (1901)
Enskilda Banken i Christinehamn (1902)
Enskilda Banken i Wenersborg (1902)

Gefleborgs Lans Enskilda Bank (1903)
Gotlands Enskilda Bank (1902)
Gotheborgs Privat Bank (1901)
Hallands Enskilda Bank (1902)
Helsinglands Enskilda Bank (1903)
Hernosands Enskilda Bank (1903)
Kalmar Enskilda Bank (1902)
Malare–Provinsernas Enskilda Bank (1902)
Norrbottens Enskilda Bank (1903)
Norrkopings Enskilda Bank (1902)
Ost-Gota Bank (1902)
Privat Banken i Orebro (1902)
Skaraborgs Lans Enskilda Bank (1902)
Skanska Priwat-Banken (1901)
Smalands Privat Bank (1902)
Stockholms Enskilda Bank (1902)
Stora Kopparbergs Lans och Berglags Enskilda Bank (1902)
Sundvalls Enskilda Bank (1903)
Sodermanlands Enskilda Bank (1902)
Uplands Enskilda Bank (1903)
Wermlands Provincial Bank (1901)

Nearly all of the above notes are rare and seldom available.

SWITZERLAND (Schweiz)

After the French occupation and the founding of the Helvetian Republic in 1803, renewed in 1815, the everlasting neutrality policy was established. In 1848 changes were made in the Constitution to strengthen the union of the States.

1 Franken = 100 Rappen

Concordat Notes

Uniform bank notes of the various Concordat banks with their individual names and authorized signatures imprinted. The notes issued from 1883 show the figure of Helvetia at left. The following banks issued Concordat notes (all R–RRR):

1.	Aargauische Bank, Aarau	50 Franken
2.		100 Franken
3.		500 Franken
4.		1,000 Franken
5.	Appenzell-Ausserhodische Kantonalbank, Herisau	50 Franken
6.		100 Franken
7.		500 Franken
8.	Appenzell-Innenhodische Kantonalbank, Appenzell	50 Franken
9.		100 Franken
10.	Banca Cantonale Ticinese, Bellinzona	50 Franken
11.		100 Franken
12.		500 Franken
13.		1,000 Franken
14.	Banca della Svizzera Italiana, Lugano	50 Franken
15.		100 Franken
16.		500 Franken
17.	Banca Popolare di Lugano	50 Franken
18.		100 Franken
19.		500 Franken
20.	Bank in Basel	50 Franken
21.		100 Franken
22.		500 Franken
23.		1,000 Franken
24.	Bank in Luzern	50 Franken
25.		100 Franken
26.		500 Franken
27.	Bank in St. Gallen	50 Franken
28.		100 Franken
29.		500 Franken
30.		1,000 Franken

31.	Bank in Schaffhausen	50	Franken
32.		100	Franken
33.		500	Franken
34.	Bank in Zurich	50	Franken
35.		100	Franken
36.		500	Franken
37.		1,000	Franken
38.	Banque Cantonale Fribourgeoise	50	Franken
39.		100	Franken
40.		500	Franken
41.		1,000	Franken
42.	Banque Cantonale Neuchateloise	50	Franken
43.		100	Franken
44.		500	Franken
45.	Banque Cantonale Vaudoise, Lausanne	50	Franken
46.		100	Franken
47.		500	Franken
48.		1,000	Franken
49.	Banque Commerciale Neuchateloise	500	Franken
50.		100	Franken
51.		500	Franken
52.	Banque du Commerce de Geneva	50	Franken
53.		100	Franken
54.		500	Franken
55.		1,000	Franken
56.	Banque de l'Etat de Fribourg	50	Franken
57.		100	Franken
58.		500	Franken
59.	Banque de Geneve	50	Franken
60.		100	Franken
61.		500	Franken
62.		1,000	Franken
63.	Banque Populaire de la Gruyere, Bulle	50	Franken
64.		100	Franken
65.		500	Franken
66.	Basellandschaftliche Kantonalbank, Liestal	50	Franken
67.		100	Franken
68.		500	Franken
69.		1,000	Franken
70.	Baseler Kantonalbank, Basel	50	Franken
71.		100	Franken
72.		500	Franken
73.		1,000	Franken
74.	Caisse d'Amortissement de la Dette publique a Fribourg	50	Franken
75.		100	Franken
76.		500	Franken
77.	Credit Agricole et Industriel de la Broye, Estavayer	50	Franken
78.		100	Franken
79.	Credit Gruyerien, Bulle	50	Franken
80.		100	Franken

81.	Credito Ticinese, Locarno	50	Franken
82.		100	Franken
83.		500	Franken
84.	Ersparnis-Cassa des Kantons Uri, Altdorf	50	Franken
85.		100	Franken
86.	Glarner Kantonalbank, Glarus	50	Franken
87.		100	Franken
88.		500	Franken
89.	Graubundner Kantonalbank, Chur	50	Franken
90.		100	Franken
91.		500	Franken
92.	Kantonalbank von Bern	50	Franken
93.		100	Franken
94.		500	Franken
95.	Kantonalbank Schwyz	50	Franken
96.		100	Franken
97.		500	Franken
98.		1,000	Franken
99.	Kantonale Spar-und Leihkasse von Nidwalden, with "Unterwalden nid dem Walde"		
100.		50	Franken
101.	As #99 with "Nidwalden"	100	Franken
102.		50	Franken
103.	Luzerner Kantonalbank	100	Franken
104.		50	Franken
105.		100	Franken
106.		500	Franken
107.	Obwaldener Kantonalbank, Sarnen	1,000	Franken
108.		50	Franken
109.	St. Gallische Kantonalbank	100	Franken
110.		50	Franken
111.		100	Franken
112.		500	Franken
113.	Schaffhauser Kantonalbank	1,000	Franken
114.		50	Franken
115.		100	Franken
116.	Solothurnische Bank	500	Franken
117.		50	Franken
118.		100	Franken
119.		500	Franken
120.	Solothurner Kantonalbank	1,000	Franken
121.		50	Franken
122.		100	Franken
123.		500	Franken
124.	Spar-und Leihcasse des Kantons Luzern	1,000	Franken
125.		500	Franken
126.	Thurgauische Hypothekenbank, Frauenfeld	1,000	Franken
127.		50	Franken
128.		100	Franken
		500	Franken

129.	Thurgauische Kantonalbank, Weinfelden	50 Franken
130.		100 Franken
131.		500 Franken
132.	Toggenburger Bank, Lichtensteig	50 Franken
133.		100 Franken
134.		500 Franken
135.	Zurcher Kantonalbank	50 Franken
136.		100 Franken
137.		500 Franken
138.		1,000 Franken
139.	Zuger Kantonalbank	50 Franken
140.		100 Franken
141.		500 Franken

All of the above notes are R–RRR above their face value.

Schweizerische Nationalbank (Swiss National Bank)

Founded in 1905, the Bank issued types similar to the Concordat issues but with a white cross in a red rosette at the upper right and changed text.

142.	1.2.1907	50 Franken, green	R

180 × 115

143.		100 Franken, blue	R
144.		500 Franken, green	RR
145.		1,000 Franken, violet	RRR

New type notes

Notes #146–150 read "Gesetz vom 6. Okt. 1905," many date and signature varieties

146.	dates from 1. 1.1910	50 Franken, green. Woman's head. Woodcutter on reverse	50.00
147.		100 Franken, blue. Woman's head. Mower on reverse	R
148.		500 Franken, red. Woman of Appenzell. Appenzell knitter on reverse	RR
149.		1,000 Franken, violet. Woman's head. Foundry on reverse	RRR

150.	dates from 1.12.1911	20 Franken, blue, green and brown. Woman's head, "Vreneli"	20.00
151.	dates from 1. 8.1913	5 Franken. William Tell with background of Rutli Alp	
		a. Light brown (first issue)	12.50
		b. Dark brown (later issue)	—
152.	1.1.1918	100 Franken, blue and brown. Tell and Tellskapelle. Head of Tell in medallion at left. Letters "T.W." at lower left, "R.K." at lower right	50.00
153.		100 Franken, blue and brown. As #152 but altered portrait of Tell in medallion. Letters "Ekn. R.K." at lower right	RR

Die Eidgenossische Staatskasse (Confederation State Treasury)

154.	10.8.1914	5 Franken, blue. Liberty at left, Arnold v. Winkelried at right. German text	15.00
155.		5 Franken, blue. As #154 but French text	15.00
156.		5 Franken, blue. As # 154 but Italian text	25.00
157.		10 Franken, blue. Liberty at left, Tell at right. German text	20.00

127 × 83

158.		10 Franken, blue. As #157 but French text	20.00
159.		10 Franken, blue. As #157 but Italian text	37.50
160.		20 Franken, blue. Liberty at left, Arnold v. Winkelried right. German text	30.00
161.		20 Franken, blue. As #160 but French text	30.00
162.		20 Franken, blue. As #160 but Italian text	50.00

Darlehnkasse der schweizerischen Eidgenossenschaft (State loan office of the Swiss Confederation)

| 163. | 9.9.1914 | 25 Franken, dark green and yellow brown | 30.00 |

Treasury notes of 1 and 2 franken (dated 27.4.1915) and 100 franken (dated 9.9.1914) were printed but not issued.

Swiss National Bank

Notes as previous issues but text reads "Gesetz vom 7.4.1921."

| 164. | | 20 Franken, blue, green and brown. Type of #150 | 25.00 |

165.	1.1.1923	100 Franken, blue. Type of #147	R
166.		500 Franken, red. Type of #148	RR
167.		1,000 Franken, violet. Type of #149	RRR

Notes as previous issue but text reads "Gesetzgebung uber die Schweizerische National Bank." Many date and signature variations.

168.	dates to 18. 4.1929	20 Franken, blue, green and brown. Type of #150	10.00
169.	dates to 20. 1.1949 and 29.10.1955	50 Franken, green. Type of #146	20.00
170.	dates to 20. 1.1949	100 Franken, blue. Type of #147	30.00

200 × 127

171.	dates to 20. 1.1949	500 Franken, red. Type of #148	—
172.	dates to 16.10.1947 and 29. 4. 1955	1,000 Franken, violet. Type of #149	—

New Note Types

Many date and signature varieties

173.	21. 6.1929–28. 3.1952	20 Franken, blue. Pestalozzi	8.50
174.	dates from 25. 8.1955	10 Franken, red brown. Gottfried Keller	—
175.	dates from 1. 7.1954	20 Franken, blue. H. Dufour	—
176.	dates from 1. 7.1955	50 Franken, green. Girl's head	—
177.	dates from 25.10.1956	100 Franken, blue. Boy's head	—
178.	dates from 31. 1.1957	500 Franken, red brown. Woman's head	—
179.	dates from 30. 9.1954	1,000 Franken, violet. Woman's head	—

TURKEY (Turkiye)

During the 19th century, Turkey was forced out of the Balkan area. In the Balkan War of 1913 Turkey lost nearly all of her remaining European territories. Sultan Mohammed VI (1918–22) was deposed in 1922 and a new republic established. The first president of the republic was Kemal Ataturk.

1 Ghurush (piastre, later kurus) = *40 Para*
1 Pound (lira) = *100 Kurus*

Imperial Ottoman Bank, so-called "Kaime" Notes

Dates of Issue: *I٣٩٣* = 1293 (1876), *I٣٩٤* = 1294 (1877), *I٣٩٥* = 1295 (1878), *I٣٣I* = 1331 (1913),   *I٣٣٢* = 1332 (1914),   *I٣٣٣* = 1333 (1915).

Numerals of value: *I* = 1, *٢* = 2, *٣* = 3, *٤* = 4, *٥* = 5, *٦* = 6, *٧* = 7 , *٨* = 8, *٩* = 9, *I٥* = 10, *٢٥* = 20, *٥٥* = 50, *I٥٥* = 100.

The early dates on the following notes follow the Moslem calendar (A.H.) beginning with the year 1 equal to A.D. 622, the date of Mohammed's flight from Mecca.

1.	1876/77	1 Ghurush, grey to grey blue	
		a. Round stamp (15 mm) with 1294 on reverse. Line stamp with 1877	$1.00
		b. Round stamp (18 mm) with 1295 on reverse. Line stamp with 1877	2.00
2.		5 Ghurush, red brown	
		a. Round stamp with 1293 on reverse. Box stamp with 1876	2.50
		b. As # 2a but 1877, unwatermarked paper	2.00
		c. As #2b but paper watermarked with letters	2.50
		d. As #2b but 1294	1.50
3.		10 Ghurush, lilac on light green.	
		a. Round stamp with 1293 on reverse. Box stamp with 1876	3.00
		b. Round stamp with 1293 on reverse. Box stamp with 1877	5.00
4.		20 Ghurush, brown lilac on yellow	
		a. Round stamp with 1293 on reverse. Box stamp with 1876	6.50
		b. Round stamp with 1293 on reverse. Box stamp with 1877	5.00
		c. Round stamp with 1294 on reverse. Box stamp with 1877	3.50

5. 1876/77 50 Ghurush, brown lilac on yellow. Vertical format
            a. Round stamp with 1293 on reverse. Box stamp
               with 1876   6.50
            b. As #5a but 1877   5.00
            c. As #5a but 1294/1877   5.00
            d. As #5c but 1295   5.00

6. 100 Ghurush, brown lilac on grey. Vertical format
            a. Round stamp with 1293 on reverse. Oval stamp
               with 1876   6.50
            b. As #6a but 1877   5.00
            c. As #6a but 1294/1877   5.00

178 × 112

7. 50 Ghurush, light blue. Round stamp with 1295 on
    reverse. Box stamp with 1877. Horizontal format   7.50

8. 100 Ghurush, red brown. Horizontal format
            a. Round stamp with 1294 on reverse. Box stamp
               with 1877   10.00
            b. Round stamp with 1295 on reverse. Box stamp
               with 1877   12.50

During World War I and continuing until 1933, the Imperial Ottoman Bank issued notes that had no legal tender status as their face value exceeded their exchange value. The 1, 2, 5, 50 and 100 pound values are RR–RRR.

Notes of the Finance Ministry

Text and figures in Arabic script

9. 30 March 1331 (1915) 1 Pound, blue frame. Background rose,
                       green and brown   17.50
10.   5 Pounds   37.50
11. 18 Oct. 1331 (1915) ¼ Pound, green background   3.50
12.   ½ Pound, rose background   7.50
13.   1 Pound, brown and multicolored back-
                    ground   12.50

14.	18 Oct. 1331 (1915)	5	Pounds, blue frame, rose, blue and brown background
			30.00
15.	16 Dec. 1331 (1915)	$\frac{1}{2}$	Pound on left or right half of 1 pound note #9
			37.50
16.		$\frac{1}{2}$	Pound on left or right half of 1 pound note #13
			12.50
17.		$2\frac{1}{2}$	Pounds on left or right half of 5 pounds note #10
			50.00
18.		$2\frac{1}{2}$	Pounds on left or right half of 5 pounds note #14
			25.00
19.	22 Jan. 1331 (1916)	5	Piastres, brown background
			1.50
20.		20	Piastres, violet background
			3.00
21.		$\frac{1}{4}$	Pound, green background
			3.50
22.		$\frac{1}{2}$	Pound, rose background
			6.50
23.		1	Pound, brown frame, blue, green and rose background
			8.50
24.	2 March 1332 (1916)	$\frac{1}{8}$	Pound on left or right half of $\frac{1}{4}$ pound note #11
			R
25.	23 May 1332 (1916)	1	Piastre, green. River with palms and caravan
			1.00
26.		$2\frac{1}{2}$	Piastres, rose. The Dardanelles
			1.25
27.		1	Pound
			R
28.		5	Pounds
			RR
29.		25	Pounds
			RRR
30.		100	Pounds
			RRR
31.		1,000	Pounds
			RRR
32.	6 August 1332 (1916)	5	Piastres, olive-green background. White paper
			1.25
33.		20	Piastres, orange background
			2.50
34.		$\frac{1}{2}$	Pound, rose background. Brownish paper, light blue and yellow
			5.00

175 × 96

35.		1	Pound, green border, blue, green and rose background
			a. Paper watermarked with hook design
			12.50
			b. Paper watermarked with small quatrefoils
			12.50

36.	6 August 1332 (1916)	5 Pounds, blue border, multicolored background	20.00
37.		10 Pounds, brown border, light blue background	37.50
38.		50 Pounds, light blue and yellow brown	
		a. Paper watermarked with hook design	R
		b. Paper watermarked with honeycomb and letters	R
39.		50 Pounds. As #38b but four stamps on reverse and "2eme Emission"	RR
40.		50 Pounds. As #38b but two stamps on reverse and "3eme Emission"	RR
41.		500 Pounds	RR
42.		50,000 Pounds	RRR
43.	4 February 1332 (1917)	5 Piastres, green background. Bluish paper	2.00
44.		20 Piastres, brown background. Bluish paper	3.00
45.		½ Pound, red background. Violet paper	5.00

170 × 91

46.		1 Pound, brown border, violet, rose and green background	
		a. Paper watermarked with hook design	7.50
		b. Paper watermarked with small quatrefoils	8.50
47.		2½ Pounds, orange and green	15.00
48.		10 Pounds, brown border, light blue background	37.50
49.		25 Pounds	R
50.		100 Pounds	RR

51.	28 March 1333 (1918)	1 Pound	12.50
52.		2½ Pounds, brown border, multicolored background	20.00
53.		5 Pounds, blue border, green and multicolored background	37.50
54.		25 Pounds, brown border, light blue background	R
55.		100 Pounds	RR
56.		1,000 Pounds	RRR

Postage Stamp Currency

Unissued postage stamps (#57 and #58) or tax stamps (#59) pasted on colored cardboard

57.	(1917)	5 Para, carmine on yellow or rose cardboard. Gun emplacement	1.25
58.		10 Para, green on bluish, greenish, yellowish or rose cardboard. Hagia-Sofia Mosque	1.25
59.		10 Para on 1 piastre, green and rose on bluish, yellowish or rose cardboard. Camel	3.50

Notes of the Finance Ministry

All notes with text in arabic and "Law no. 701 of 30. Dec. 1341 (1925)"

60.	1 Pound, green. Peasant with two oxen	3.50

170 × 91

61.	5 Pounds, blue. Springing wolf in middle	7.50
62.	10 Pounds, violet. Springing wolf at right	12.50
63.	50 Pounds, blue. Kemal Ataturk at right. View of Afyonkarahisar and mountain on reverse	25.00
64.	100 Pounds, green. Kemal Ataturk at right. View of new city of Ankara on reverse	50.00
65.	500 Pounds, red brown. Gok-Medres Mosque at left. Kemal Ataturk at right	R
66.	1,000 Pounds, dark blue. Kemal Ataturk at right. Railroad canyon on reverse	RR

Turkiye Cumhuriyet Merkez Bankasi (Central Bank of Turkey)

All notes with Latin letters and date "11 Haziran (June) 1930." Pre World War II issue, obverse portrait of Kemal Ataturk without moustache.

67.	2½ Pounds, green. Memorial at the National Plaza on reverse	2.00
68.	5 Pounds, dark blue. Memorial in Ankara on reverse	3.50
69.	10 Pounds, red brown. Citadel of Ankara on reverse	6.50
70.	50 Pounds, violet. Farm house and Angora sheep on reverse	10.00
71.	100 Pounds, dark brown. The Dardanelles on the reverse	25.00
72.	500 Pounds, olive green. Rumeli Hisar castle on reverse	R
73.	1,000 Pounds, blue. Memorial in Ankara on reverse	RR

Turkiye Cumhuriyet Merkez Bankasi (Central Bank of Turkey)

All notes have Latin letters and the date "11 Haziran (June) 1930." Obverse portrait of Ismet Inonu (with moustache) facing half left.

74.	50 Kurus, dark brown and lilac. Bank building on reverse. Printed by Bradbury (not issued)	.75
75.	50 Kurus, brown and green. Bank building on reverse. Printed by Reichs Printing Office	2.00
76.	1 Pound, lilac. The Bosphorus on reverse	2.50
77.	2½ Pounds, dark brown. Family home on reverse	3.50
78.	5 Pounds. Three girls on reverse	5.00

155 × 65

79.	10 Pounds, brown and red brown. Three peasant girls on reverse	7.50
80.	10 Pounds, light brown. Sultan Ahmed fountain in Istanbul on reverse	8.50
81.	10 Pounds, red. As #80 but later issue	7.50
82.	50 Pounds, violet. Sheep on reverse	15.00
83.	50 Pounds, blue. As #82 but later issue	12.50
84.	100 Pounds, dark brown. Girl with grapes on reverse Also known half printed	20.00
85.	100 Pounds, violet. Rumeli Hisar castle on reverse	20.00
86.	500 Pounds, olive green. Rumeli Hisar castle on reverse	37.50
87.	500 Pounds, olive green. Student	37.50
88.	1,000 Pounds, blue. Memorial in Ankara	R
89.	1,000 Pounds, blue. Boy Scout	R

Turkiye Cumhuriyet Merkez Bankasi (Central Bank of Turkey)

All notes with Latin letters and date "11 Haziran (June) 1930." Obverse portrait of Kemal Ataturk without moustache facing front. Post-war issue.

90.	2½ Pounds, lilac. Reverse lilac, bank building	1.25
91.	2½ Pounds, lilac. As #90 but brown reverse	1.00
92.	2½ Pounds, lilac. As #90 but red reverse	1.00
93.	2½ Pounds, lilac. As #90 but green reverse	.75
94.	5 Pounds, blue. Reverse blue, three peasant girls. Without name of printer	1.50
95.	5 Pounds, blue. As #94 but different guilloche (ornament) on obverse. Reverse blue. Printed by Bradbury	1.25
96.	5 Pounds, blue. As #95 but green reverse	1.25
97.	10 Pounds, green. Reverse green, river and Maritza Bridge. Without name of printer	3.00
98.	10 Pounds, green. As #97 but red-brown reverse. Without name of printer	2.50
99.	10 Pounds, green. As #97 but different guilloche on obverse. Reverse brown. Printed by Thomas De La Rue	2.50
100.	10 Pounds, green. As #99 but green reverse	2.00
101.	10 Pounds, green. As #99 but red-brown reverse	2.00
102.	50 Pounds, brown. Reverse brown, soldier with arms. Printed by Bradbury Wilkinson	—
103.	50 Pounds, brown. As #102 but orange reverse	—
104.	50 Pounds, brown. As #102 but dark rose reverse	—
105.	50 Pounds, brown. As #102 but grey-green reverse	—

159 × 74

106.	50 Pounds, brown. As #102 but brown reverse without name of printer	—
107.	50 Pounds, brown. As #106 but different guilloche on obverse	—
108.	100 Pounds, olive green. Reverse olive green, park with bridge in Ankara. Printed by Bradbury	—
109.	100 Pounds, olive green. As #108 but light blue reverse	—
110.	100 Pounds, brown. As #108 but different guilloche on obverse. Without name of printer	—
111.	500 Pounds, brown. Plaza and mosque in Istanbul on reverse	—
112.	500 Pounds, grey brown. As #111	—
113.	1,000 Pounds, violet. The Bosphorus on reverse	—

Turkiye Cumhuriyet Merkez Bankasi (Central Bank of Turkey)

All notes with Latin letters and date "11 Haziran (June) 1930." Obverse shows portrait of Kemal Ataturk facing half left.

114.   5 Pounds, violet and multicolored. Waterfall on reverse   —
115.   10 Pounds, green   —
116.   20 Pounds, brown. Memorial on reverse   —
117.   100 Pounds, green. Park with bridge in Ankara on reverse   —
118.   100 Pounds, olive green. As #117 but different guilloche   —
119.   500 Pounds, brown. Plaza and Mosque of Sultan Ahmed in Istanbul on reverse   —
120.   500 Pounds, grey violet. As #119   —

English notes with overprint

Issued during the World War I campaign of Gallipoli in Palestine and Iraq

R1.   60 Piastres on 10 shillings, red. British note #85 with overprint in Arabic letters   37.50
R2.   120 Piastres on 1 pound, black. British note #86 with overprint in Arabic letters   R

YUGOSLAVIA

The Kingdom of Yugoslavia was formed after the break-up of the Austro-Hungarian Empire in 1918 from Serbia, Croatia, and Slovenia. King Alexander I ruled from 1921 until 1934, followed by his son, King Peter II, who was under the guardianship of a regent until 1941. Yugoslavia was occupied by German troops during World War II who supported the independent states of Serbia and Croatia. Since 1945 Yugoslavia has been a Federated People's Republic.

1 Dinar = 100 Para

Finance Ministry Notes

Notes of the Austro-Hungarian Bank with machine overprint МИНИСТАРСТВО ФИНАНСИЈА КРАЉЕВСТВА СРБА ХРВАТА И СЛОВЕНАЦА (Ministarstvo Finansija Kraljevstva Srba, Hrvata i Slovenaca)

1.	(1919)	10 Kronen (dated 2.1.1915). Austria #19	$7.50
2.		20 Kronen (dated 2.1.1913). Austria #13	R

162 × 99

3.	50 Kronen (dated 2.1.1914). Austria #15	10.00
4.	100 Kronen (dated 2.1.1912). Austria #12	7.50
5.	1,000 Kronen (dated 2.1.1902). Austria #8	20.00

Numerous local and state hand overprints exist on Austro-Hungarian bank notes, also Serbian overprints on Bulgarian notes. At the time of the second Yugoslavian overprint on the Austrian notes, a stamp was attached to each. The text on the stamp reads "Kraljevstvo Srba Hrvata i Slovenaca." On the stamps affixed to the 10, 20 and 50 kronen notes the text was in three languages—Serbian, Croatian and Slovenian—and only one type of stamp was used. The stamp fastened to the 100 and 1,000 kronen notes had text in only one language, Serbian, Croatian or Slovenian, thus there were three different types of stamps.

6.	10 Kronen. Orange stamp, three languages. Woman's head to left	1.00
7.	20 Kronen. Lilac stamp, three languages. Woman's head to left	1.25
8.	50 Kronen. Green stamp, three languages. Woman's head to left	2.50
9.	100 Kronen. Brown stamp	
	a. Serbian (Cyrillic alphabet)	2.00
	b. Croatian	2.00
	c. Slovenian	2.00
10.	1,000 Kronen. Blue, brown and orange stamp	
	a. Serbian (Cyrillic alphabet)	1.50
	b. Croatian	1.50
	c. Slovenian	1.50

Ministarstvo Finansija Kraljevstva Srba, Hrvata i Slovenaca (Finance Ministry Notes)

Newly printed notes without overprint

11.	1. 2.1919	½ Dinar, brown, rose and green	.25
12.	(1919)	1 Dinar, brown. Helmeted man's head at left	.25
13.	21. 3.1921	25 Para (¼ dinar), blue and olive. Buildings in middle	.25

Notes overprinted in kronen values "kypha-kruna-kron." Various colors were used for the overprint.

14.	1. 2.1919	½ Dinar = 2 Kronen. Note #11 with red overprint	.40
15.	(1919)	1 Dinar = 4 Kronen. Note #12 with red overprint	.50
16.	(1919)	5 Dinar = 20 Kronen, lilac. Helmeted man's head at left	.65
17.	1. 2.1919	10 Dinar = 40 Kronen, blue. Blacksmith at left	.75
18.		20 Dinar = 80 Kronen, green. Farmer plowing with oxen at left	1.50

174 × 110

19.	(1919)	100 Dinar = 400 Kronen, lilac. Cupids at left and right	25.00
20.		1,000 Dinar = 4,000 Kronen, grey violet. Six allegorical figures	R

Narodna Banka Kraljevine Srba Hrvata i Slovenaca (National Bank of the Kingdom of the Serbs, Croats and Slovenes)

21.	1.11.1920	10 Dinar, blue. Man with wagon wheel at left	1.50
22.	30.11.1920	100 Dinar, violet and yellow. Seated woman with sword at right	8.50
23.		1,000 Dinar, multicolored. St. George and the dragon at left	R
24.		1,000 Dinar, multicolored. As #23 but blue overprint on man's head (Karageorge), colored rosettes overprinted above and below	37.50
25.	26. 5.1926	10 Dinar, multicolored. Woman's head at right	1.25

Narodna Banka Kraljevine Jugoslavije (National Bank of the Kingdom of Yugoslavia)
НАРОДНА БАНКА КРАЉЕВИНЕ ЈУГОСЛАВИЈЕ

26.	1.12.1929	10 Dinar, multicolored. As #25	3.00
27.		100 Dinar, violet and yellow. As #22	
		a. Paper watermarked with head of Karageorge	3.50
		b. Paper watermarked with head of Alexander I	1.00
28.	1.12.1931	50 Dinar, brown and multicolored. Head of King Alexander I at left (first issued in 1941 as a Serbian note)	.75
29.		1,000 Dinar, blue green and brown. Head of Queen Marie at left	1.00

171 × 104

30.	15. 7.1934	100 Dinar, blue and multicolored. Woman with boy at right (not issued)	12.50
31.	6. 9.1935	500 Dinar, green. King Alexander I at left	2.00
32.		1,000 Dinar, multicolored. Group of six people with three horses and a lion (not issued)	15.00
33.	6. 9.1936	20 Dinar, brown and blue. King Peter II in middle	1.00
34.		10,000 Dinar, brown, yellow green and blue. King Peter II at left (not issued)	RR
35.	22. 9.1939	10 Dinar, green. Head of King Peter II at left	1.25

Srpska Narodna Banka (Serbian National Bank) СРПСКА НАРОДНА БАНКА

36.	1. 5.1941	10 Serbian Dinar, green. Arms at left. Reverse of #35 overprinted	1.25
37.		20 Serbian Dinar, brown. Man's head (Vuc Karadzic) at left	.75
38.		100 Serbian Dinar, violet and yellow. Note #27 overprinted	1.00
39.		1,000 Serbian Dinar on 500 dinar, multicolored. Three seated women (the 500 dinar note was not issued without overprint)	1.50
40.	1. 8.1941	50 Serbian Dinar, brown and multicolored. Woman's head at left	.75
41.	1.11.1941	500 Serbian Dinar, brown and multicolored. Woman in national costume in middle	
		a. Paper watermarked with head of King Alexander I	.75
		b. Paper watermarked with woman's head	.50
42.	1. 5.1942	20 Serbian Dinar, blue. As #37 (not issued)	6.50
43.		50 Serbian Dinar, brown. Man's head (Njegos) at left	.75

163 × 84

44.		100 Serbian Dinar, brown and multicolored. Shepherd playing flute, sheep in background (not issued)	25.00
45.		500 Serbian Dinar, brown and multicolored. Seed sower at right	1.50
46.		1,000 Serbian Dinar, brown and multicolored. Blacksmith at left, woman in costume at right	
		a. Paper watermarked with head of King Peter II	1.00
		b. Paper watermarked with woman's head	2.00
47.	1. 1.1943	100 Serbian Dinar, brown and blue. St. Sava at left	.75

Demokratska Federativna Jugoslavija (Democratic Federation of Yugoslavia)

48.	1944	1 Dinar, olive brown. Soldier's head and rifle at right	.25
49.		5 Dinar, blue. Type of #48	.25

50.	1944	10	Dinar, black and orange. Type of #48	.35
51.		20	Dinar, orange. Type of #48 (three control number varieties)	.50
52.		500	Dinar, brown and green. Type of #48 (two control number varieties)	4.50
53.		1,000	Dinar, dark green. Type of #48 (two control number varieties)	7.50
54.	(undated)	50	Dinar, violet. Type of #48 (two control number varieties)	1.00
55.		100	Dinar, dark green and violet (two control number varieties)	.75

Gospodarska Banka za Istru Rijeku i Slovensko Primorje (State Bank for Istria, Fiume and the Slovenian Coast)

56.	1945	1	Jugolire, brown. Woman with soldier's cap at left	1.00
57.		5	Jugolire, green. Sail boat at right on reverse	.50
58.		10	Jugolire, brown and green. Type of #57	.75
59.		20	Jugolire, violet and green. Type of #57	.75
60.		50	Jugolire, red brown. Type of #57 at right (two control number varieties)	1.50
61.		100	Jugolire, brown and blue. Type of #57 (two control number varieties)	5.00

134 × 75

| 62. | | 500 | Jugolire, green. Type of #57 | 6.50 |
| 63. | | 1,000 | Jugolire, lilac and light brown. Farmer plowing with oxen at right on reverse | 7.50 |

Narodna Banka Federativne Narodne Republike Jugoslavije (National Bank of the Federated People's Republic of Yugoslavia)

64.	1. 5.1946	50	Dinar, brown. Miner at left	.25
65.		100	Dinar, brown and multicolored. Blacksmith at left, farmer at right	.50
66.		500	Dinar, brown. Soldier with rifle at right	3.00
67.		1,000	Dinar, brown. Woman with produce at right	2.50

149 × 77

68.	1. 5.1953	100 Dinar, multicolored. Four workers and two steam engine wheels	6.50
69.	1. 5.1955	100 Dinar, red. Woman in costume at left	.50
70.		500 Dinar, green. Woman with sickle at left	1.50
71.		1,000 Dinar, brown. Worker at left	3.00
72.		5,000 Dinar, blue. Relief of Mestrovic at left	12.50

Narodna Banka Jugoslavije (National Bank of Yugoslavia)

73.	1. 5.1963	100 Dinar, red. As #69	1.25
74.		500 Dinar, green. As #70	2.50
75.		1,000 Dinar, brown. As #71	5.00
76.		5,000 Dinar, blue. As #72	17.50

Currency Reform, 1965: *100 old Dinar = 1 new Dinar*

77.	1. 8.1965	5 Dinar, green. Woman with sickle at left (format 134 × 64 mm)	—
78.		10 Dinar, brown. Worker at left (format 143 × 66 mm)	—
79.		50 Dinar, blue. Relief of Mestrovic at left (format 151 × 72 mm)	—
80.		100 Dinar, red. Equestrian statue "Peace"	—
81.	1. 5.1968	5 Dinar, green. Woman with sickle at left (format 123 × 59 mm)	—
82.		10 Dinar, brown. Worker at left (format 131 × 63 mm)	—
83.		50 Dinar, blue. Relief of Mestrovic at left (format 139 × 66 mm)	—

Savings Bank of Laibach Province

Issued during the German occupation, one side in Slovenian, the other in German

R1.	14. 9.1944	50 Lire, red. Peasant woman with produce	2.50
R2.		100 Lire, blue. Peasant with scythe	2.00
R3.		500 Lire, green. Man in costume	4.50
R4.		1,000 Lire, brown. Woman's head	6.50
R5.	28.11.1944	½ Lira, green. Child in costume	1.00
R6.		1 Lira, dark brown. Spire and dragon	.75

R7.	2 Lire, brown. Woman and child	1.00
R8.	5 Lire, brown red. Man in costume	1.00
R9.	10 Lire, violet. Woman's head with costume cap	1.25

Many essays in various printing and overprint colors are known with text differences and such items as the 2 lire illustration appearing on the 1 lira note.

Montenegro, Italian Occupation

Yugoslavian notes stamped "Verificato."

R10.	(1941)	10 Dinar (dated 22.9.1939). Note #35 with stamp	5.00
R11.		20 Dinar (dated 6.9.1936). Note #33 with stamp	7.50
R12.		50 Dinar (dated 1.12.1931). Note #28 with stamp	3.50
R13.		100 Dinar (dated 1.12.1929). Note #27 with stamp	
		a. Paper watermarked with head of Karageorge	6.50
		b. Paper watermarked with head of King Alexander I	2.00
		Error: 100 Dinar of 30.11.1920 with stamp	R

Partisan Notes

Gospodarsko Financni Odbor Osvobodilne Fronte

M1.	50 Lit, orange	.75
M2.	100 Lit, lilac brown and blue (with and without control numbers)	1.00
	Also known with stamp "25RM," probably a forgery.	
M3.	500 Lit, red brown on grey olive	7.50
M4.	1,000 Lit, red brown on grey olive	12.50
M5.	5,000 Lit, red brown on grey olive	20.00
M6.	10,000 Lit, red brown on grey olive	25.00

Denarni Zavod Slovenije

M7.	20.2.1944–12.3.1944	1 Liro, blue green. Control number in black	2.00
		Error: No text on reverse	12.50
M8.		5 Lir, blue on light blue. Control number in black	2.50
M9.		10 Lir, red. Control number in black	5.00
		German propaganda note: Obverse as M9, reverse "Ta denar je prav . . ."	R
M10.		1 Liro, blue on olive. Control number in red	1.00
M11.		5 Lir, blue on grey. Control number in red	1.25
M12.		10 Lir, brown on grey violet. Control number in black	3.50
M13.		100 Lir, brown on light brown. Control number in black	5.00
M14.	Handwritten dates	1,000 Lir, green. Value handwritten	8.50

Izvršni Odbor Ocvobodilne Fronte Slovenskega Narodna

M15.	8.10.1943	20 RM, blue and red. Woman with bread, farmer and blacksmith	7.50
M16.		50 RM, green and red. Type of M15	10.00
M17.		500 RM. Type of M15	15.00

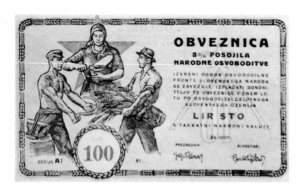

153 × 91

M18.	100 Lir, blue and red. Type of M15	10.00
M19.	100 Lit, brown. Agricultural work at left and right	7.50
M20.	1,000 Lit, brown. Type of M19	12.50
M21.	10,000 Lit, brown. Type of M19	20.00

Potrdilo (Partisan Certificates)

Values and dates handwritten, crude printing or reproduction.

Kanalski O.N.O.O. (O.F.)

M22.	100 Lir	10.00
M23.	600 Lir, lilac. Tito at right	10.00

Narodni Osvobodilni Svet za Primorsko Slovenijo

M24.	100 Lir	6.50
M25.	300 Lir	10.00
M26.	400 Lir	10.00
M27.	1,000 Lir, blue. Tito at right	7.50
M28.	5,500 Lir	12.50
M29.	10,000 Lir, green. Tito at right	12.50

200 × 103

M30.   12,000 Lir, green. Tito at right   15.00

Okrožni Odbor O.F. za Zapadno Primorsko

M31.   128 Lir, blue. Tito at right   20.00

Okrožni Odbor O.F. za Slov. Istro

M32.   100 Lir, blue grey   10.00
M33.   400 Lir, blue grey   15.00
M34.   500 Lir, blue grey   10.00

OOOF (Okrožni Odbor O.F.) za Brkine

M35.   600 Lit, black   10.00

Okrožni N.O.O. za Brkine

M36.   1,000 Lir, green. Tito at right   7.50

Okrožni Narodno Osvobodilni Odbor za Brda

M37.   50 Lir, lilac. Tito at right   10.00
M38.   10,000 Lir, grey. Tito at right   12.50

Okrožni Narodno Osvobodilni Odbor za Kras

M39.   200 Lir, grey   5.00
M40.   500 Lir, grey   11.50

Okrožni Narodno Osvobodilni Odbor za Gorisko

M41.   250 Lir, green. Tito at right   10.00
M42.   1,000 Lir, green. Tito at right   10.00

Okrožni Narodna Osvobodilni Odbor za Idrijsko

M43.	100 Lir, grey	5.00

Okrožni Narodno Osvobodilni Odbor za Basko

M44.	50 Lir	5.00
M45.	100 Lir	7.50
M46.	400 Lir, grey. Red star at right	10.00
M47.	500 Lir, grey. Red star at right	10.00
M48.	5,000 Lir	12.50